ELECTROCHEMICAL DATA

SOLE DISTRIBUTORS FOR THE U.S.A. AND CANADA:
ELSEVIER PRESS, INC., 402 LOVETT BOULEVARD, HOUSTON
(TEXAS) AND 300 PARK AVENUE, NEW YORK (N.Y.) —
FOR THE BRITISH COMMONWEALTH, EXCEPT CANADA:
CLEAVER-HUME PRESS, LTD., 42a SOUTH AUDLEY STREET,
LONDON, W.I.

ELECTROCHEMICAL DATA

by

B. E. CONWAY, Ph.D., D.I.C.

The Chester Beatty Research Institute
London

ELSEVIER PUBLISHING COMPANY

AMSTERDAM   HOUSTON   LONDON   NEW YORK

1952

Library of Congress Card No. 52–5652

PRINTED IN THE NETHERLANDS BY
FA. BOOSTEN & STOLS, MAASTRICHT

356750

PREFACE

In any work of reference, particularly of numerical data, the problems of comprehensiveness, critical assessment of accuracy and validity of data, inclusion of older yet reliable data and the production of a concise and easily usable book are difficult to solve simultaneously without some degree of compromise being made. In the production of *A Textbook of Electrochemistry* by G. KORTÜM and J. O'M. BOCKRIS it was considered appropriate to include a chapter containing a representative selection of useful electrochemical data. At the same time, however, the general need for a more comprehensive collection of data in the expanding field of electrochemistry was realised and the compilation of data for a separate reference work was undertaken.

In this resulting work, the main aim has been to bring together for easy reference information on various aspects of electrochemistry for which exact data of known accuracy are available in the literature. Qualitative data of unknown reproducibility have, on the whole, been omitted. However, besides information on pure electrochemistry, data have been included on some more quantitative aspects of applied electrochemistry. Thus, sections are included which provide modern data on the electrochemistry of fused salts and liquid silicates and also on applications in the field of biophysics, for example, electrophoretic mobilities and diffusion constants of biologically important materials, oxidation-reduction potentials in biological systems. Provision of data in this field, although not extensive, was felt to be of value on account of the growing importance of the applications of physical chemistry and physical methods in general to biological problems.

If is the author's pleasure to record his indebtedness to the many chemists, to whom appropriate references are made in the text who have co-operated with the author in sending him some of their latest experimental data which were unpublished at the time of compilation of the tables. In this way it has been possible in a number of instances to quote very recent data.

The author also wishes to acknowledge permission to reproduce some figures from the following works: *Oxidation-reduction potentials in bacteriology and biochemistry*, by L. F. HEWITT (Livingstone, Edinburgh), *The physical chemistry of electrolytic solutions*, by H. S. HARNED and B. B. OWEN (Reinhold Publ. Corp., New York), and *Metals reference book*, by C. J. SMITHELLS (Butterworths, London).

Particular thanks are due to Dr. J. O'M. BOCKRIS of Imperial College, London, for his comments on the manuscript, for suggestions for improvements and additions to the text and for many valuable discussions concerning the value and validity of data included in the work. The author is also indebted to Dr. H. ROSENBERG, Miss E. M. PRESS, and Messrs. I. A. AMMAR, L. BRAYBON and P. G. TOWLSON for their assistance in checking proofs of the numerical data.

The Chester Beatty Research Institute,   B. E. CONWAY
London

May, 1952

CONTENTS

VIII. Electrochemistry of melts at high temperatures 261

IMPORTANT SYMBOLS USED IN THE TABLES

a/b Axial ratio of assymmetrical particles

a_i Activity of a substance i

a Mean activity of an electrolyte

c Velocity of light

c_i Concentration in mol or equiv./l. of substance i

C Capacity

D Diffusion coefficient

$\overline{D}$ Integral diffusion coefficient

D_0 Diffusion coefficient at infinite dilution

e_0 Standard electrode potential

e_0 Electron or electron charge

E Electromotive force

E_0 Standard e.m.f. of half elements

f_0 Osmotic coefficient

$f_{\pm}$ Activity coefficient of electrolyte

f_u Activity coefficient of non-electrolyte

f/f_0 Frictional ratio

F The Faraday

G Free heat content

$H^{\neq}$ Heat of activation

h PLANCK's constant

H Enthalpy

i Current density or current

i_0 Exchange current density

$I_{(m)}$ Ionic strength at molality m

$\overline{J}$ Partial molal heat capacity

k BOLTZMANN's constant, also salting-out constants

K Thermodynamic equilibrium constant

K' Non-thermodynamic equilibrium constant

K_A, K_B Thermodynamic acid or basic dissociation constant, respectively

K_w Ionic product of water

l Ionic mobility at infinite dilution

$\bar{L}$ Partial molal heat content

m Concentration in mol/ 1000 g. solvent; also mass

M Concentration in mol/l. solvent, (see also c_i), also molecular weight

$\left.\begin{array}{c}n_+\\n_-\end{array}\right\}$ Transference number of ion

N Molar fraction

N_A AVOGADRO's number

P Pressure

q Electric charge

r Distance, radius

R Gas Constant, also electric resistivity and molar refraction

S Entropy

S_0 Sedimentation constant at infinite dilution

t Time, also temperature °C.

T Absolute temperature

U Electrophoretic mobility

$\bar{V}$ Partial molar volume

V Volume or dilution in l./mol

z_i Valence of ion i

α Polarisability, also constant in slope in TAFEL equation

γ Surface tension, also stoichiometric activity coefficient

Γ_i Ionic concentration of ion i

ε Dielectric constant

ζ Electrokinetic potential

η Overpotential, also viscosity

$\varkappa$ Specific conductance

$1/\varkappa$ Radius of ionic atmo-

sphere. Other symbols used are defined in the text.

Λ_∞ Equivalent conductance at infinite dilution

Λ_v Equivalent conductance at finite concentration

μ Dipole moment

ν Number of ions arising from dissociation of an electrolyte

ϱ Density

σ Charge density per sq. cm.

Φ_v Apparent molar volume

ψ Electric potential

CHAPTER I

UNIVERSAL CONSTANTS AND RATIOS AND SOME CONVERSION FACTORS

The tables of universal constants and ratios are those given by R. T. BIRGE (*Rev. Mod. Phys.*, 1941, **13**, 233), and represent the most consistent and modern set of values available. The values of the electrochemical equivalents of the elements given in Chapter IX are based on a rounded figure of 96,500 coulombs for F used by ROUSCH (*Trans. Electrochem. Soc.*, 1938, **73**, 285) which gives 1·11793 mg./int. coulomb as the electrochemical equivalent for silver instead of 1·11800 given by BIRGE. However, this difference is within experimental error as the uncertainty in F is, according to BIRGE (see Table I, 1), 10 int.coulomb/g.equiv. Some important universal ratios such as mass of proton : mass of electron and the specific electron charge are also included.

A table of dimensions and definitions of electrical units is given in Table I, 2, and the magnitudes of the units in the electro-magnetic and electrostatic unit systems are tabulated.

Some useful conversion factors for energy and pressure units are also given.

TABLE I, 1

PRINCIPAL CONSTANTS AND RATIOS

Acceleration due to the earth's
gravitational field g_0 (Standard) $= 980 \cdot 665$ cm.sec.$^{-2}$.
g_{45} $= 980 \cdot 616$ cm.sec.$^{-2}$ *.

Standard atmospheric pressure
(the standard atmosphere) A_0 $= (1 \cdot 013246 \pm 0 \cdot 000004) \cdot 10^6$ dyne cm.$^{-2}$at.$^{-1}$

A_{45} $= (1 \cdot 013195 \pm 0 \cdot 000004) \cdot 10^6$ dyne cm.$^{-2}$at.$^{-1}$

1 litre $= 1000$ ml. $= 1000 \cdot 078 \pm 0 \cdot 002$ cc.

Volume of ideal gas $(0 \, °C., \; A_0)$ $= (22 \cdot 4146 \pm 0 \cdot 0006) \cdot 10^3$ cm.^{3}mol^{-1}
$= (22 \cdot 4140 \pm 0 \cdot 006)$ litre.mol^{-1}

Volume of ideal gas $(0 \, °C., \; A_{45})$ $= (22 \cdot 4157 \pm 0 \cdot 0006) \cdot 10^3$cm.^{3}mol^{-1}
$= 22 \cdot 4151 \pm 0 \cdot 0006$ litre.mol^{-1}

Ice point $= 273 \cdot 16 \pm 0 \cdot 01 \, °K.$

Normal calorie $=$ Heat required to raise the temperature of 1 g. water from $14 \cdot 5$ to $15 \cdot 5 \, °C.$

Joule equivalent $= 4 \cdot 1855 \pm 0 \cdot 0004$ abs.joule.cal.$^{-1}$
$= 4.1847 \pm 0.0003$ int.joule.cal.$^{-1}$

Avogadro's Number, N_A $= (6 \cdot 0228 \pm 0.0011) \cdot 10^{23}$ mol^{-1}

Specific gravity of mercury $(0 \, °C., A_0)$ referred to air free water at its maximum density $= 13 \cdot 59542 \pm 0 \cdot 00005.$

Density of mercury $(0 \, °C., \; A_0)$ $= 13 \cdot 59504 \pm 0 \cdot 00005$ g.cm.$^{-3}$

Planck's constant $h = (6 \cdot 624 \pm 0 \cdot 002) \cdot 10^{-27}$ erg.sec.

Velocity of light in vacuum $c = (2 \cdot 99776 \pm 0 \cdot 00004) \cdot 10^{10}$ cm. sec.$^{-1}$

The faraday $F = 96501 \pm 10$ int. coulomb/g.equiv.

F (chemical scale) ** $\begin{cases} = 96487 \pm 10 \text{ abs. coulomb/g.equiv.} \\ = 9648 \cdot 7 \pm 1 \text{ abs. e.m.u. /g.equiv.} \end{cases}$

$F' = cF = (2 \cdot 89247 \pm 0 \cdot 00030) \cdot 10^{14}$ abs. e.s.u./g.equiv.

F (physical scale) ** $= 96514 \pm 10$ abs. coulomb/g.equiv.
$= 9651 \cdot 4 \pm 1$ abs. e.m.u./g.equiv.
$= (2.89326 \pm 0 \cdot 00030) \cdot 10^{14}$ abs. e.s.u./g.equiv.

1 abs. electron volt $= 10^8 \, e_0 = 10^8 \, F/N_A = (1 \cdot 60203 \pm 0 \cdot 00034) \cdot 10^{-12}$ erg.

Energy in cal./mol for 1 e.v./molecule $= 23052 \pm 3$ cal.mol^{-1}

Gas constant $R = (8 \cdot 31436 \pm 0 \cdot 00038) \cdot 10^7$ erg.deg.$^{-1}$mol^{-1}
$= 1 \cdot 98646 \pm 0 \cdot 00021$ cal.deg.$^{-1}$mol^{-1}

Boltzmann constant $k = R/N_A = (1 \cdot 38047 \pm 0 \cdot 00026) \cdot 10^{-16}$ ergs.deg.$^{-1}$.

---

* Suffices 0 and 45 refer to $0°$ and $45°$ of latitude respectively.
** In the "chemical scale" the equivalent weight is defined with reference to the normal isotopic mixture: $^{16}O + ^{17}O + ^{18}O = 16 \cdot 00000$, whilst on the physical scale it is defined with reference to the isotope $^{16}O = 16 \cdot 00000.$

TABLE I, 1 (*Continued*)

Electrochemical equivalents:

$$Ag = 1 \cdot 11800 . 10^{-3} \text{ g./int.coulomb.}$$
$$= (1 \cdot 11807 \pm 0 \cdot 00012) . 10^{-3} \text{ g./abs.coulomb.}$$
$$I = (1 \cdot 315026 \pm 0 \cdot 000025) . 10^{-3} \text{ g./int.coulomb.}$$
$$= (1 \cdot 31535 \pm 0 \cdot 00014) . 10^{-3} \text{ g./abs.coulomb.}$$

International volt = that potential difference which applied across a conductor of resistance one int.ohm causes a current of one int.ampère to flow.

International ohm = Resistance opposed to a constant current by a column of mercury at $0 °C.$, $14 \cdot 4521$ g. in mass, of constant cross-sectional area and $106 \cdot 300$ cm. in length.

Coulomb (practical unit) = Quantity of electricity transferred by a current of 1 ampère flowing for 1 second.

International ampère = that uniform current which will deposit $0 \cdot 00111800$ g. Ag per second from a standard $AgNO_3$ solution.

For definitions of absolute electrostatic and electromagnetic units of charge etc., see Table I, 2.

International amp. $= 0 \cdot 99986 \pm 0 \cdot 00002$ abs.amps.
,, ohm $= 1 \cdot 00048 \pm 0 \cdot 00002$ abs.ohm.
,, coulomb $= 0 \cdot 99986 \pm 0 \cdot 00002$ abs.coulomb.
,, henry $= 1 \cdot 00048 \pm 0 \cdot 00002$ abs.henry.
,, volt $= 1 \cdot 00034 \pm 0 \cdot 00003$ abs.volt.
,, joule $= 1 \cdot 00020 \pm 0 \cdot 00004$ abs.joule.

Atomic wt. of electron $= F/e_0^-/m_e = (5 \cdot 4862 \pm 0 \cdot 0017) . 10^{-4}$ (physical scale),
or $(5 \cdot 4847 \pm 0 \cdot 0017) . 10^{-4}$ (chemical scale).

Mass of electron $m_e = e_0^- /e_0^- /m_e = (F/N_A)/e_0^-/m_e = (9 \cdot 1066 \pm 0 \cdot 0032) . 10^{-28}$ g.

Mass of H atom $= H/N_A = (1 \cdot 67339 \pm 0 \cdot 00031) . 10^{-24}$ g.

Mass of proton $= (1 \cdot 67248 \pm 0 \cdot 00031) . 10^{-24}$ g.

Ratio $\dfrac{\text{Mass H atom}}{\text{Mass electron}} = 1837 \cdot 5 \pm 0 \cdot 5.$

Ratio $\dfrac{\text{Mass proton}}{\text{Mass electron}} = 1836 \cdot 5 \pm 0 \cdot 5.$

Specific charge of proton $= e_0^-/\text{mass of proton} = 9578 \cdot 7 \pm 1 \cdot 0$ abs.e.m.u.g.$^{-1}$.

Electron charge $e_0^- = F/N_A = (1 \cdot 60203 \pm 0 \cdot 00034) . 10^{-20}$ abs.e.m.u.
$= (4 \cdot 8025 \pm 0 \cdot 0010) . 10^{-10}$ abs.e.s.u.

Specific electron charge $e_0^-/m_e = (1 \cdot 7592 \pm 0 \cdot 0005) . 10^7$ abs.e.m.u.g.$^{-1}$.
$= (5 \cdot 2736 \pm 0 \cdot 0015) . 10^{17}$ abs.e.s.u.g.$^{-1}$.

Ratio of e.s.u.: e.m.u. units of electrical charge =
c = velocity of light, (see above).
$h/e_0^- = (4 \cdot 1349 \pm 0 \cdot 0007) . 10^{-7}$ erg.sec.e.m.u.$^{-1}$.
$= (1 \cdot 3793 \pm 0 \cdot 0002) . 10^{-17}$ erg.sec.e.s.u.$^{-1}$.

References:
R. T. BIRGE, *Rev. Mod. Phys.*, 1941, **13**, 233.
See also:
U. STILLE *Z. Physik*, 1943, **121**, 24.
H. L. CURTIS, *J. Res. Nat. Bur. Stand.*, 1944, **33**, 235.

TA

Units are those proposed by the Report of

A has the value 1 in e.s.u. or e.m.u. if ε and μ are

In e.s.u. $\varepsilon = 1$, $\mu = 1$

ε and μ are connected by $\dfrac{1}{\mu\varepsilon} = c^2$ and $\varepsilon\mu = L^{-2}T^2$. m, L ar

Quantity	Symbol	Defining equation	Electrostatic unit	Electromagnetic unit
Charge	q	Force $=$ $\dfrac{Aqq'}{\varepsilon r^2}$ $i = \dfrac{dq}{dT}$	Unit charge repels an equal charge 1 cm. away in vac. with force of 1 dyne.	Unit charge per s is delivered by u current.
Current	i	$i = dq/dT$ $H = 2\pi\, a\, n\, i/r$ $=$ magnetic field in coil of area a and radius r of n turns.	Unit current delivers unit charge/ sec.	Unit current flow round 1 cm. arc circle of radius 1 produces unit mag tic field at cen
Potential difference or e.m.f.	E or $\Delta\psi$	Energy $= E\,V$ Rate of working $= E\,i$	Unit e.m.f. confers on unit charge abil to perform 1 erg of work.	
Resistance	R	$E = i\,R$	Unit resistance allows unit e.m.f. to p duce passage of unit current.	
Energy	w	$w =$ force . distance	Unit energy is expended when 1 dy acts through 1 cm.	
Power	Ψ	Power $= dw/dT$	Unit energy per sec.	
Capacity	C	Energy $= \dfrac{q^2}{2C}$	Conductor on which unit charge can be placed with expenditure of 1 erg of work.	

LECTRICAL UNITS

rnational Congress on Physics, London, 1934.

ctric constant and permeability of free space respectively.
.m.u. $\varepsilon = 1/c^2$, $\mu = 1$.
the standard notations for mass, length and time respectively.

Practical unit	Practical unit in		e.m.u. e.s.u.	Dimensions of unit expressed in e.s.u.	Dimensions of unit expressed in e.m.u.
	e.s.u.	e.m.u.			
ulomb	$3 \cdot 10^9$	10^{-1}	c	$\varepsilon^{1/2} m^{1/2} L^{3/2} T^{-1}$	$\mu^{-1/2} m^{1/2} L^{1/2}$
père	$3 \cdot 10^9$	10^{-1}	c	$\varepsilon^{1/2} m^{1/2} L^{3/2} T^{-2}$	$\mu^{-1/2} m^{1/2} L^{1/2} T^{-1}$
lt	$1/3 \cdot 10^{-2}$	10^8	$1/c$	$\varepsilon^{-1/2} m^{1/2} L^{1/2} T^{-1}$	$\mu^{1/2} m^{1/2} L^{3/2} T^{-2}$
m	$1/9 \cdot 10^{-11}$	10^9	$1/c^2$	$\varepsilon^{-1} L^{-1} T$	$\mu L T^{-1}$
ule	10^7	10^7	1	$m L^2 T^{-2}$	$L^2 T^{-2}$
tt	10^7	10^{-9}	1	$m L^2 T^{-3}$	$\mu^{-1} L^{-1} T^2$
rad	$9 \cdot 10^{11}$	10^{-9}	c^2	εL	

TABLE I

Quantity	Symbol	Defining equation	Electrostatic unit	Electromagnetic unit
Inductance	L	$E = L\, di/dT$		Conductor in which unit change of current sec. produces unit e.m.f. has unit L.
Magnetic pole	m	Force $= \dfrac{A}{\mu} \cdot \dfrac{mm'}{r^2}$		Unit pole repels equal pole 1 cm. away with force of 1 dyne.
Magnetic flux	$\varPhi$	$d\varPhi/dT = -E$		Unit e.m.f. is induced in a circuit when through it changes at the rate of 1 unit (maxwell/sec.)
Magnetic induction or flux density	B	$\int B dS = \varPhi$	Unit magnetic flux per cm.^{2} (gauss)	
Magnetic field intensity	H	$\int H dl = 4\pi\, ani$ where l is the length of circuit carrying a current of i. Force on pole $m = mH$		Magnetomotive force round a circuit $=$ work done in taking unit pole round it $=$ line integral of magnetic field intensity $=$ force exerted on unit N pole unit $= 1$ oersted.
Electric field intensity	F	$-F=$ differential of ψ with respect to distance	Space variation of potential or electric intensity $=$ force exerted on unit positive charge.	

ntinued)

Practical unit	Practical unit in		e.m.u. e.s.u.	Dimensions of unit expressed in e.s.u.	Dimensions of unit expressed in e.m.u.
	e.s.u.	e.m.u.			
nry	$1/_9 . 10^{-11}$	10^9	$1/c^2$	$\varepsilon^{-1}L^{-1}T^2$	μL
. 10^8 maxwells 4π volt/sec.	$1/_3 . 10^{-2}$	10^8	$1/c$	$\varepsilon^{-1/2}m^{1/2}L^{1/2}$	$\mu^{1/2}m^{1/2}L^{1/2}T^{-1}$
0^8 maxwells = 1 volt/sec.	$1/_3 . 10^{-2}$	10^8	$1/c$	$\varepsilon^{-1/2}m^{1/2}L^{1/2}$	$\mu^{1/2}m^{1/2}L^{3/2}T^{-1}$
0^8 gauss = 1 olt sec./cm.^{2}	$1/_3 . 10^{-2}$	10^8	$1/c$	$\varepsilon^{-1/2}m^{1/2}L^{-3/2}$	$\mu^{1/2}m^{1/2}L^{-1/2}T^{-1}$
$^{-1}$ oersted	$3 . 10^9$	10^{-1}	c	$\varepsilon^{1/2}m^{1/2}L^{1/2}T^{-2}$	$\mu^{-1/2}m^{1/2}L^{-3/2}T^{-1}$
olt/cm.	$1/_3 . 10^{-2}$	10^8	$1/c$	$\varepsilon^{-1/2}m^{1/2}L^{-1/2}T^{-1}$	$\mu^{1/2}m^{1/2}L^{1/2}T^{-2}$

TABLE I, 3

CONVERSION FACTORS

ENERGY FACTORS

These are factors by which the given value must be multiplied to obtain that value in the sought units.

Given \ Sought	erg/ molecule	cm.$^{-1}$ $\left(\dfrac{1}{h}\right)$/ molecule	e-volt/ molecule	cal./molecule
erg/molecule	1	$5 \cdot 048 \cdot 10^{15}$	$6 \cdot 252 \cdot 10^{11}$	$1 \cdot 441 \cdot 10^{16}$
cm.$^{-1}\left(\dfrac{1}{h}\right)$/molecule	$1 \cdot 981 \cdot 10^{-16}$	1	$1 \cdot 239 \cdot 10^{-4}$	$2 \cdot 854$
e-volt/molecule	$1 \cdot 599 \cdot 10^{-12}$	$8 \cdot 074 \cdot 10^{3}$	1	$2 \cdot 304 \cdot 10^{4}$
cal./molecule	$6 \cdot 942 \cdot 10^{-17}$	$0 \cdot 3501$	$4 \cdot 340 \cdot 10^{-5}$	1

TABLE I, 3 (Continued)

PRESSURE FACTORS

(For method of use of these factors, see above)

Sought / Given	dyne/cm.²	g./cm.²	kg./m.²	mm. Hg	atmosphere	pound/in.²	pound/ft.²
dyne/cm.²	1	$1{\cdot}0198 \, . \, 10^{-3}$	$1{\cdot}0198 \, . \, 10^{-2}$	$7{\cdot}5010 \, . \, 10^{-4}$	$9{\cdot}8697 \, . \, 10^{-7}$	$1{\cdot}4504 \, . \, 10^{-5}$	$2{\cdot}0887 \, . \, 10^{-3}$
g./cm.²	980·6	1	10	$7{\cdot}3551 \, . \, 10^{-1}$	$9{\cdot}6777 \, . \, 10^{-4}$	$1{\cdot}4223 \, . \, 10^{-2}$	2·0481
kg./m.²	98·06	10^{-1}	1	$7{\cdot}3551 \, . \, 10^{-2}$	$9{\cdot}6777 \, . \, 10^{-5}$	$1{\cdot}4223 \, . \, 10^{-3}$	$2{\cdot}0481 \, . \, 10^{-1}$
mm.Hg	1332	1·3595	13·595	1	$1{\cdot}3158 \, . \, 10^{-3}$	$1{\cdot}9337 \, . \, 10^{-2}$	2·7845
atmosphere	1,013,200	1033·3	10,333	760	1	14·696	2116·32
pound/in.²	68,944	70·308	708·12	51·715	$6{\cdot}8046 \, . \, 10^{-2}$	1	144
pound/ft.²	478·78	$4{\cdot}883 \, . \, 10^{-1}$	4·883	$3{\cdot}591 \, . \, 10^{-1}$	$4{\cdot}7252 \, . \, 10^{-4}$	$6{\cdot}945 \, . \, 10^{-3}$	1

For accuracy of data see values quoted in Table I, 1.

Electrical Units: For conversion factors for electrical units see Table I, 2.

CHAPTER II

GENERAL DATA ON PHYSICAL PROPERTIES

In this chapter an attempt has been made to include some of the more important data on general physical properties which bear relevance to the electrochemistry of solids and solutions. From the large amount of material available in the literature on physcial properties of elements and compounds it has been necessary, in order not disproportionately to emphasise this chapter in a monograph of electrochemical data, to include only a selection of these data.

In Table II, 1, some physical properties of common organic compounds, some of which are used as non-aqueous solvents in electrochemistry, are tabulated.

The ionic entropies in Table II, 2 are relative to $S_{0H^{.}} = 0$. The absolute entropy of $H^{.}$ given by LEE and TAI as —5·4 e.u. is controverted by BOCKRIS and PARSONS (*Trans. Faraday Soc.*, 1951, **47**, 914) who suggest a value of —4·6 e.u. which appears to be more satisfactory for the conversion of the relative entropies given in the Table to absolute entropies.

The interatomic bond distances and ionic radii are those given by PAULING in 1927 (*J. Am. Chem. Soc.*, 1927, **49**, 771). Although some controversy exists concerning correct assignment of bond distances, this early but comprehensive list of ionic radii and bond distances appears to be satisfactory (L. PAULING, "The Nature of the Chemical Bond", Cornell Univ. Press, Ithaca, 1948).

The values of electron work function for various metals are particularly susceptible to traces of surface impurity, *e.g.* adsorbed films on the metals. The data given by KLEIN and LANGE (*Z. Elektrochem.*, 1938, **44**, 561) have been chosen in this chapter and the values given by these authors are not subject to serious criticism. Successive ionisation potentials of some elements also determined by KLEIN and LANGE are tabulated. These values of work function and ionisation potentials are of use in computation of the energetics of electrode processes.

The most modern set of values given by SMITHELLS has in part been used in the table of electrical resistivities of metals.

Refractive indices of some common organic compounds are given in Table II, 1, whilst molar and ionic refractions of a number of salts and ions are given in Table II, 5. Refractive indices of ethanol-water mixtures for the complete composition range 0 - 100 % ethanol are given for Na_D radiation in Table II, 4.

Table II, 3 gives values of polarisabilities of some ions and molecules. This table is followed by a series of compilations of data on the dielectric constants of solids, pure liquids, aqueous, non-aqueous liquid mixtures, and electrolytic solutions. Table II, 28 summarises many values of dielectric increment in water of amides and dipolar ions (e.g., peptides) of biological importance. The values of dielectric constant of water are those given by WYMAN (Phys. Rev., 1930, 35, 623) and also the later values of WYMAN and INGALLS (J. Am. Chem. Soc., 1938, 60, 1182) who corrected WYMAN's earlier results for the thermal expansion of the resonator used in the measurements. Both sets of values are given since some of the earlier computations of theoretical limiting slopes of molal heat contents, heat capacities and molal volumes utilised this uncorrected data.

Table II, 11 gives values of a number of properties of liquids of various types. The types have been divided with respect to the kind of interaction predominating in the liquid structure, viz. dipolar, H bonding; some data for close-packed liquids are also given.

Results of measurements of densities of fused salts and fused salt mixtures are more appropriately located with the material concerned with the electrochemistry of melts at high temperatures and will accordingly be found in Chapter VIII.

Compound	Cryoscopic const. for 1 g.mol. in 1000 g. solvent	Ebullioscopic const. for 1 g.mol. in 1000 g. solvent	Viscosity in c.g.s. unit	Sp. conductance in mho.cm.$^{-1}$	Dielectr constan (static
n-Pentane			0·002395 (20°)	$< 2 . 10^{-10}$ [47]	1·845 (20°)
n-Hexane		2·33 [132]	0·00337 (15°)		1·904 (15°)
n-Heptane			0·00333 (40°)		1·973 (20°) (
n-Octane		4·02 [83]	0·00542 (20°)		1·962 (20°) (
Cyclohexane	20·2 [24]	2·75 [27]	0·01056 (15°)		2·012 (25°) (
Benzene	5·227 [65]	2·587 [27]	0·00696 (15°)	5·32 - 4·43 . 10^{-17} (18°) [63]	2·292 (15°) (
Toluene		3·33 [27]	0·00623 (15°)	1·4 . 10^{-14} (30)	2·366 (25°) (
Methanol		0·84 [66]	0·00544 (25°) [41]	3 . 10^{-7} (25°) [157]	31·2 (20°) (

ORGANIC COMPOUNDS

Dipole moment Debyes	Specific heat	Refractive index	Boiling pt. °C.	Freezing pt. °C.	Density $\left(\varrho\,\tfrac{t_1}{t_2}\right)$ †
(61)	0·54 (16·8 °C.) (97)	1·35746 D 20° (32)	36·00 (178)	—129·63 (178)	0·62632 20° 4°vac. (178)
(161)	0·53546 (17·71°) (98)	1·37486 D 20° (124)	68·71 (178)	—95·39 (178)	0·69545 20° 4°vac. (178)
(127)	0·527 (21·04°) (110)	1·38764 D (20°) (32)	98·4 (178)	—90·62 (178)	0·68365 20° 4° (178)
(32)	0·526 (25·14°) (98)	1·39743 D (20°) (124)	125·667 (178)	—56·798 (178)	0·69855 25° 4° (178)
(116) (162)	0·4411 (19·3°) (29)	1·42623 D (20°) (77)	80·738 (178)	6·554 (178)	0·77389 25° 4° (178)
(80) (103)	0·41441 (21·80°) (164)	1·50110 D (20°) (146)	80·103 (178)	5·533 (178)	0·87368 25° 4° (178)
0·4 (101)	0·4059 (25°) (165)	1·49682 D (20°) (140)	110·623 (178)	—94·991 (178)	0·86231 25° 4° (178)
1·664 (169) 1·698 (142)	0·5966 (19·85°) (33)	1·33057 D (15°) (73)	64·75 (146)	—97·68 (139)	0·78662 25° 4° (43)

TABLE I

Compound	Cryoscopic const. for 1 g. mol. in 1000 g. solvent	Ebullioscopic const. for 1 g. mol. in 1000 g. solvent	Viscosity in c.g.s. unit	Sp.conductance in mho.cm.$^{-1}$	Dielectric constan (static)
Ethanol	c. 3 (10)	1·20±0·021 (130)	0·01200 (20°) (15)	1·35 . 10^{-9} (25°) (28)	25·00 (20°) (1
n-Propanol		1·59 (9)	0·019666 (25°) (145)	9·17 . 10^{-9} (18°) (62)	22·2 (20°) (1
iso-Propanol			0·02430 (20°) (46)	0·51 . 10^{-6} (25°) (160)	13·8 (18°) (1
n-Butanol			0·03378 (15°) (141)	9·12 . 10^{-9} (25°) (62)	17·7 (17.2°) (1
iso-Butanol		2·01 (9)	0·04703 (15°) (141)	0·8 . 10^{-7} (25°) (153)	17·95 (25°)
Ethylene glycol			0·1733 (25°) (35)	1·16 . 10^{-6} (25°) (93)	41·2 (20°) (1
Glycerol	3·27 - 3·69 (102)		10·69 (20°) (1)	0·9 . 10^{-7} (25°) (51)	15·3 (21°) (1
Diethyl ether	1·79 (13)	2·16 (9)	0·00247 (15°) (141)	⩽ 3·7 . 10^{-13} (25°) (104)	4·376 (20°) (10

ued)

ole ent oyes	Specific heat	Refractive index	Boiling pt. °C.	Freezing pt. °C.	Density $\left(\varrho \frac{t_1}{t_2}\right)$ †
96 (89) 02 142)	0·588 (24·9°) (95)	1·3614 D (20°) (21)	78·33 (23)	—114·49 (134)	0·785063 20° 4° (146)
55 169) (89)	0·531 (18°) (96)	1·38543 D (20°) (21)	97·18 ± 0·01 (23)	—126·10 (96)	0·80335 20° 4° (79)
59 035 (31)	0·596 (20°) (99)	1.37538 D (25°) (145)	82.258 (23)	—89·5 (137)	0·7830 25° (85)
56 169)	0·565 (20·9°) (95)	1·39711 C (20°) (180)	117·72±0·01 (53)	—90·2 (139)	0·81337 15° 4° (139)
9 (81)	0·716 (21°) (78)	1·3939 D (25°) (141)	108·10 (141)	—108·0 (26)	0·80576 15° 4° (141)
8 (129)	0·575 (19·9°) (99)	1·4329 D (16°) (73)	197·2 (129)	—12·3 (129)	1·113068 20° 4° (111)
	0·5795 (26·3°) (49)	1·47289 D (20°) (118)	290·6 (9)	18·18 (49)	1·2613 20° 4° (17)
5 (87)	0·551 (16·84°) (122)	1·35555 D (15°) (141)	34·60 (141)	—116·3 (134)	0·71925 15° 4° (141)

TABLE

Compound	Cryoscopic const. for 1 g.mol. in 1000 g. solvent	Ebullioscopic const. for in g.mol. in 1000 g. solvent	Viscosity in c.g.s. unit	Sp. conductance in mho.cm.$^{-1}$	Dielec const. (stat
1 : 4 Dioxan	4·8±0·3 [37]	3·27 [57]	0·01255 (25°) [57]	5 . 10^{-15} (25°) [71]	2·2 (20°
Acetone	2·40 [94]	1·725 [67]	0·003371 (15°) [141]	5·5 . 10^{-8} (25°) [156]	21·4 (20°
Formic acid	2·77 [171]	2·4 [6]	0·016376 (24·96°) [133]	6·2 . 10^{-5} (25°) [120]	57·0 (21°
Acetic acid	3·9 [59]	3·075 (v. dry) [11]	0·01232 (20°) [46]	11·2 . 10^{-9} (25°) [104]	6·1 (20°
Acetic anhydride		3·53 [11]	0·0110 (18°) [42]	0·48 . 10^{-6} (25°) [151]	20·7 (18·
Methyl acetate		2·061 [121]	0·00382 (20·3°) [2]	1·923 . 10^{-4} (17°) [4]	8·0 (19.
Ethyl acetate		2·83 [26]	0·00424 (25°) [46]	< 1 . 10^{-9} (25°) [70]	6·1 (20°
Ethyl chloride	·	1·95 [5]	93·7 . 10^{-5} (0°)	< 3 . 10^{-9} (0°) [176]	6·2 (170°, in conta liquid)

nued)

ole nent ebyes	Specific heat	Refractive index	Boiling pt. °C.	Freezing pt. °C.	Density $\left(\varrho\, \frac{t_1}{t_2}\right)$ †
45 [112]	0·415 (18°) [113]	1·4202 D (25°) [65]	101·50 [37]	11·65 [71]	1·02802 25°/4° [113]
±0·02 [169]	0·5176 (20°) [165]	1·36157 D (15°) [141]	56·11 [39]	—94·82 [134]	0·78985 20°/4°vac. [141]
19 [168]	0·5134 (17·66°) [119]	1·37348 He (15°) [139]	100·8 [139]	8·40 [44]	1·22647 15°/4° [139]
04 [20]	0·488 (19·5°) [99]	1·3698 D (25°) [72]	118·10 [18]	16·63 [117]	1·04922 20°/4° [139]
8 [177]	0·432 (23·56°) [14]	1·39229 He (15°) [139]	140·0 [139]	—73·1 [139]	1·0810 20°/4° [139]
74 [169]	0·502 (18·42°) [159]	1·36143 D (20°) [86]	57·323 [134]	—98·05 [134]	0·9273 25°/4° [134]
81 [92]	0·459 (20·44°) [143]	1·37243 D (20°) [72]	77·112 [139]	—83·60 [175]	0·90053 20°/4° [138]
05 [45]	0·3636 (—28·59°) [105]	1·3790 D (0°) [148]	12·28 [149]	—138·30 [135]	0·91708 6°/6° [100]

TABLE

Compound	Cryoscopic const. for 1 g.mol. in 1000 g. solvent	Ebullioscopic const. for in g.mol. in 1000 g. solvent	Viscosity in c.g.s. unit	Sp. conductance in mho.cm.$^{-1}$	Dielect consta (stati
Chloroform	4·90 [8]	3·66 - 3·91 [10]	0·00596 (15°) [140]	$< 10^{-10}$ (25°) [155]	4·6417 ± (25°)
Carbon tetrachloride	29·8 [13]	4·88 [7]	0·00958 (19·91°) [90]	$4 . 10^{-18}$ (18°) [47]	2·219 ± (25°)
Trichlorethylene		4·43 [158]	0·005490 (25°) [56]	Immeasurably small [155]	3·42 (10°)
Nitrobenzene	6·89 [112]	5·27 [12]	0·0182 (25°) [154]	$1·22 . 10^{-8}$ (23·6°) [114]	34·093±((25°)
Carbon disulphide		2·35 [9]	0·00367 (20°) [133]	$\leqslant 3·7 . 10^{-3}$ (25°) [104]	2·63 (20°)

tinued)

pole ment ebyes	Specific heat	Refractive index	Boiling pt. °C.	Freezing pt. °C.	Density $\left(\varrho\,\frac{t_1}{t_2}\right)$ †	
·18 [92]	0·2251 (19·9°) [110]	1·44858 D (15°) [140]	61·27 [140]	—63·49 [138]	1·49845 [140]	15° 4°
[115]	0·2022 (19·9°) [110]	1·41040 D (20°) [50]	76·75 [50]	—22·96 [138]	1·58471 [50]	25° 4°
·8 [148]	0·223 (20°) [58]	1·479141 D (17°) [106]	86·95 [135]	—86·4 [135]	1·4649 [38]	20° 4°
·24 [173]	0·3442 (30°) [163]	1·55261 D (20°) [19]	209·6 [144]	5·77 ± 0·02 [84]	1·1983 [146]	25° 4°
[170]	0·242 (20°) [33]	1·63189 D (15°) [141]	46·25 [141]	—111·53 [142]	1·2632 [52]	20° 4°

	Cryoscopic constant	Ebullioscopic constant	Viscosity in c.g.s. unit	Sp.conductance in mho.cm.$^{-1}$	Dielectr constar
Accuracy of figures in the respective columns.	± 0.2 - ± 0.3	± 0.08-± 0.10	$\pm 1\%$	$\pm 1\%$ but see SCHROEDER*	± 0.01 except w otherwi stated

* N.B. SCHROEDER and JAFFÉ (1, 2) have shown that conductances of ordinarily pure organic materials may considerably be reduced by pre-electrolysis.

^{1}) J. SCHROEDER, *Ann. Phys.*, 1909, **29**, 125.

^{2}) G. JAFFÉ, *ibid.*, 1909, **28**, 326.

† Density; $\varrho \frac{20°}{4°}$ *for example* = density at 20 °C. relative to H_2O at 4 °C., where $t_1 = 20°$, and $t_2 = 4$ °C.; "vac" indicates corrected for vacuum.

Refractive indices: letters D, C and He refer to the Na_D Na_C and He_γ lines respectively used for the measurements.

References:

1 M. P. APPLEBYE, *J. Chem. Soc.*, 1910, 2000.
2 T. TITANI, *Bull. Inst. Res. Japan*, 1927, 671; *Bull. Chem. Soc. Japan*, 1927, 4, 95.
3 O. A. BALL, *J. Chem. Soc.*, 1930, 570.
4 A. BARTOLI, *Gazz. chim. Ital.*, 1894, **24**, II, 156.
5 E. BECKMANN and F. JUNKER, *Z. anorg. Chem.*, 1907, **55**, 380.
6 E. BECKMANN, *Z. physik. Chem.*, 1907, **57**, 129, 140.
7 E. BECKMANN, *Z. physik. Chem.*, 1907, **58**, 543.
8 E. BECKMANN and O. FAUST, *Z. physik. Chem.*, 1915, **89**, 246.
9 B. C. MacEWEN, *J. Chem. Soc.*, 1923, **123**, 2279.
10 E. BECKMANN and O. LIESCHE, *Z. physik. Chem.*, 1914, **88**, 23.
11 E. BECKMANN, *Z. physik. Chem.*, 1914, **88**, 419.
12 E. BECKMANN and G. LOCKEMANN, *Z. physik. Chem.*, 1907, **60**, 385.
13 E. BECKMANN and P. WÄNTIG, *Z. anorg. Chem.*, 1910, **67**, 17.
14 D. BERTHELOT, *Ann. Chim.*, 1876, **9**, (5), 295.
15 E. C. BINGHAM and R. F. JACKSON, *Sci. Pap. Bur. Standards*, 1917, 298.
16 R. BOCK, *Z. Physik*, 1925, **31**, 534.
17 P. S. ALBRIGHT, *J. Am. Chem. Soc.*, 1937, **59**, 2098.
18 B. P. ALPERT and P. J. ELVING, *Ind. Eng. Chem.*, 1949, **41**, 2864.
19 K. BRAND and K. W. KRANZ, *J. prakt. Chem.*, 1927, **115**, (2), 143.
20 B. BRIEGLEB, *Z. physik. Chem.*, 1930, **10**, (B), 205.
21 D. L. POLLOCK, A. R. COLLETT and C. L. LAZZELL, *J. Phys. Chem.*, 1946, **50**, 23.

ntinued)

Dipole moment Debyes	Specific heat	Refractive index	Boiling pt. °C.	Freezing pt. °C.	Density $\left(\varrho\,{}^{t_1}_{t_2}\right)$ †
± 0·1 Debye	±0·002— ±0·0005 for 4 sig. fig.	± 0·00004	± 0·02 — 0·04	± 0·02 — 0·04	± 0·0005 — 0·00005

[22] R. F. BRUNEL, J. L. CRENSHAW and E. TOBIN, *Chem. News*, 1921, **122**, 256, 269, 281.

[23] C. B. KRETSCHMER and R. WIEBE, *J. Am. Chem. Soc.*, 1949, **71**, 1793, 3176.

[23a] J. F. CARLEY and L. W. BERTELSEN, *Ind. Eng. Chem.*, 1949, **41**, 2806.

[24] G. BRUNI and M. AMADORI, *Atti dell Inst. Veneto*, 1910-11, **70**, II, 1113.

[25] P. J. CARLISLE and A. A. LEVINE, *Ind. Eng. Chem.*, 1932, **24**, 1164.

[26] B. H. CARROLL, G. K. ROLLEFSON and J. H. MATHEWS, *J. Am. Chem. Soc.*, 1926, **47**, 1791.

[27] J. M. CUETO, *Quim. Indust.*, 1926, **3**, 113, *Chem. Zentr.*, 1926, II, 614.

[28] P. S. DANNER and J. H. HILDEBRAND, *J. Am. Chem. Soc.*, 1922, **44**, 2824.

[29] J. G. ASTON, G. J. SZASZ and H. L. FINK, *J. Am. Chem. Soc.*, 1931, **53**, 3876.

[30] DI COMMOX, *Nuovo Cim.*, 1903, **3**, (5), 97.

[31] H. L. DONLE, *Z. physik. Chem.*, 1931 **14**, (B), 326.

[32] F. L. HOWARD, T. W. MEARS *et al.*, *J. Res. Nat. Bur. Stand.*, 1947, **38**, 365.

[33] K. K. KELLEY, *J. Am. Chem. Soc.*, 1929, **51**, 180, 779 and 1145.

[34] P. DRUDE, *Z. physik. Chem.*, 1897, **23**, 267.

[35] A. F. DUNSTAN, *Z. physik. Chem.*, 1905, **51**, 732.

[36] G. EDGAR, G. CALINGAERT and R. E. MARKER, *J. Am. Chem. Soc.*, 1929, **51**, 1483.

[37] B. PESCE and M. V. LAGO, *Gazz. chim. Ital.*, 1944, **74**, 131.

[38] E. ERDMANN, *J. prakt. Chem.*, 1912, **85**, (2), 78.

[39] K. CLUSIUS and W. RINGER, *Z. physik. Chem.*, 1940, **A. 187**, 186.

[40] P. EVERSHEIM, *Ann. Physik*, 1902, **8**, (4), 539.

[41] G. JONES and H. J. FORNWALT, *J. Am. Chem. Soc.*, 1938, **60**, 1683.

[42] B. PESCE, *Gazz. chim. Ital.*, 1940, **70**, 710.

[43] E. F. FIOCK, D. C. GINNINGS and W. B. HOLTON, *J. Research Nat. Bur. Standards*, 1931, **6**, 881.

[44] J. LANGE, *Z. physik. Chem.*, 1940, **A. 187**, 27.

[45] O. FUCHS, *Z. Physik*, 1930, **63**, 824.

[46] H. M. CHADWELL, *J. Am. Chem. Soc.*, 1926, **48**, 1912.

[47] C. B. GATES, *J. Phys. Chem.*, 1912, **16**, 454.

[48] G. T. GERLACH, *Chem. and Ind.*, 1884, **7**, 277.

[49] See ref. 17.

[50] D. R. STULL, *J. Am. Chem. Soc.*, 1937, **59**, 2726.

[51] J. S. Guy and H. C. Jones, *Am. Chem. J.*, 1911, **46**, 137.

[52] J. H. Mathews, *J. Am. Chem. Soc.*, 1926, **48**, 562.

[53] W. D. Harkins and E. W. Wampler, *J. Am. Chem. Soc.*, 1931, **53**, 850.

[54] H. Harris, *J. Chem. Soc.*, 1925, **127**, 1049.

[55] R. J. W. LeFevre, *Trans. Faraday Soc.*, 1938, **34**, 1127.

[56] W. Herz, *Z. Elektrochem.*, 1917, **23**, 24.

[57] W. Herz and E. Lorentz, *Z. physik. Chem.*, 1929, **140**, 406.

[58] W. Herz and W. Rathman, *Chem. Z.*, 1913, **37**, 621.

[59] K. Hess, *Ber.*, 1930, **63**, 518.

[60] M. M. Hicks-Bruun and J. H. Bruun, *J. Research Nat. Bur. Standards*, 1932, **8**, 525.

[61] K. Hojendahl, *Dissertation*, Copenhagen, 1928.

[62] H. Hunt and H. T. Briscoe, *J. Phys. Chem.*, 1929, **33**, 1945.

[63] G. Jaffé, *Wiedemann's Ann.*, 1908, **25**, (4), 267.

[64] G. Jaffé, *Wiedemann's Ann.*, 1909, **28**, (4), 326.

[65] C. H. Schneider and C. C. Lynch, *J. Am. Chem. Soc.*, 1943, **65**, 1063.

[66] H. C. Jones, *Z. physik. Chem.*, 1899, **31**, 114.

[67] H. C. Jones, *Am. Chem. J.*, 1902, **27**, 16.

[68] A. Kailen and R. Obogi, *Monatsh.*, 1925, **45**, 215.

[69] C. H. Kao and Shao-Yuan Ma, *Sci. Rep. Tsing Hua Univ.*, 1932, A. **1**, 181; *Chem. Zentr.*, 1932, 3076.

[70] J. Kendall and P. M. Gross, *J. Am. Chem. Soc.*, 1920, **42**, 1776.

[71] See ref. 37.

[72] F. Fischer and C. Zerbe, *Brennstoff Chem.*, 1923, **4**, 17.

[73] A. G. Dorochewsky, *J. Russ. Phys. Chem. Soc.*, 1911, **43**, 66.

[74] H. Landolt and H. Jahn, *Z. physik. Chem.*, 1892, **10**, 289.

[75] K. F. Lowe, *Ann. Physik*, 1898, **66**, 390.

[76] T. M. Lowry, *J. Chem. Soc.*, 1914, **105**, 81.

[77] A. F. Forziati and A. R. Glascow, *J. Res. Nat. Bur. Stand.*, 1946, **36**, 129.

[78] W. Luginin, *Ann. Chim. Phys.*, 1898, **13**, (7), 289.

[79] H. Lund and J. Bjerrum, *Ber.*, 1931, **64**, 210.

[80] R. W. Lunt and M. A. G. Rau, *Proc. Roy. Soc.*, 1930, A. **126**, 213.

[81] P. C. Mahanti and R. N. Das Guta, *Indian J. Phys.*, 1929, **3**, 467.

[82] B. J. Mair, *J. Research Nat. Bur. Standards*, 1932, **9**, 457 (Rep. 482).

[83] C. Mascarelli and I. Musatty, *Gazz. chim. Ital.*, 1911, **41**, I, 80.

[84] N. B. Massy, F. L. Warren and J. H. Wolfenden, *J. Chem. Soc.*, 1932, 91.

[85] J. H. Mathews, *J. Am. Chem. Soc.*, 1926, **48**, 562.

[86] H. M. Huffmann, G. S. Parks and M. Barmore, *J. Am. Chem. Soc.*, 1931, **53**, 3876.

[87] L. Meyer, *Z. physik. Chem.*, 1920, **95**, 349.

[88] G. Middleton and F. C. Hymas, *Analyst*, 1931, **56**, 238.

[89] J. B. Miles, *Phys. Rev.*, 1929, **34**, 964.

[90] C. C. Miller, *Proc. Roy. Soc.*, 1924, A. **106**, 724.

[91] See ref. 55.

[92] H. Muller and K. Sack, *Physikal. Z.*, 1930, **31**, 815.

[93] R. Muller, V. Rascha and M. Wittmann, *Monatsh.*, 1927, **48**, 659.

94 H. Osaka, *Bull. Inst. Phys. Chem. Res.*, Japan, 1928, **7**, 873; *English Edition*, 1928, 80.

95 G. S. Parks, *J. Am. Chem. Soc.*, 1925, **47**, 338.

96 G. S. Parks and H. M. Huffman, *J. Am. Chem. Soc.*, 1926, **48**, 2788.

97 G. S. Parks and H. M. Huffman, *Ind. Eng. Chem.*, 1931, **23**, 1138.

98 G. S. Parks, H. M. Huffman and M. Barmore, *J. Am. Chem. Soc.*, 1933, **55**, 2733.

99 D. C. Ginnings and R. J. Corruccini, *Ind. Eng. Chem.*, 1948, **40**, 1990.

100 O. Fuchs, *Z. Physik*, 1930, **63**, 824.

101 H. Poltz, O. Steil and O. Strasser, *Z. physik. Chem.*, 1932, **17**, (B), 155.

102 N. A. Pushin and A. A. Glagoleva, *J. Chem. Soc.*, 1922, **121**, 2820.

103 W. R. Pyle, *Phys. Rev.*, 1931 **38**, (2), 1057.

104 M. Rabinowitsch, *Z. physik. Chem.*, 1926, **119**, 59, 70.

105 J. Gordon and W. F. Giauque, *J. Am. Chem. Soc.*, 1948, **70**, 1506.

106 V. H. Veley, *Proc. Roy. Soc.*, 1910, A. **82**, 217.

107 T. W. Richards, E. K. Carver and W. C. Schumb, *J. Am. Chem. Soc.*, 1919, **41**, 2019.

108 T. W. Richards and F. Barry, *J. Am. Chem. Soc.*, 1915, **37**, 993.

109 See ref. 86.

110 G. S. Parks, H. M. Huffmann and B. Thomas, *J. Am. Chem. Soc.*, 1930, **52**, 1032.

111 C. N. Rieber *et al.*, *Ber.*, 1925, **58**, 969.

112 H. M. Roberts and C. R. Bury, *J. Chem. Soc.*, 1923, 2037.

113 See ref. 37.

114 W. Rudolph, *Dissertation, Leipzig*, 1911.

115 R. Sanger, *Physikal. Z.*, 1926, **27**, 556.

116 R. Sangewald and A. Weissberger, *Physikal. Z.*, 1929, **30**, 268.

117 W. O. Pool, H. J. Harwood and A. W. Ralston, *J. Am. Chem. Soc.*, 1945, **67**, 775.

118 L. T. C. Schey, *Rec. trav. Chim.*, 1899, **18**, 181.

119 J. W. Stout and L. H. Fisher, *J. Chem. Phys.*, 1941, **9**, 163.

120 H. I. Schlesinger and A. W. Martin, *J. Am. Chem. Soc.*, 1914, **36**, 1589.

121 J. Schroeder and H. Steiner, *J. prakt. Chem.*, 1909, **79**, 49.

122 G. S. Parks and H. M. Huffmann, *J. Am. Chem. Soc.*, 1926, **48**, 2788; 1930, **52**, 4381.

123 O. Schumann, *Ann. Physik.*, 1881, **12**, (3), 40.

124 See ref. 77.

125 R. H. Smith and D. H. Andrews, *J. Am. Chem. Soc.*, 1931, **53**, 3644.

126 C. P. Smyth and H. E. Rogers, *J. Am. Chem. Soc.*, 1930, **52**, 1824.

127 C. P. Smyth and W. N. Stoops, *J. Am. Chem. Soc.*, 1928, **50**, 1883.

128 C. P. Smyth and W. N. Stoops, *J. Am. Chem. Soc.*, 1929, **51**, 3312.

129 C. P. Smyth and W. S. Walls, *J. Am. Chem. Soc.*, 1931, **53**, 2115.

130 H. C. S. Snethlage, *Z. physik. Chem.*, 1915, **90**, 13.

131 C. A. Taylor and W. H. Rinkenbach, *Ind. Eng. Chem.*, 1926, **18**, 676.

132 R. Teubner, *Dissertation, Leipzig*, 1928.

133 O. Faust, *Z. physik. Chem.*, 1912, **79**, 97.

134 M. Wojciechowski and E. Smith, *Rocz. Chem.*, 1937, **17**, 118.

135 See ref. 105.

[136] J. TIMMERMANS, *Bull. Soc. Chim. Belg.*, 1914, **27**, 334.

[137] J. TIMMERMANS, *Bull. Soc. Chim. Belg.*, 1927, **36**, 502.

[138] L. A. K. STAVELY and A. GUPTA, *Trans. Faraday Soc.*, 1949, **45**, 50.

[139] J. TIMMERMANS and M. HENNAUT-ROLAND, *J. Chim. Phys.*, 1930, **27**, 401.

[139a] E. E. ROGER, *J. Am. Chem. Soc.*, 1938, **60**, 2699.

[140] See ref. 77.

[141] B. B. ALLEN and S. P. LINGO, *J. Phys. Chem.*, 1939, **43**, 425.

[142] J. D. STRANATHAN, *J. Chem. Phys.*, 1938, **6**, 395.

[143] G. S. PARKS, H. M. HUFFMANN and M. BARMORE, *J. Am. Chem. Soc.*, 1933, **55**, 2733.

[144] M. T. TORAL and E. MOLES, *Anal. Fis. Quim.*, 1933, **31**, 735.

[145] V. C. G. Trew and G. M. C. WATKINS, *Trans. Faraday Soc.*, 1933, **29**, 1310.

[146] G. E. COATES and J. E. COATES, *J. Chem. Soc.*, 1944, 77.

[147] H. ULICH and W. NESPITAL, *Z. physik. Chem.*, 1932, **16**, (B), 221.

[148] O. FUCHS, *Z. Physik*, 1930, **63**, 824.

[149] See ref. 106.

[150] J. WADE and R. W. MERRIMAN, *J. Chem. Soc.*, 1912, **101**, 2429.

[151] P. WALDEN, *Z. physik. Chem.*, 1906, **54**, 129.

[152] P. WALDEN, *Z. physik. Chem.*, 1910, 70, 569.

[153] P. WALDEN, *Z. physik. Chem.*, 1912, **78**, 275.

[154] P. WALDEN, *Bull. Acad. Sci. Petersburg*, 1913, 564; *Chem. Zentr.*, 1913, II, 331.

[155] P. WALDEN, *Z. physik. Chem.*, 1930, **147**, (A), 1.

[156] P. WALDEN and E. J. BIRR, *Z. physik. Chem.*, 1931, **153**, (A), 1.

[157] P. WALDEN, H. ULICH and G. BUSCH, *Z. physik. Chem.*, 1926, **114**, 275.

[158] P. WALDEN, S. ZASTROW and L. ROUDOLF, *Ann. Acad. Sci. Fennicae*, 1929, **29**, No. 23.

[159] G. WEISSENBERGER, F. SCHUSTER and H. PAMER, *Monatsh.*, 1925, **46**, 287.

[160] J. L. WHITMAN and D. M. HURT, *J. Am. Chem. Soc.*, 1930, **52**, 4762.

[161] J. W. WILLIAMS, *Z. physik. Chem.*, 1928, **138**, 75.

[162] J. W. WILLIAMS, *J. Am. Chem. Soc.*, 1930, **52**, 1831.

[163] J. W. WILLIAMS and F. DANIELS, *J. Am. Chem. Soc.*, 1924, **46**, 903.

[164] G. D. OLIVER, M. EASTON and H. M. HUFFMANN, *J. Am. Chem. Soc.*, 1948, **70**, 1502.

[165] R. D. VOLD, *J. Am. Chem. Soc.*, 1937, **59**, 1515.

[166] See ref. 55.

[167] R. WILLSTATTER and V. L. KING, *Ber.*, 1913, **46**, 534.

[168] K. L. WOLF, *Physikal. Z.*, 1930, **31**, 227.

[169] K. L. WOLF and W. J. GROSS, *Z. physik. Chem.*, 1931, **14**, (B), 305.

[170] C. T. ZAHN, *Phys. Rev.*, 1930, **35**, (2), 848.

[171] U. ZANNINOVICH-TESSARIN, *Gazz. chim. ital*, 1896, **26** (i), 311; *Z. physik. Chem.*, 1896, **19**, 251.

[172] A. J. ZMACZYNSKI, *J. Chim. Phys.*, 1930, **27**, 503.

[173] F. FAIRBROTHER, *J. Chem. Soc.*, 1934, 1846.

[174] G. S. HOOPER and C. A. KRAUS, *J. Am. Chem. Soc*, 1934, **56**, 2265.

[175] E. L. SKAU, *J. Phys. Chem.*, 1933, **37**, 609.

[176] E. WERTYPOROCH and T. FIRLA, *Z. physik. Chem.*, 1932, **162**, (A) 398.

[177] C. T. Zahn, *Physik. Z.*, 1933, **34**, 570.
[178] National Bur. Standards U.S.A., American Petroleum Research, *Project* 44.
[179] See ref. 55.
[180] D. C. Jones, *J. Chem. Soc.*, 1929, 799.

TABLE II, 2

ENTROPIES S_0 OF IONS IN AQUEOUS SOLUTION AT 25 °C.
(in cal.degree^{-1}. mol^{-1}), with reference to $S_{0, \mathrm{H}^{\cdot}} = 0$

H·	0·00		Se···	−48 †	Ir····	−106	
Li·	4·7	± 1·0	Y···	−34 †	U····	−67·9 †	
Na·	14·0	± 0·4	Ga···	−69 †	OH′	2·49 ± 0·06	
K·	24·2	± 0·2	In···	−42 †	F′	2·3 ± 2	
Rb·	28·7	± 0·7	Tl···	−35 †	Cl′	13·50	†
Cs·	31·8	± 0·6	As···	−60 †	Br′	19·7	†
NH4·	26·6	± 0·6 *	Sb···	−43 †	I′	25·3	†
Ag·	17·54	± 0·15	V···	−65 †	IO3′	28·0 ± 1·0	
Ag(NH3)·′	57·8	± 1·0	Cr···	−65 †	HS′	14·9 ± 1·0	
Tl·	30·5	± 0·4	Mn···	−59 †	HSO3′	32·6 ± 1·5	
Hg2··	19·7	± 3	Fe···	−61 ± 5	SO3″	3 ± 3	
Be··	−27	†	Rh···	−60 †	HSO4′	30·6 ± 2	
Mg··	31·6	± 3	Si····	−177 †	SO4″	4·4 ± 0·5 *	
Ca··	−12·7	± 0·6 *	Ti····	−109 †	NO3′	29·9 ± 1	
Sr··	−7·3	± 1·5	Ge····	−157 †	H2PO4′	21·6 ± 0·3 *	
Ba··	2·3	± 0·3	Zr····	−81 †	HPO4″	8·7 ± 1·0 *	
Cu··	−26·5	± 1·0	Sn····	−95 †	PO4‴	−52 ± 2 *	
Zn··	−25·7	± 1·0	Pb····	−84 †	H2AsO4′	28 ± 1·0 *	
Cd··	−16·4	± 1·5	Th····	−65 †	HCO3′	22·2 ± 0·8	
Sn··	−4·9	± 1·0	V····	−114 †	CO3″	−13·0 ± 1·0	
Pb··	3·9	± 0·9	Nb····	−101 †	C2O4″	9·6 ± 1·0	
Fe··	−25·9	± 1·0	Mo····	−103 †	CN′	25 ± 5	
Co··	−27	†	Te····	−79 †	MnO4′	46·7 ± 0·4	
Ni··	−31	†	Ru····	−108 †	CrO4″	10·6 ± 1·0	
Mn··	−19·1	†	W····	−103 †			
Al···	−76	± 10	Os····	−104 †			

References:

W. M. Latimer, K. S. Pitzer and W. V. Smith, *J. Am. Chem. Soc.*, 1938, **60**, 1829.
* C. C. Stephenson, *J. Am. Chem. Soc.*, 1944, **66**, 1436.
† A. F. Kapustinsky, *Acta Physicochim. U.R.S.S.*, 1941, **14**, 503.

[1] For conversion to absolute entropies a value of S_0 for H· given by R. Parsons and J. O'M. Bockris (*Trans. Faraday Soc.*, 1951. **47**, 914), as —4·6 e.u. may be used.
[2] Entropies of rare earth metal ions are given by A. F. Kapustinsky (*loc. cit.*).

TABLE II, 3

TOTAL (ELECTRONIC + ATOMIC) POLARISABILITIES (α_0) OF IONS AND MOLECULES

Ion or molecule		$\alpha_0 . 10^{24}$ cm.^{3}	Ion or molecule		$\alpha_0 . 10^{24}$ cm.^{3}
Li·	Ref. 1	0·075 ±0·02	Ce····	Ref. 5	1·20
Na·	,, 1	0·21 ±0·02	F′	,, 1	0·99 ±0·02
K·	,, 1	0·87 ±0·02	Cl′	,, 2	3·02 ±0·02
Rb·	,, 1	1·81 ±0·02	Br′	,, 1	4·17 ±0·02
Cs·	,, 1	2·79 ±0·02	I′	,, 1	6·28 ±0·02
Cu·	,, 5	1·81	O″	,, 5	2·76
Ag·	,, 5	1·85 ±0·02	S″	,, 5	5·90
Be··	,, 5	0·035	Se″	,, 5	6·42
Mg··	,, 1	012 ±0·02	Te″	,, 5	9·60
Ca··	,, 5	0·531	He	,, 1	0·20
Sr··	,, 1, 5	1·42 ±0·02	Ne	,, 1	0·392
Ba··	,, 5	1·69	A	,, 1	1·63
Cu··	,, 5	0·670	Kr	,, 1	2·46
Zn··	,, 5	0·114	Xe	,, 1	4·00
Cd··	,, 5	0·96	Na	,, 3	29·7
Hg··	,, 5	1·99	Hg	,, 3	10·43
Pb··	,, 5	4·34	H_2	,, 4	0·787 ±0·02
Al···	,, 1	0·065 ±0·02	O_2	,, 3	1·36 ±0·01
Se···	,, 5	0·382	N_2	,, 3	1·73 ±0·02
Y···	,, 5	1·02	CO	,, 4	1·844 ±0·02
La···	,, 5	1·58	H_2O	,, 3	1·444 ±0·02
C····	,, 5	0·012	H_2S	,, 3	3·642 ±0·02
Si····	,, 1	0·034 ±0·02	SO_2	,, 3	3·774 ±0·02
Ti····	,, 5	0·272	N_2O	,, 3	2·921 ±0·02
Zr····	,, 5	0·800	O_3	,, 3	2·845 ±0·02

References:

[1] M. BORN and W. HEISENBERG, Z. *Physik*, 1924, **23**, 388.
[2] C. F. J. BÖTTCHER, *Rec. Trav. Chim.*, 1943, **62**, 325.
[3] C. CUTHBERTSON, *Proc. Roy. Soc.*, 1909, A. **83**, 171; *Phil. Trans.*, 1914, 213.
[4] A. VAN ITTERBEEK and K. DE CLIPELIER, *Physica*, 1948, **14**, 349.
[5] F. C. FRANK, *Trans. Faraday Soc.*, 1937, **33**, 513.

TABLE II, 4

REFRACTIVE INDICES (n) OF ETHANOL-WATER MIXTURES AT 25 °C. FOR Na_D RADIATION

wt.% H_2O	$n^{25°}_{Na_D}$	wt.% H_2O	$n^{25°}_{Na_D}$	wt.% H_2O	$n^{25°}_{Na_D}$
0 *	1·35912	34	1·36227	68	1·35314
1	1·35952	35	1·36216	69	1·35264
2	1·35991	36	1·36204	70	1·35213
3	1·36030	37	1·36191	71	1·35160
4	1·36063	38	1·36177	72	1·35104
5	1·36092	39	1·36162	73	1·35047
6	1·36118	40	1·36146	74	1·34989
7	1·36141	41	1·36130	75	1.34927
8	1·36162	42	1·36113	76	1·34864
9	1·36181	43	1·36094	77	1·34800
10	1·36198	44	1·36075	78	1·34734
11	1·36213	45	1·36055	79	1·34668
12	1·36226	46	1·36035	80	1·34600
13	1·36239	47	1·36014	81	1·34531
14	1·36251	48	1·35992	82	1·34463
15	1·36261	49	1·35969	83	1·34394
16	1·36269	50	1·35946	84	1·34323
17	1·36276	51	1·35921	85	1·34251
18	1·36282	52	1·35895	86	1·34180
19	1·36287	53	1·35867	87	1·34109
20	1·36290	54	1.35839	88	1·34039
21	1·36293	55	1·35810	89	1·33969
22	1·36294	56	1·35780	90	1·33899
23	1·36294	57	1·35749	91	1·33830
24	1·36293	58	1·35716	92	1·33762
25	1·36290	59	1·35683	93	1·33694
26	1·36287	60	1·35647	94	1·33626
27	1·36283	61	1·35612	95	1·33560
28	1·36278	62	1·35573	96	1·33495
29	1·36272	63	1·35534	97	1·33432
30	1·36265	64	1·35493	98	1·33371
31	1·36257	65	1·35451	99	1·33311
32	1·36248	66	1·35407	100	1·33252
33	1.36238	67	1·35361		

* Extrapolated; accuracy of $n^{25°}_{Na_D}$ ± 0·00003.

T. A. SCOTT, J. Phys. Chem., 1946, 50, 406.

TABLE II, 5

MOLAR REFRACTION R OF SALTS IN AQUEOUS SOLUTION AT 25 °C. AT INFINITE
DILUTION FOR THE WAVE LENGTH 5875·62 Å. (Na_{D_2}).

R cm.³	NaCl	KCl	NaBr	$1/2SrCl_2$	NH_4NO_3	$1/2Na_2SO_4$
	9·232	11·296	12·825	19·980	15·317	7·547

Accurate to ±0·005 cm.³

A. KRUIS, Z. Physik. Chem., 1936, B. 34, 51.

TABLE II, 5 (Continued)

GRAM IONIC REFRACTION FOR IONS IN AQUEOUS SOLUTION AT 25 °C. AT
INFINITE DILUTION FOR WAVE LENGTH 5875·62 Å.

Ion	R cm.³	Reference	Ion	R cm.³	Reference
Na˙	0·200	1	F′	2·60	2
K˙	2·264	1	Cl′	9·032	1
NH_4˙	4·30	1	Br′	12·625	1
$1/2Sr$˙˙	0·958	1	I′	19·23	1
$1/2Ba$˙˙	2·185	2	$1/2SO_4$″	7·347	1
$1/2Ca$˙˙	0·355	2	OH′	5·10	2
$1/2Mg$˙˙	0·90	2	ClO_4′	13·240	1
$1/2Zn$˙˙	0·30	1	H_2O	3·7156	1

References:

[1] A. KRUIS, Z. physik. Chem., 1936, B. 34, 51.
[2] Optical properties of electrolytic solutions. G. KORTÜM, Sammlung Chem. und Chem. tech. Vorträge, Stuttgart, 1936, 43, 57.
See also L. PAULING, Proc. Roy. Soc., 1927, 114 A, 181.

TABLE II, 6

CRYSTAL IONIC RADII OF ELEMENTS

Element	radii in Å	Element	radii in Å
H′	2·08 (2·08)	Ge ⃛⃛	0·53 (0·76)
He	(0·93)	As ⃛⃛⃛	0·47 (0·71)
Li˙	0·60 (0·60)	Se ⃛⃛⃛	0·42 (0·66)
Be˙˙	0·31 (0·44)	Br ⃛⃛⃛⃛	0·39 (0·62)
B⃛	0·20 (0·35)	Ge⁗	2·72 (3·71)
C⃛⃛	0·15 (0·29)	As‴	2·22 (2·85)
N⃛⃛⃛	0·11 (0·25)	Se″	1·98 (2·32)
O⃛⃛⃛	0·09 (0·22)	Br′	1·95 (1·95)
F⃛⃛⃛⃛	0·07 (0·19)	Kr	(1·69)
C⁗	2·60 (4·14)	Rb˙	1·48 (1·48)
N‴	1·71 (2·47)	Sr˙˙	1·13 (1·32)
O″	1·40 (1·76)	Y⃛	0·93 (1·20)
F′	1·36 (1·36)	Zr⃛⃛	0·80 (1·09)
Ne	(1·12)	Nb⃛⃛⃛	0·70 (1·00)
Na˙	0·95 (0·95)	Mo⃛⃛⃛⃛	0·62 (0·93)
Mg˙˙	0·65 (0·82)	Ag˙	1·26 (1·26)
Al⃛	0·50 (0·72)	Cd˙˙	0·97 (1·14)
Si⃛⃛	0·41 (0·65)	In⃛	0·81 (1·04)
P⃛⃛⃛	0·34 (0·59)	Sn⃛⃛	0·71 (0·96)
S⃛⃛⃛⃛	0·29 (0·53)	Sb⃛⃛⃛	0·62 (0·89)
Cl⃛⃛⃛⃛⃛	0·26 (0·49)	Te⃛⃛⃛⃛	0·56 (0·82)
Si⁗	2·71 (3·84)	I⃛⃛⃛⃛⃛	0·50 (0·77)
P‴	2·12 (2·79)	Sn⁗	2·94 (3·70)
S″	1·84 (2·19)	Sb‴	2·45 (2·95)
Cl′	1·81 (1·81)	Te″	2·21 (2·50)
Ar	(1·54)	I′	2·16 (2·16)
K˙	1·33 (1·33)	Xe	(1·90)
Ca˙˙	0·99 (1·18)	Cs˙	1·69 (1·69)
Sc⃛	0·81 (1·06)	Ba˙˙	1·35 (1·53)
Ti⃛⃛	0·68 (0·96)	La⃛	1·15 (1·39)
V⃛⃛⃛	0·59 (0·88)	Ce⃛⃛	1·01 (1·27)
Cr⃛⃛⃛⃛	0·52 (0·81)	Au˙	1·37 (1·37)
Mn⃛⃛⃛⃛⃛	0·46 (0·75)	Hg˙˙	1·10 (1·25)
Cu˙	0·96 (0·96)	Tl⃛	0·95 (1·15)
Zn˙˙	0·74 (0·88)	Pb⃛⃛	0·84 (1·06)
Ga⃛	0·62 (0·81)	Bi⃛⃛⃛	0·74 (0·98)

Univalent crystal radii of ions are given in brackets. Accurate to ±1%.

L. PAULING, J. Am. Chem. Soc., 1927, 49, 771; Idem, Nature of the Chemical Bond Ithaca, 1948.

TABLE II, 7
INTERATOMIC COVALANT BOND DISTANCES IN Å.

	H 0·30				
	B	C	N	O	F
Single-bond radius	0·88	0·77	0·70	0·66	0·64
Double-bond ,,	0·76	0·67	0·61	0·57	0·55
Triple-bond ,,	0·68	0·60	0·55	0·51	
		Si	P	S	Cl
Single-bond radius		1·17	1·10	1·04	0·99
Double-bond ,,		1·07	1·00	0·95	0·90
Triple-bond ,,		1·00	0·93	0·88	
		Ge	As	Se	Br
Single-bond radius		1·22	1·21	1·17	1·14
Double-bond ,,		1·12	1·11	1·08	1·05
		Sn	Sb	Te	I
Single-bond radius		1·40	1·41	1·37	1·33
Double-bond ,,		1·30	1·31	1·28	1·24

Bond	Substance	Method [1]	One-half of obs. distance	Assigned * radius
C–C	Diamond	X-ray *	0·771	0·77
F–F	F_2 (g)	E.D. [2]	0·73	0·64
Si–Si	Si (c)	X-ray	1·17	1·17
P–P	P_4 (g)	E.D. [3]	1·10	1·10
P–P	P (c) (black)	X-ray [4]	1·09	1·10
S–S	S_8 (c)	X-ray [5]	1·05	1·04
S–S	S_8 (g)	E.D. [6]	1·05	1·04
Cl–Cl	Cl_2 (g)	Sp. *	0·992	0·99
Ge–Ge	Ge (c)	X-ray	1·22	1·22
As–As	As_4 (g)	E.D. [3]	1·22	1·21
As–As	As (c)	X-ray	1·25	1·21
Se–Se	Se (c)	X-ray	1·16	1·17
Br–Br	Br_2 (g)	Sp.	1·140	1·14
Sn–Sn	Sn (c) (grey)	X-ray	1·40	1·40
Sb–Sb	Sb (c)	X-ray	1·43	1·41
Te–Te	Te (c)	X-ray	1·38	1·37
I–I	I_2 (g)	Sp.	1·33	1·33

c ≡ crystal;   g ≡ gas.   Accuracy: ±1 - 3%.

* See discussion in PAULING, *Nature of the Chemical Bond*, Ithaca, 1948.

TABLE II, 7 (*Continued*)

References:

[1] "X-ray" signifies the X-ray study of crystals, E.D. the electron-diffraction study of gas molecules, and Sp. the spectroscopic study of gas molecules.

[2] L. O. BROCKWAY, *J. Am. Chem. Soc.*, 1938, **60**, 1348.

[3] L. R. MAXWELL, V. M. MOSLEY and S. B. HENDRICKS, *J. Chem. Phys.*, 1935, **3**, 698.

[4] B. HULTGREN and B. E. WARREN, *Phys. Rev.*, 1935, **47**, 808. Approximately the same value is found also in amorphous red phosphorus, amorphous black phosphorus, and liquid phosphorus, C. D. THOMAS and N. S. GINGRICH, *J. Chem. Phys.*, 1938, **6**, 659.

[5] B. E. WARREN and J. T. BURWELL, *J. Chem. Phys.*, 1935, **3**, 6.

[6] L. R. MAXWELL, S. B. HENDRICKS and V. M. MOSLEY, *Phys. Rev.*, 1936, **49**, 199.

TABLE II, 8

ELECTRON WORK FUNCTIONS OF METALS

Metal	Electron Work Function in e.volt	Metal	Electron Work Function in e.volt	Metal	Electron Work Function in e.volt
Li	1·40	Cu	4·46	Te	4·70
Be	3·10	Zn	3·66	Ba	1·73
Na	1·60	Ga	3·80	Ta	3·96
Mg	3·58	Ge	4·50	W	4·38
Al	3·38	Se	4·42	Os	4·55
K	1·60	Zr	3·60	Ir	4·57
Ca	3·33	Mo	4·48	Pt	4·52
Ti	4·14	Ru	4·52	Au	4·46
V	4·44	Rh	4·52	Hg	4·50
Cr	4·38	Pd	4·49	Tl	3·84
Mn	4·14	Ag	4·44	Pb	3·94
Fe	4·40	Cd	4·00	Bi	4·17
Co	4·21	Sn	4·09	Th	3·46
Ni	4·32	Sb	4·14	U	4·32

Accuracy: ±0·03 e.volt.

O. KLEIN and E. LANGE, *Z. Elektrochem.*, 1938, **44**, 558.

TABLE II, 9

SUCCESSIVE IONISATION POTENTIALS (*I*) OF THE ELEMENTS IN ELECTRON VOLTS

Metal	I_{Me}.	I_{Me}..	I_{Me}...	I_{Me}....
Be	9·28	27·4	—	—
Mg	7·61	22·6	—	—
Al	5·96	24·1	53·0	—
Ca	6·09	17·9	—	—
Cr	6·74	23·3	50·3	—
Mn	7·39	23·1	—	—
Fe	7·83	24·3	—	—
Ni	7·61	25·8	—	—
Zn	9·36	27·2	—	—
As	10·5	30·6	58·8	—
Se	9·70	—	—	—
Sr	5·67	16·7	—	—
Mo	7·06	—	—	—
Cd	8·96	25·8	—	—
Sn	7·03	21·8	52·3	92·8
Ba	5·19	15·1	—	—
W	8·1	—	—	—
Pt	8·9	—	—	—
Pb	7·38	22·4	—	98·2

Accuracy: ±0·05 e.volt.

O. KLEIN and E. LANGE, Z. *Elektrochem.*, 1938, *44*, 561.

TABLE II, 10

ELECTRICAL RESISTIVITIES (R_0) OF METALS AT 0 °C. AND THEIR TEMPERATURE COEFFICIENTS α

$$\left[\alpha = \frac{1}{R_0} \cdot \frac{R_{100} - R_0}{100} \; ; \quad R_0 \text{ in ohm cm.} \; . \; 10^{-6} \right]$$

	R_0	α		R_0	α
Al	2·5	0·0043	Hg	94·07	— *
Sb	40	0·0050	Mo	5·7	0·0033
As	36	0·0039	Ni	6·7	0·0064
Ba	50 - 75	—	Nb	17	0·003
Be	12·2	—	Os	9·5	0·0042
Bi	115	0·0045	Pd	10·7	0·0037
Cd	7·7	0·0042	Pt	10·5	0·0039
Ca	∼ 5	0·0033	K	6·7	0·0052 (0 °C.—m.p.)
C	∼ 30	—	Re	21	0·0031
Ce	70	—	Rh	5	0·0046
Cs	19	0·0044	Rb	12·5	0·0052
Cr	14	—	Ru	14	—
Co	9·7	0·0033	Ag	1·6	0·0041
Cu	1·55	0·0043	Na	4·3	0·0055 (0 °C.—m.p.)
Ga	50	0·0040 (0 °C.—m.p.)	Sr	30	0·0038
Ge	∼300	—	Ta	15	0·0031
Au	2·4	0·0034	Tl	17	0·0051
Hf	32	—	Th	18	—
In	8·3	0·0040	Sn	13	0·0045
Ir	5·3	0·0040	Ti	55	0·0054
Fe	10	0·0065	W	5·3	0·0048
La	55	—	U	∼400	—
Pb	19	0·0042	V	∼170	—
Li	8·5	0·0045	Zn	5·9	0·0041
Mg	4·4	0·0040	Zr	41	0·0044
Mn	∼150	—			

* Temp. dependence is given by

$$R_t = 94·077 \cdot 10^{-6} \left[1 + 0·8862 \, (t \cdot 10^{-3}) + 1·1057 \, (t - 30) \cdot 10^{-6} \right],$$

where t is in °C.

Metals Reference Book, SMITHELLS, Butterworths, London, 1949.

TABLE II, 11

PROPERTIES OF MOLECULAR AND METALLIC LIQUIDS

1. Molecular Liquids, non-polar

Liquid	T_F	T_B	L_F	L_B	B	A	η	$\mu \cdot 10^{18}$ e.s.u.	Ref.
A	84·0	87·5	0·27	1·50	0·524	1·24	2·83		1
N_2	63·4	77·4	0·47	1·34	0·468	0·762	3·11		1
CO	66·2	81·2	0·22	1·41	0·463	0·951	3·21		1
CH_4	89·2	111·8	0·24	2·20	0·740	0·347	2·25		2
O_2	54·8	70·2	0·106	1·67	0·406	1·945	8·09		1
C_2H_4	103·8	169·4	—	—	0·739	2·01	7·24		2

2. Molecular liquids, dipolar

C_2H_5Br	154·0	311·0	—	6·6	1·12	6·25	25	1·86	3
CH_3I	206·9	315·6	—	6·5	1·12	7·11	11	1·65	3
C_2H_5I	164·5	345·2	—	7·25	1·25	7·08	35	1·65	3
C_3H_7I	161·6	375·4	—	—	1·41	6·54	56	1·65	3

3. Molecular liquids, H-bonded

H_2O	273·1	373·1	1·43	9·68	3·05	0·59	18		3
CH_3OH	175·2	337·5	0·53	8·4	1·84	2·49	50	1·67	3
C_2H_5OH	155·5	351·5	1·14	9·4	2·34	2·11	500	1·70	3
C_3H_7OH	146·0	370·8	—	9·9	3·16	0·97	5500	1·66	3
C_4H_9OH	183·2	390·7	2·22	10·4	3·46	0·72	1000	1·66	3
$(CH_3)_3C.OH$	298·5	355·8	1·58	9·6	5·62	0·036	50	1·66	3
HCOOH	281·4	373·5	0·33	5·8	2·49	2·44	24	1·45	3
CH_3COOH	289·6	391·1	0·35	5·8	1·93	4·22	12	1·04	3
C_3H_7COOH	251·0	414·1	0·65	7·6	1·78	5·12	19	0·88	3

References:
[1] N. S. RUDENKO and C. W. SCHUBNIKOW, *Physik. Z. Sovietunion*, 1934, **6**, 470.
[2] *ibid.*, 1935, **8**, 179.
[3] A. G. WARD, *Trans. Faraday Soc.*, 1937, **33**, 88 (quoted).

TABLE II, 11 (*Continued*)

METALLIC LIQUIDS — CLOSE PACKED STRUCTURE

Metal	T_F	T_B	L_F	L_B	B	A $\times 10^4$	η	Ref.
Na	370·5	1153	0·61	25	0·96	21·5	7·9	1, 2
K	335·3	1033	0·57	21	1·15	9·75	5·5	1, 2
Cu	1356	2573	2·75	116	—	—	37	3
Ag	1233	2223	2·63	59·5	4·87	56·9	41·4	2, 4
Zn	692·4	1180	1·74 *	24	2·92	41·4	33·4	2
Cd	593·9	1040	1·48	26	1·585	66·2	25·3	2
Hg	234·2	630	0·57	14	0·598	55·5	20·1	2
Sn	504·8	2533	1·73 *	18	1·603	41·3	20·3	5
Pb	600·5	1893	1·31 *	46	2·32	40·8	28·5	2, 3
Sb	903·5	1653	2·92 *	45	2·92	28·8	14·6	3
Bi	544	1723	2·70 *	46	1·715	38·2	18·6	5

Notes:
* Values of J. H. AWBERY and E. GRIFFITHS, *Proc. Phys. Soc.*, 1926, **38**, 378.
Mean of S. ERK's values (*Z. Physik.*, 1928, **47**, 892) and a careful determination published later (*J. Am. Chem. Soc.*, 1928, **50**, 2878 by E. C. BINGHAM and T. R. THOMPSON). B, A and η are related by the viscosity equation $\eta = Ae^{B/RT}$, where A is such that the calculated viscosities are in poises((c.g.s. system). In the table η is given in millipoises, B, L_F and L_B in k.cal./g.mol and T_F, T_B in °K., where L_F and L_B are the latent heats of fusion and vaporisation and T_F, T_B the melting and boiling points, respectively, at 1at. (A_{45}) pressure.

References:
1 F. SAUERWALD, *Z. Metallkunde*, 1934, **26**, 259.
2 K. GERING and F. SAUERWALD, *Z. anorg. Chem.*, 1935, **223**, 205.
3 A. BIENAS and F. SAUERWALD, *ibid.*, 1927, **161**, 51.
4 W. RADECKER and F. SAUERWALD, *ibid.*, 1931, **203**, 156.
5 F. SAUERWALD and K. TOPLER, *ibid.*, 1926, **157**, 117.

TABLE II, 12

DENSITIES AND VAPOUR PRESSURES OF SOME METHANOL-WATER MIXTURES

Temp. °C.	Density g./ml. (10% Methanol)	Density g./ml. (20% Methanol)
0	0·9842	0·9721
5	0·9839	0·9709
10	0·9834	0·9696
15	0·9825	0·9681
20	0·9813	0·9663
25	0·9799	0·9644
30	0·9782	0·9622
35	0·9763	0·9598
40	0·9742	0·9572

Temp. °C.	Vapour Press.(mm. Hg 0°C.) (10% Methanol)	Vapour Press.(mm. Hg 0°C.) (20% Methanol)
0	6·57	8·58
5	9·35	12.50
10	13·11	17·30
15	18·18	23·90
20	24·90	32·65
25	33·7	43·8
30	45·1	58·7
35	59·6	77·1
40	78·1	100·6

Accuracy of densities $\pm$ 0·0001; of vapour pressures $\pm$ 0·05 - 0·1 mm. Hg. Composition of solution given as wt.%.

H. S. HARNED and H. C. THOMAS, *J. Am. Chem. Soc.*, 1936, **57**, 1666.

TABLE II, 13

DENSITIES AND VAPOUR PRESSURES OF SOME ETHANOL-WATER MIXTURES

Temp. °C.	Density g./ml. (10% Ethanol)	Density g./ml. (20% Ethanol)
0	0·9841	0·9772
10	0·9839	0·9725
20	0·9818	0·9686
25	0·9804	0·9664
30	0·9787	0·9639
40	0·9747	0·9585

Temp. °C.	Vapour Press. mm. Hg (10% Ethanol)	Vapour Press. mm. Hg (20% Ethanol)
0	6·1	7·7
10	12·4	15·3
20	23·5	28·5
25	38·0	45·5
30	51·5	61·9
40	78·5	91·1

Composition is given as wt.%.

A. PATTERSON and W. A. FELSING, *J. Am. Chem. Soc.*, 1942, **64**, 1478.

TABLE II, 14

VAPOUR PRESSURES OF SATURATED SOLUTIONS AT 25 °C. IN TERMS
OF WATER ACTIVITY

(The system is that of the solid stable in contact with saturated solution at 25 °C.
* a_w = water activity.)

Solid phase	* a_w	Solid phase	a_w
$K_2Cr_2O_7$	0·9800	$NaBr . 2H_2O$	0·577
KNO_3	0·9248	$Mg(NO_3)_2 . 6H_2O$	0·5286
$BaCl_2 . 2H_2O$	0·9019	$LiNO_3 . 3H_2O$	0·4706
KCl	0·8426	$K_2CO_3 . 2H_2O$	0·4276

TABLE II, 14 (Continued)

Solid phase	a_w	Solid phase	a_w
KBr	0·8071	$MgCl_2 . 6H_2O$	0·3300
NaCl	0·7528	$K(C_2H_3O_2) . 1·5H_2O$	0·2245
$NaNO_3$	0·7379	$LiCl . H_2O$	0·1105
$SrCl_2 . 6H_2O$	0·7083	$NaOH . H_2O$	0·0703

Symbols are defined in the following table.
R. H. STOKES and R. A. ROBINSON, *Ind. Eng. Chem.*, 1949, **41**, 2013; cf. also loc. cit. p. 2014.

TABLE II, 15

CONCENTRATIONS OF SOLUTIONS GIVING SPECIFIED VAPOUR PRESSURES AT 25 °C.

* a_w	H_2SO_4		NaOH		$CaCl_2$	
	m	%	m	%	m	%
0·95	1·263	11·02	1·465	5·54	0·927	9·33
0·90	2·224	17·91	2·726	9·83	1·584	14·95
0·85	3·025	22·88	3·840	13·32	2·118	19·03
0·80	3·730	26·79	4·798	16·10	2·579	22·25
0·75	4·398	30·14	5·710	18·60	2·995	24·95
0·70	5·042	33·09	6·565	20·80	3·400	27·40
0·65	5·686	35·80	7·384	22·80	3·796	29·64
0·60	6·341	38·35	8·183	24·66	4·188	31·73
0·55	7·013	40·75	8·974	26·42	4·581	33·71
0·50	7·722	43·10	9·792	28·15	4·990	35·64
0·45	8·482	45·41	10·64	29·86	5·431	37·61
0·40	9·304	47·71	11·54	31·58	5·912	39·62
0·35	10·21	50·04	12·53	33·38	6·478	41·83
0·30	11·25	52·45	13·63	35·29	7·183	44·36
0·25	12·47	55·01	14·96	37·45	—	—
0·20	13·94	57·76	16·67	40·00	—	—
0·15	15·81	60·80	19·10	43·32	—	—
0·10	18·48	64·45	23·05	47·97	—	—
0·05	23·17	69·44	—	—	—	—

* a_w = water activity = p/p_0, where p = vapour pressure of solution, and p_0 = vapour pressure of pure water; m = molality = mols of (anhydrous) solute per 1000 grams of water; % = percentage of (anhydrous) solute by weight.

R. H. STOKES and R. A. ROBINSON, *Ind. Eng. Chem.*, 1949, **41**, 2013.

TABLE II, 16

APPARENT MOLAR VOLUMES (φ) OF TETRA-ETHYLAMMONIUM IODIDE IN WATER

0 °C.		
Molality	Density ratio * ϱ	φ
0·09993	1·007502	180·75
0·25005	1·018100	181·50
0·50013	1·034765	181·37

25 °C.		
0·0004437	1·000015	22
0·0010267	1·000061	19
0·0050013	1·000351	187
0·0100051	1·000713	186
0·0199685	1·001444	185
0·0499761	1·003571	185·5
0·0998798	1·007078	185·5
0·4997866	1·033012	185·55
0·9990455	1·061608	184·70
1·49977725	1·086331	184·21

40 °C.		
0·0199685	1·001436	68·3
0·0499761	1·003555	186·74
0·0998798	1·007000	187·28
0·4997866	1·032614	187·31
0·9990435	1·061028	186·25
1·4977723	1·085477	185·78
1·998605	1·110394	183·27

85 °C.		
0·19986	1·013756	191·74
0·49938	1·031880	193·35
0·99973	1·059000	193·00
1·9992	1·103804	191·89
2·9919	1·139460	190·70

TABLE II, 16 (*Continued*)

* Density ratio $\varrho = \dfrac{\text{density of solution}}{\text{density of water}}$

J. BOWLER REED, Ph. D. *Thesis*, London, 1950.

TABLE II, 17

PARTIAL MOLAR VOLUMES $(\overline{V}_2)$

OF TETRA-ETHYLAMMONIUM IODIDE AT INFINITE DILUTION IN WATER

Temp. °C.	$\overline{V}_2$
0	181·2
25	185·3
40	187·4
85	190·9

APPARENT AND PARTIAL MOLAR VOLUMES

OF TETRA-ETHYLAMMONIUM BROMIDE AT 0 °C. IN WATER

Molality	ϱ	φ	$\overline{V}_2$
0·10	1·00401	169·87	170·3
0·20	1·00785	170·74	

J. BOWLER REED, Ph. D. *Thesis*, London, 1950.

TABLE II, 18

DIELECTRIC CONSTANTS OF IONIC CRYSTALS

Substance	ε Static dielectric constant	ε_0 High frequency dielectric constant	Substance	ε Static dielectric constant
LiF	9·27	1·92	PbO	26
LiCl	11·05	2·75	PbS	18
LiBr	12·1	3·16	PbSO$_4$	14
LiI	11·03	3·80	Pb(NO$_3$)$_2$	17
NaF	6·0	1·74	PbCO$_3$	24
NaCl	5·62	2·25	CuO	18
NaBr	5·99	2·62	FeO	14
NaI	6·60	2·91	TiO$_2$	114
KF	6·05	1·85	SnO$_2$	24
KCl	4·68	2·13	HgCl$_2$	14
KBr	4·78	2·33	PbMoO$_4$	24
KI	4·94	2·69	Pb$_5$Cl(PO$_4$)$_3$	47·5
RbF	5·91	1·93		
RbCl	5·0	2·19		
RbBr	5·6	2·33	PbO to Pb$_5$Cl(PO$_4$)$_3$:	
RbI	5·0	2·63	*Reference 2.*	
AgCl	12·3	4·01		
AgBr	13·1	4·62		
MgO	9·8	2·95		
CaO	11·8	3·28		
SrO	13·3	3·31		
CsCl	7·20	2·60		
CsBr	6·51	2·78		
CsI	5·65	3·03		
NH$_4$Cl	6·96	2·62		
TlBr	29·8	5·41		
TlCl	31·9	5·10		
CuCl	10·0	3·57		
CuBr	8·0	4·08		
ZnS	8·3	5·07		
BeO	7·35	2·95		
CaF$_2$	8·63	1·99		
SrF$_2$	7·69	2·08		
BaF$_2$	7·33	2·09		

LiF to BaF$_2$: *Reference 1.*

[1] K. HOJENDAHL, *Kgl. Danske Vidensk. Selskab*, 1938, **16**, 2.
[2] F. C. FRANK, *Trans. Faraday Soc.*, 1937, **33**, 513.

T.

DIELECTRIC CONSTANTS OF DIOXAN-WATER MIXTURES

Dioxan wt.%	Temperature °C.					
	0	10	20	30	40	50
0	88·31	78·86	69·16	59·34	49·37	39·ʃ
10	84·25	75·06	65·68	56·24	46·71	37·ʒ
20	80·37	71·43	62·38	53·30	44·19	35·ʒ
30	76·73	67·98	59·24	50·52	41·80	33·ʒ
40	73·12	64·70	56·26	47·88	39·54	31·ʒ
50	69·85	61·59	53·43	45·38	37·41	29·ʒ
60	66·62	68·50	50·75	43·01	35·39	28·(
70	63·50	55·77	48·20	40·76	33·48	26·ʃ
80	60·58	53·07	45·77	38·63	31·67	25·(

Measured at wave length of 150 m. by a resonance method.

Accuracy ± 0·01.

TＡ

DIELECTRIC CONSTANTS OF KEＴ

Temp. °C.	Acetone	Methyl Ethyl Ketone	Methyl Propyl Ketone	Di-Ethyl Ketone
—80	34·5			
—69	31·1	27·16	21·96	
—40	28·42	24·58	20·19	19·77
—20	25·91	22·27	18·39	19·37
0	23·65	20·30	16·82	18·90
20	21·45	18·51	15·45	17·00
40	19·38	16·80	14·08	15·31
60		15·29	12·87	13·83
80		13·89	11·73	12·52
100			10·78	11·49
120				
140				
160				

Accuracy ±0·01 - 0·02.

CTRIC CONSTANT OF WATER AT VARIOUS TEMPERATURES

			Temperature °C.			
60	70	80	90	95	98	100
9·84	20·37	12·19	6·16	3·91	2·73	2·11
8·17	19·25	11·58	5·93	3·82	2·70	2·10
6·60	18·20	10·99	5·71	3·74	2·68	2·10
5·12	17·20	10·44	5·50	3·65	2·65	2·10
3·72	16·26	9·91	5·30	3·57	2·62	2·10
2·40	15·37	9·41	5·10	3·49	2·60	2·09
1·15	14·52	8·93	4·91	3·41	2·57	2·09
9·97	13·73	8·48	4·73	3·33	2·55	2·09
8·86	12·97	8·05	4·56	3·25	2·52	2·09

G. AKERLÖF and O. A. SHORT, *J. Am. Chem. Soc.*, 1936, **58,** 1241.

RIOUS TEMPERATURES

ethyl iso-Butyl Ketone	Methyl n-Amyl Ketone	Di-Propyl Ketone	Methyl Hexyl Ketone
18·81			
17·37			
15·91	14·27	15·10	12·53
14·50	13·13	13·80	11·45
13·11	11·95	12·60	10·39
11·78	10·85	11·42	9·42
10·68	9·93	10·36	8·70
9·75	9·08	9·46	8·01
8·90	8·27	8·65	7·42
	7·61	8·00	6·90
	7·10		6·49
			6·10

R. H. COLE, *J. Chem. Phys.*, 1941, **9,**25 1.

TABLE II, 21

DIELECTRIC CONSTANT OF WATER. VARIATION WITH TEMPERATURE

t °C.	ε	t °C.	ε	t °C.	ε
0	88·00	25	78·54	55	68·32
5	86·04	30	76·75	60	66·74
10	84·11	35	75·00	70	63·68
15	82·22	40	73·28	80	60·76
18	81·10	45	71·59	90	57.98
20	80·36	50	69·94	100	55·33

Values for the dielectric constant are accurate to $\pm 0\cdot15$.

J. WYMAN, *Phys. Rev.*, 1930, **35**, 623.

See also J. WYMAN and E. N. INGALLS, *J. Am. Chem. Soc.*, 1938, **60**, 1182.

TABLE II, 22

DIELECTRIC CONSTANT (ε) OF WATER AND DEUTERIUM OXIDE AT VARIOUS TEMP. t °C.
REVISED VALUES

$$\varepsilon \text{ at } 25 \text{ °C., } H_2O, = 78\cdot54$$
$$\varepsilon \text{ at } 25 \text{ °C., } D_2O, = 78\cdot25$$

At various temperatures, for D_2O

$$\varepsilon = 78\cdot25 \left\{1 - 4\cdot617 \cdot 10^{-3} (t - 25) + 1\cdot22 \cdot 10^{-5} (t - 25)^2 - 2\cdot7 \cdot 10^{-8} (t - 25)^3\right\}$$

and for H_2O

$$\varepsilon = 78\cdot54 \left\{1 - 4\cdot579 \cdot 10^{-3} (t - 25) + 1\cdot19 \cdot 10^{-5} (t - 25)^2 - 2\cdot8 \cdot 10^{-8} (t - 25)^3\right\}$$

TEMPERATURE COEFFICIENTS

$$\frac{1}{\varepsilon} \left(\frac{d\varepsilon}{dt}\right)$$

t °C.	0	20	40	60	80	100
D_2O	—0·00470	—0·00463	—0·00457	—0·00453	—0·00452	—0·00456
H_2O	—0·00466	—0·00459	—0·00454	—0·00451	—0·00452	—0·00459

J. WYMAN and E. N. INGALLS, *J. Am. Chem. Soc.*, 1938, **60**, 1182.

TABLE II, 23

DIELECTRIC CONSTANT (ε) OF HCN AT VARIOUS TEMPERATURES

Temp. °C.	ε	Temp. °C.		ε
—15 (Supercooled)	213·2	10		133·3
—13·3 (F.p.)	205·5	15		123·5
—10	191·9	18		118·3
—5	173·7	20		114·9
0	158·1	25		106·8
5	144·8	25·7	(B.p.)	105·7

$$-\frac{d\log_{10}\varepsilon}{dt} = 0\cdot0079. \quad \text{Accuracy } \pm\, 0\cdot01 - 0\cdot2\%.$$

J. COATES et al., J. Chem. Soc., 1944, 77.

TABLE II, 24

DIELECTRIC CONSTANTS OF METHANOL-WATER MIXTURES FROM 5 °C. TO 55 °C.

wt.% Methanol	Temp. °C.					
	5·00	15·00	25·00	35·00	45·00	55·00
0·00	86·10	82·19	78·48	74·94	71·50	68·13
10·00	81.68	77·83	74·18	70·68	67·32	64·08
20·00	77·38	73·59	69·99	66·52	63·24	60·06
30·00	72·80	69·05	65·55	62·20	58·97	55·92
40·00	67·91	64·31	60·94	57·70	54·62	51·69
50·00	62·96	59·54	56·28	53·21	50·29	47·53
60·00	57·92	54·71	51·67	48·76	46·02	43·42
70·00	52·96	49·97	47·11	44·42	41·83	39·38
80·00	48·01	45·24	42·60	40·08	37·70	35·46
90·00	42·90	40·33	37·91	35·65	33·53	31·53
95·00	39·98	37·61	35·38	33·28	31·29	29·43
100·00	36·88	34·70	32·66	30·74	28·92	27·21

Accuracy, $\pm0\cdot1\%$.

P. S. ALBRIGHT and L. J. GOSTING, J. Am. Chem. Soc., 1946, **68**, 1061.

TABLE II, 25

DIELECTRIC CONSTANTS (ε) OF NITROMETHANE-DIOXANE MIXTURES

CH_3NO_2 wt.%	ε	CH_3NO_2 wt.%	ε
0·0	2·2	73·5	28·4
38·8	15·6	82·0	31·9
52·2	20·3	89·9	35·0
64·1	24·7	100·0	39·4

Values of ε were measured using a SHEDLOVSKY bridge as a substitution bridge with a calibrated air condenser parallel to the cell. Corrections for lead capacity were made by comparison with standard liquids.

R. M. FUOSS and G. I. CATHERS, *J. Polymer Sci.*, 1949, **4**, 97.

TABLE II, 26

DIELECTRIC CONSTANTS (ε) OF AQUEOUS ELECTROLYTE SOLUTIONS AT 25 °C. FOR
WAVE LENGTHS OF 3 AND 10 cm.

ε_s = static dielectric constant of the solution.

Salt	Normality	$\varepsilon_{3\,cm.}$	$\varepsilon_{10\,cm.}$	ε_s
LiCl	0·5	26·0	10·7	71·2
	1·0	23·3	8·0	64·2
	1·5	20·2	5·0	57·0
	2·0	17·0	—	51·0
RbCl	0·5	25·0	8·9	73·5
	1·0	23·2	9·4	68·5
	1·5	22·0	—	63·5
	2·0	20·2	—	58·5
KCl	0·5	25·9	10·5	73·5
	1·0	23·6	6·8	68·5
	1·5	21·8	—	63·5
	2·0	18·4	—	58·5
BaCl$_2$	1·0	22·2	8·8	64·0
	2·0	16·9	—	51·0
HCl	0·25	26·0	7·8	72·5
	0·5	26·3	—	69·0
NaOH	0·25	26·6	11·7	73·0
	0 5	24·7	4·9	68·0

TABLE II, 26 (*Continued*)

Salt	Normality	$\varepsilon_{3\,cm.}$	$\varepsilon_{10\,cm.}$	ε_s
KI	0·198	27·2	10·4	75·0
	0·396	25·1	11·1	72·0
NaF	0·415	25·0	7·4	73·0
	0·830	24·0	8·4	69·0
$LaCl_3$	0·52	25·2	8·9	71·0
	1·04	22·0	7·8	64·0
KF	0·242	27·9	8·8	75·0
	0·484	25·7	7·3	72·0
NaI	0·428	25·1	8·3	71·0
	0·856	20·8	—	64·0
$MgCl_2$	0·468	25·2	13·0	71·0
	0·935	23·0	8·1	64·5
Na_2SO_4	0·5	26·4	—	73·0
	1·0	25·1	—	67·0
	2·0	20·8	—	60·5

Accuracies: $\varepsilon_{3\,cm.}$, $\pm 1\cdot 0$, $\varepsilon_{10\,cm.}$, ± 3, ε_s, ± 2.
For frequency dependence of ε see original paper.
J. B. HASTED, D. M. RITSON and C. H. COLLIE, *J. Chem. Phys.*, 1948, **16**, 1.

TABLE II, 27

RADIO FREQUENCY ABSORPTION IN AQUEOUS ELECTROLYTE SOLUTIONS

Electrolyte	Molarity c	Wavelength λ for max. power loss.	Characteristic constant K, $= \lambda c$
NaCl	0·015	1100	16·5
	0·020	850	12·0
	0·031	530	16·4
	0·082	200	16·4
	0·2	80	16·0
HCl	0·0054	530	2·86
	0·014	200	2·80
	0·036	80	2·88

TABLE II, 27 (*Continued*)

Electrolyte	Molarity *c*	Wavelength λ for max. power loss.	Characteristic constant $K, = \lambda c$
CaCl$_2$	0·0072	1100	8·10
	0·015	530	7·95
	0·04	200	8·00
	0·1	80	8·00
SrCl$_2$	0·015	530	7·95
	0·04	200	8·00
LaCl$_3$	0·008	510	4·08
	0·0105	380	4·00
	0·019	212	4·04

J. FORMAN and D. J. CRISP, *Trans. Faraday Soc.*, 1946, **42B**, 186.

TABLE II, 28

VALUES OF MOLAR DIELECTRIC INCREMENT IN WATER OF DIPOLAR IONS
AND RELATED SUBSTANCES OF BIOLOGICAL IMPORTANCE

Substance	Dielectric Increment and Reference ($\sim$)
Glycine	22·6 [1], 23·0 [2], 26·4 [4], 30 [3]
α-Alanine	23·2 [1], 23·6 [2], 27·7 [4]
α-Aminobutyric acid	23·2 [1]
α-Aminovaleric acid	22·5 [1]
DL-α-Valine	25 [6]
L-α-Leucine	25 [6]
β-Alanine	34·6 [1], 35 [7], 42·3 [2]
β-Aminobutyric acid	32·4 [1], 36 [8]
γ-Aminobutyric acid	51 [7]
γ-Aminovaleric acid	54·8 [1]
δ-Aminovaleric acid	63 [7]
ε-Aminocaproic acid	77·5 [1], 73 [7]
ζ-Aminoheptylic acid	87 [7]
L-Asparagine	28·4 [4], 20·4 [9]
L-Glutamine	20·8 [9]
D-Glutamic acid	26 [6]

TABLE II, 28 (*Continued*)

Substance	Dielectric Increment and Reference ($\sim$)
L-Aspartic acid	27·8 [4]
DL-Proline	21 [6]
N-Phenyl glycine	c. 30 [10]
Ornithine	51 [8]
Sarcosine	24·5 [6]
D-Arginine	62 [11]
Taurine	41 [6]
Creatine	32·2 [9]
Glycocyamine	30 [9]
Acetyl histidine	62 [9]
Glycine dipeptide	70·6 [1], 70 [6], 70·5 [12], 80 [3]
Glycine tripeptide	113 [1], 128 [12]
Glycine tetrapeptide	159 [1]
Glycine pentapeptide	215 [1]
Urea *	3·4 [4], 3·15 [17], 2·72 [18]
Thiourea	4 [4]
Methylurea	3·7 [6]
Ethylurea	1 [7]
Propylurea	1 [7]
Urethan	—4·3 [6]
Biuret	—6·3 [6]
Semicarbazide	0 [6]
Thiosemicarbazide	c. 0 [6]
Dimethylurea (asymm.)	c. 0 [6]
Dimethylurea (symm.)	3 [6]
Malonamide	4·3 [6]
Succinamide	c. —1 [6]
Acetamide	c. —0·8 [6]
dl-Malamide	2 [8]
Benzamide	—4·1 [4]
Sulphamide	7 [19]
Hydantoin	—6·4 [7]
Pyrrolidine	—1·0 [7]
Pyridine	—4·2 [7]
2 : 5 Dioxopiperazine	—10 [6]
Glycineanhydride	—10 [6]
Hydroxylamine	—0·8 [8]

* Increment not linear with concentration. Limiting value of increment at zero concn. is given.

TABLE II, 28 (*Continued*)

Substance	Dielectric Increment and Reference (∼)
Acetanilide	—4 [4]
Acetonitrile	—1·74 [4]
m-Dihydroxybenzene	—6 [8]
o-Dihydroxybenzene	c. —6 [8]
p-Dihydroxybenzene	—6·4 [8]
Glycine hexapeptide	234 [1]
Glycine heptapeptide (in 5·14M urea)	290 [19]
Glycylalanine	71·8 [9]
Analylglycine	71 [9]
Leucylglycine	62 [12], 68·4 [9]
Glycylleucine	54 [7], 74·6 [9], 70 [12]
N-Methyl-leucylglycine	67 [9]
Glycylphenylalanine	70·4 [9]
Phenylalanylglycine	56·7 [9]
D-Leucylglycylglycine	120·4 [9], 54 [7], 112 [12]
$\varepsilon:\varepsilon'$-Diguanidodi-(α-thio-*n*-caproic acid)	151 [9]
$\varepsilon:\varepsilon'$-Diaminodi-(α-thio-*n*-caproic acid)	131 [13]
Lysylglutamic acid	345 [13]
Glycinebetaine	24—27 [8], 18·2 [14]
α-Aminovalerianic acid betaine	60 [3]
ξ-Aminopentadecylic acid betaine	220 (70 °C.) [3]
π-Aminoheptadecylic acid betaine	190 (80 °C.) [3]
Pyridine betaine	18·5 [14], 20·5 [3]
o-Benzbetaine	18·7 [11], 20 [10]
m-Benzbetaine	48·4 [14], 58 [10]
p-Benzbetaine	72·4 [14], 68 [10], 62 [3]
Thiobetaine	23 [8]
Dimethylphenyl glycine	17 [10]
o-Aminobenzoic acid	low [15]
m-Aminobenzoic acid	41 [15]
p-Aminobenzoic acid	c. 0 [15]
m-$(CH_3)_3N^{\cdot}$. C_6H_4 . CH=CH . COO′	71 [16]
p-$(CH_3)_3N^{\cdot}$. C_6H_4 . CH=CH . COO′ (trans)	100 [16]
p-$(CH_3)_3N^{\cdot}$. C_6H_4 . CH=CBr . COO′ (trans)	102 [16]
m-$(CH_3)_3N^{\cdot}$. C_6H_4 . CH=C(C_6H_5) . COO′ (cis)	25 [16]
m-$(CH_3)_3N^{\cdot}$. C_6H_4 . CH=C . (C_6H_5) . COO′ (trans)	90 [16]
Phenol	—6·6 [4]
Benzoic acid	67 [4]
Aniline	—7·6 [4]

TABLE II, 28 (Continued)

References:

[1] J. WYMAN and T.[L. MCMEEKIN, J. Am. Chem. Soc., 1933, 55, 908.

[2] G. HEDESTRAND, Z. physik. Chem., 1928, 135, 36.

[3] I. HAUSSER, Sitzungsber. Heidelberg. Akad. Wiss., 1935, No. 6, 41 pp.

[4] G. DEVOTO, Gazz. chim. Ital., 1930, 60, 520.

[5] J. WYMAN, Chem. Rev., 1936, 19, 213.

[6] G. DEVOTO, Gazz. chim. Ital., 1931, 61, 897.

[7] G. DEVOTO, ibid., 1933, 63, 50.

[8] G. DEVOTO, ibid., 1934, 64, 76.

[9] J. P. GREENSTEIN and J. WYMAN, J. Am. Chem. Soc., 1935, 57, 637.

[10] G. DEVOTO, Gazz. chim. Ital., 1934, 64, 371.

[11] G. DEVOTO, Z. physiol. Chem., 1933, 222, 227.

[12] L. CAVALLARO, Arch. Sci. biol., 1934, 20, 567

[13] J. P. GREENSTEIN, J. WYMAN and E. J. COHN, J. Am. Chem. Soc., 1935, 57, 637.

[14] J. T. EDSALL and J. WYMAN, J. Am. Chem. Soc., 1935, 57, 1964.

[15] G. DEVOTO, Gazz. chim. Ital., 1933, 63, 247.

[16] G. DEVOTO, Z. Elektrochem., 1934, 40, 641.

[17] G. DEVOTO, Gazz. chim. Ital., 1933, 63, 119.

[18] J. WYMAN, J. Am. Chem. Soc., 1933, 55, 4116.

[19] G. DEVOTO, Atti accad. Lincei, 1931, 24, 432.

TABLE II, 29

DIPOLE MOMENTS OF AMINO ACID ESTERS

Substance	$\mu \cdot 10^{18}$ e.s.u.
Glycine ethyl ester	2·11
α-Alanine ethyl ester	2·09
α-Aminobutyric acid ethyl ester	2·13
α-Aminovaleric acid ethyl ester	2·13
Valine ethyl ester	2·11
α-Aminocaproic acid ethyl ester	2·13
β-Alanine ethyl ester	2·14
β-Aminobutyric acid ethyl ester	2·11

Accurate to $\pm 0 \cdot 01 \cdot 10^{-18}$ e.s.u.

J. WYMAN, Chem. Rev., 1936, 19, 213.

TABLE II, 29 (*Continued*)

DIPOLE MOMENTS OF AMIDES

Substance	$\mu . 10^{18}$ e.s.u.	Ref.
Urea	4·56	1
Thiourea	4·89	1
Symm.-dimethylurea	4·8	2
Tetraethylurea	3·3	3
Propylurea	4·1	3
Acetamide	3·6	3
Sulphamide	3·9	3
Benzamide	3·6	3
Valeramide	3·7	4
Caproamide	3·9	4

For comprehensive list of dipole moments see *Trans. Faraday Soc.*, 1934, **30,** General Discussion.

[1] W. D. KUMLER and G. M. FOHLEN, *J. Am. Chem. Soc.*, 1942, **64**, 1944.
[2] E. C. E. HUNTER and J. R. PARTINGTON, *J. Chem. Soc.*, 1933, 87.
[3] G. DEVOTO, *Gazz. Chim. Ital.*, 1933, **63**, 491.
[4] J. WYMAN, *Chem. Rev.*, 1936, **19**, 213.

TABLE II, 30

DIPOLE MOMENTS OF SOME HORMONES AND RELATED COMPOUNDS IN DIOXAN

Substance	$\mu . 10^{18}$ e.s.u.
Cholestane-3(β) : 7(α)-diol	2·31
Cholestane-3(β) : 7(β)-diol	2·55
Cholestane	2·98
Δ^5-Cholestane-3(β)ol-7 one	3·79
Androsterone	3·70
β-Androsterone	2·95
Δ^5-Androstene-3(β) : 17(α)-diol	2·89
Δ^5-Androstene-3(β) : 17(β)-diol	2·69
Δ^5-Androstene-3(β)ol-17 one	2·46
Testosterone	4·32
cis-Testosterone	5·17
Δ^4-Androstene-3 : 17 dione	3·32
Isophorone	3·96

Ethylenic $>C=C<$ in a six membered ring and conjugated with, $>C=O$ increases the dipole moment approximately by 1 Debye. Non-conjugated $>C=C<$ in sterols decreases the dipole moment by approximately 0·49. Biological activity is not correlated with dipole moment.

W. D. KUMLER and G. M. FOHLEN, *J. Am. Chem. Soc.*, 1945, **67**, 437.

TABLE II, 31

DIPOLE MOMENTS OF SOME INORGANIC COMPOUNDS

Compound	Dipole Moment $\times 10^{18}$ e.s.u.	Reference
HF	$1\cdot92 \pm 0\cdot02$	1
HCl	$1\cdot084 \pm 0\cdot003$—$0\cdot007$	2
HBr	$0\cdot78$	3
HI	$0\cdot38$	3
DCl	$1\cdot084 \pm 0\cdot003$—$0\cdot007$	2
H_2O	$1\cdot87$	4, 5
H_2O_2	$2\cdot13 \pm 0\cdot05$	6
H_2S	$1\cdot10$	7
SO_2	$1\cdot60$	7
SO_3	$0\cdot00$	8
NH_3	$1\cdot3$	9
N_2H_4	$1\cdot84$	10
NO	$0\cdot16$	11
NO_2	$0\cdot29$	12
N_2O_4	$0\cdot37$	12
NOCl	$1\cdot83$	13
NOBr	$1\cdot87$	13
PCl_3	$0\cdot90 - 1\cdot16$	14
PCl_5	$0\cdot0$	15
CO	$0\cdot10$	11
CO_2	$0\cdot0$	11

References:

[1] N. B. HANNAY and C. P. SMYTH, J. Am. Chem. Soc., 1946, 68, 171.
[2] R. P. BELL and I. E. COOP, Trans. Faraday Soc., 1938, 34, 1209.
[3] C. T. ZAHN, Physical Rev., 1926, 27, 455.
[4] M. JONA, Physik. Z., 1919, 20, 14.
[5] E. P. LINTON, Canad. J. Research, 1932, 7, 81.
[6] J. T. RANDALL, Proc. Roy. Soc., 1937, A159, 83.
[7] H. v. BRAUNMUHL, Physik. Z., 1927, 28, 141.
[8] A. SMITS, N. F. MOERMAN and J. C. PATHUIS, Z. physik. Chem., 1937, B.35, 60.
[9] H. M. RANDALL and H. M. FOLEY, Phys. Rev., 1941, 59, 171.
[10] H. ULICH, L. F. AUDRIETH and W. NESPITAL, J. Am. Chem. Soc., 1933, 55, 673.
[11] H. E. WATSON, G. G. RAO and K. K. RAMASWARMY, Proc. Roy. Soc., 1934, 143, 558.
[12] R. W. SCHULZ, Z. physik. Chem., 1938, 109, 517.
[13] J. A. A. KETELAAR, Rec. Trav. Chim., 1943, 62, 289.
[14] J. W. SMITH, Proc. Roy. Soc., 1932, 136, 256.
[15] J. H. SIMONS and G. JESSOP, J. Am. Chem. Soc., 1931, 53, 1263.

CHAPTER III

MOLECULAR AND IONIC INTERACTION IN THE LIQUID PHASE. DATA ON ACTIVITY COEFFICIENTS, OSMOTIC COEFFICIENTS, HYDRATION, SALTING-OUT AND SALTING-IN

The tables in this chapter are concerned with activity coefficients of strong electrolytes in aqueous and non-aqueous solutions and in aqueous non-aqueous mixtures. Tables of salting-out constants which involve the activity coefficients of non-electrolytes and the salting-out ratio constant of BOCKRIS and EGAN (*Trans. Faraday Soc.*, 1948, **44**, 151) are given. Since solute solvent interactions are involved in all of these constants, it is appropriate to include in this chapter data on free energy of hydration, hydration entropy and hydration numbers. A summary of the latter for a number of ions is given in Table III, 53, whilst free energies of hydration of ions derived by BERNAL and FOWLER, WEBB, LATIMER and VERWEY are collected together in Table III, 54. The hydration numbers and hydration energies derived by different authors by different methods are considerably divergent. This arises from the fact that the assumptions involved in the different methods of approach differ considerably. A full discussion of the problem of assignment of hydration energies and hydration numbers is given by BOCKRIS (*Quart. Rev.*, 1949, **3**, 173). The free energy, heat and entropy data for hydration of non-electrolytes derived by BUTLER (*Trans. Faraday Soc.*, 1937, **33**, 229) are given in Table III, 55.

A large number of activity coefficients of strong electrolytes in water and non-aqueous solvents are given and the theoretical limiting slopes for the extrapolation of $\log f_{\pm}$ against the square root of ionic concentration or molar concentration are tabulated for various temperatures. The GRONWALL-LAMER extended terms of the DEBYE-HÜCKEL theory are also included together with mean distances of closest approach of ions in aqueous, methanolic and ethanolic solution. Theoretical limiting slopes for $\log f_{\pm}$ for dioxan water mixtures are quoted in Table III, 3 and details of new calculations of limiting slopes for activity coefficients and other parameters based upon the latest temperature dependence of dielectric constant of water are given (WYMAN and INGALLS, *J. Am. Chem. Soc.*, 1938, **60**, 1182).

In the compilation of activity coefficients and osmotic coefficients reference has been made to ʃhe excellent summary for high concentrations ($>0.1m$) by STOKES and ROBINSON (*Trans. Faraday Soc.*, 1947, **45**, 612). Tables of $f_{\pm}$ for salts at lower concentrations are given in Table III, 6.

Values of the activity of water in electrolyte solutions are given in Table III, 20 and an interesting compilation of individual ionic activity coefficients computed by KIELLAND (*J. Am. Chem. Soc.*, 1937, **59**, 1675) is quoted in Table III, 31. The very high activity coefficients of HCl in anhydrous acetic acid are given in Table III, 33. Recent unpublished data of ROBINSON on activity and osmotic coefficients of $UO_2(NO_3)_2$, UO_2Cl_2, $UO_2(ClO_4)_2$ and $Ca(ClO_4)_2$ are included in the general tables of these functions.

A number of activity and osmotic coefficients for organic acid salts are given together with activity coefficients determined by vapour pressure measurements of amino acids and peptides of biological importance.

The salting-out constant data of RANDALL and FAILEY (*Chem. Rev.*, 1927, **4**, 271) together with the later work by EGAN (*Ph. D. thesis*, London, 1950) for a large number of aqueous and non-aqueous systems are tabulated in Tables III, 50 and 51. The interesting data on salting-in by tetra-alkyl ammonium salts are given in Table III, 52.

The chapter is concluded by a set of tables of thermodynamic functions for strong electrolyte solutions comprising relative partial molal heat contents and heat capacities and relative apparent molal heat contents. Values are given for various salts at different molalities and parameters involved in the temperature dependence of the functions are tabulated for various concentrations.

TABLE III, 1

THE DEBYE-HÜCKEL EQUATION FOR AQUEOUS SOLUTIONS

Values of the constants in the equations

$$\log f_{\pm} = \frac{-A\sqrt{\Gamma_i}}{1 + B\sqrt{\Gamma_i}} \quad \text{and} \quad \log f_{\pm} = \frac{-A'\sqrt{c_i}}{1 + B'\sqrt{c_i}},$$

where the latter equation applies only for a *single* electrolyte, and the former equation is general for single or mixed electrolyte solutions of ionic concentration Γ_i or molarity c_i (where Γ is equal to $2I_{(m)}$, and $I_{(m)}$ is ionic strength).

$$\frac{B}{\mathring{a}} = \frac{\varkappa \cdot 10^{-8}}{\sqrt{\Gamma_i}} \quad \text{and} \quad \frac{B'}{\mathring{a}} = \frac{\varkappa \cdot 10^{-8}}{\sqrt{c_i}},$$

where $\mathring{a}$ is the mean distance of nearest approach of the ions measured in Å.

The valency factors w, w' and w'' are given by

$$w = \frac{1}{\nu} \sum_{1}^{\varrho} \nu_i z_i^2, \qquad w' = \frac{1}{\nu\sqrt{2}} \left\{ \sum_{1}^{\varrho} \nu_i z_i^2 \right\}^{3/2}, \qquad w'' = \left(\frac{1}{2} \sum_{1}^{\varrho} \nu_i z_i^2 \right)^{1/2} = \frac{w'}{w},$$

where ϱ is the number of types of ions derived from the electrolytic dissociation and ν is the number of ions resulting from this.

For binary electrolytes the factor w'' reduces to z $(= z_1 = z_2)$

T °C.	A	A'	$B/\mathring{a}$	$B'/\mathring{a}$
0	0·3446 w	0·4870 w'	0·2294	0·3244 w''
5	·3466	·4902	·2299	·3251
10	·3492	·4938	·2305	·3260
15	·3519	·4977	·2311	·3268
18	·3538	·5002	·2315	·3274
20	·3549	·5019	·2318	·3278
25	·3582	·5065	·2325	·3288
30	·3616	·5114	·2332	·3298
35	·3653	·5166	·2340	·3309
40	·3692	·5221	·2348	·3321
45	·3733	·5280	·2357	·3333
50	·3777	·5341	·2366	·3346
55	·3823	·5406	·2376	·3360
60	·3871	·5474	·2386	·3374
70	·3973	·5619	·2407	·3403
80	·4083	·5774	·2429	·3434
90	·4200	·5940	·2452	·3467
100	·4325	·6116	·2476	·3501

Errors in the limiting slopes A and A' do not exceed $\pm 0 \cdot 1\%$. Errors in B and B' do not exceed $\pm 0 \cdot 05\%$.

From H. S. HARNED and B. B. OWEN, *Physical Chemistry of Electrolytic Solutions*, Reinhold, Publ. Corp., New York, 1943.

See also B. B. OWEN and S. R. BRINKLEY, *Ann. N.Y. Acad. Sci.*, 1949, **51**, 753, and Table III, 2.

TABLE III, 1 (*Continued*)

EXTENDED TERMS OF THE DEBYE-HÜCKEL EQUATION

* The *extended terms* to be added to the first approximation equations for $\log f_{\pm}$ on p. 56 are:

1. For symmetrical valence types:

$$\left(\frac{e_0^2\, z^2}{\varepsilon\, k\, T\, a}\right)^3 \left[\tfrac{1}{2}\, X_3\, x - 2Y_3\, x\right] + \left(\frac{e_0^2\, z^2}{\varepsilon\, k\, T\, a}\right)^3 \left[\tfrac{1}{2}\, X_5\, x - 4\, Y_5\, x\right].$$

2. For unsymmetrical valence types:

$$-\mid z_1 z_2 \mid \left\{ \frac{1}{(10^8\, a)^2}\, (z_1 + z_2)^2\, B_2\, x - \frac{1}{(10^8\, a)^3}\, (z_1^2 - \mid z_1 z_2 \mid + z_2^2)\, (z_1 + z_2)^2\, B_3{}^*\, x \right.$$

$$\left. - \frac{1}{(10^8\, a)^3}\, (z_1^2 - \mid z_1 z_2 \mid + z_2^2)^2\, B_3\, x \right\}.$$

Where,

$$B_2\, x = \left(\frac{10^8\, e_0^2}{\varepsilon\, k\, T}\right)^2 \left[\tfrac{1}{2}\, X_2\, x - Y_2\, x\right]$$

$$B_3{}^*\, x = \left(\frac{10^8\, e_0^2}{\varepsilon\, k\, T}\right)^3 \left[\tfrac{1}{2}\, X_3'\, x - 2\, Y_3'\, x\right]$$

and

$$B_3\, x = \left(\frac{10^8\, e_0^2}{\varepsilon\, k\, T}\right)^3 \left[\tfrac{1}{2}\, X_3\, x - 2\, Y_3\, x\right].$$

PARAMETERS INVOLVED IN THE EXTENDED TERMS* OF THE DEBYE-HÜCKEL THEORY

$x = \varkappa \dot{a}$	$10^3\,[\tfrac{1}{2}X_3 - 2\,Y_3]$	$10^5\,[\tfrac{1}{2}X_5 - 4\,Y_5]$	$10^2\,[\tfrac{1}{2}X_2 - Y_2]$	$10^3\,[\tfrac{1}{2}X'_3 - 2\,Y'_3]$
0·00	0·00000	0·00000	0·000000	0·000000
·005	—·00092	—·00107	—·001482	·000009
·01	—·00351	—·00416	—·004797	·000071
·02	—·01239	—·01487	—·014784	·000423
·03	—·02497	—·02985	—·027666	·001264
·04	—·04014	—·04725	—·042363	·002693
0·05	—·05711	—·06564	—·058209	·004750
·06	—·07522	—·08394	—·074748	·007457
·07	—·09403	—·10138	—·091660	·010809
·08	—·11316	—·11737	—·108703	·014766
·09	—·13231	—·13153	—·125699	·019291
0·10	—·15130	—·14363	—·142514	·024335
·11	—·16992	—·15356	—·15905	·02986
·12	—·18802	—·16126	—·17522	·03580
·13	—·20355	—·16680	—·19097	·04211
·14	—·22240	—·17023	—·20626	·04874
0·15	—·23853	—·17166	—·22105	·05563
.16	—·25391	—·17123	—·23533	·06274
·17	—·26851	—·16910	—·24908	·07002

* T. H. GRONWALL, V. K. LAMER and K. SANDVED, *Physik. Z.*, 1929, **29**, 358; V. K. LAMER, T. H. GRONWALL and L. J. GRIEFF, *J. Phys. Chem.*, 1931, **35**, 2245.

TABLE III, 1 (*Continued*)

$x = \varkappa\mathring{a}$	$10^3\left[\tfrac{1}{2}X_3 - 2Y_3\right]$	$10^5\left[\tfrac{1}{2}X_5 - 4Y_5\right]$	$10^2\left[\tfrac{1}{2}X_2 - Y_2\right]$	$10^3\left[\tfrac{1}{2}X'_3 - 2Y'_3\right]$
·18	—·28231	—·16543	—·26230	·07743
·19	—·29530	—·16037	—·27497	·08493
0·20	—·30750	—·15409	—·28710	·09248
·21	—·31892	—·14674	—·29870	·10005
·22	—·32953	—·13847	—·30977	·10761
·23	—·33943	—·12942	—·32032	·11513
·24	—·34859	—·11973	—·33036	·12258
0·25	—·35703	—·10953	—·33991	·12994
·26	—·36478	—·09895	—·34896	·13720
·27	—·37187	—·08804	—·35755	·14433
·28	—·37832	—·07696	—·36567	·15132
·29	—·38416	—·06577	—·37335	·15816
0·30	—·38942	—·05453	—·38060	·16482
·31	—·39411	—·04335	—·38743	·17132
·32	—·39827	—·03222	—·39386	·17762
·33	—·40193	—·02131	—·39990	·18374
·34	—·40510	—·01053	—·40557	·18965
0·35	—·40780	—·00001	—·41087	·19536
·36	—·41007	+·01027	—·41583	·20087
·37	—·41193	+·02022	—·42045	·20617
·38	—·41339	+·02986	—·42475	·21116
·39	—·41448	+·03917	—·42875	·21613
0·40	—·41525	+·04810	—·43244	·22080

TABLE III, 2

THEORETICAL LIMITING SLOPES FOR UNI-UNIVALENT ELECTROLYTES IN WATER FOR
ACTIVITY COEFFICIENT, PARTIAL MOLAL VOLUME AND HEAT CONTENT

$t\,°C.$	A_f	$A'\dfrac{10^{-8}}{a}$	$^2/_3\,A_v$	$-\frac12\,W_v\dfrac{10^{-8}}{a}$	$^2/_3\,A_H$	$-\frac12\,W_H\dfrac{10^{-8}}{a}$
0	0·4883	0·3241	2·467	0·0594	339·5	28·73
5	0·4921	0·3249	2·456	0·0593	362·3	29·13
10	0·4960	0·3258	2·457	0·0595	387·0	29·78
12·5	0·4981	0·3262	2·461	0·0597	400·0	30·19
15	0·5002	0·3267	2·468	0·0599	413·5	30·65
18	0·5028	0·3273	2·479	0·0603	430·2	31·27
20	0·5046	0·3276	2·488	0·0606	441·7	31·70
25	0·5091	0·3286	2·517	0·0615	471·8	32·93
30	0·5139	0·3297	2·555	0·0626	503·7	34·30
35	0·5189	0·3307	2·601	0·0640	537·5	35·85
40	0·5241	0·3318	2·655	0·0655	573·3	37·54
45	0·5295	0·3330	2·717	0·0673	611·4	39·38
50	0·5351	0·3341	2·787	0·0692	652·1	41·43
Valency Factor	$2/\nu\,\omega^{3/2}$	$\omega^{1/2}$	$2/\nu\,\omega^{3/2}$	ω^2	$^2/_3\,\omega^{3/2}$	ω^2

For electrolytes of other valency types, multiply the figures in the Table by the relevant factor given at the foot of the columns. ω represents the valency factor $\frac12\sum_1^t \nu_i z_i^2$.

In using the Table, φ_v is expressed in ml. per mol and φ_H in 15 °C. calories per mol; a is in cm. Values of the constants are calculated using the dielectric constant data of WYMAN and INGALLS (*J. Am. Chem. Soc.*, 1938, **60**, 1182, See Table II, 22) and the universal constants given by BIRGE (*Rev. Mod. Phys.*, 1941, **13**, 233; See Table I, 1).

$$A_f = 0·4343\,\frac{1}{\nu}\left(\sum_1^Q \nu_i z_i^2\right)^{3/2}\left(\frac{\pi\,N_A\,e_0^6}{1000(\varepsilon kT)^3}\right)^{1/2}\ \text{for activity coefficients } f_\pm.$$

$$A_v = 2·303\,\nu\,RT\,A_f\,\frac{3}{2}\left(\frac{\partial\ln\varepsilon}{\partial P} - \frac13\beta\right)\ \text{for partial molal volumes } \varphi_v.$$

$$A_H = -\,2·303\,\nu\,RT^2\,A_f\,\frac{3}{2}\left(\frac{\partial\ln\varepsilon}{\partial T} + \frac{1}{T} + \frac13 a\right)\ \text{for partial molal heat content } \varphi_H.$$

$$a = \text{expansibility} = -\frac{\partial\ln c}{\partial T}\ ;\qquad \beta = \text{compressibility with pressure } P = \\ = \frac{\partial\ln c}{\partial P}\ .$$

TABLE III, 2 (*Continued*)

$$W_v = -2 \cdot 303 \; v \; RT \; A_f \; A' \; \frac{1}{2} \left(\frac{\partial \ln \varepsilon}{\partial P} - \beta - \frac{2 \partial \ln a}{\partial P} \right)$$

$$W_H = 2 \cdot 303 \; v \; RT^2 \; A_f A' \; \frac{1}{2} \left(\frac{\partial \ln \varepsilon}{\partial T} + \frac{1}{T} + a - 2 \frac{\partial \ln a}{\partial T} \right)$$

where $A'c^{1/2} = \varkappa a = \left(\sum_1^{\varrho} v_i z_i^2 \right)^{1/2} \left(\frac{4 \, \pi \, N_A e_0^2}{1000 \, \varepsilon kT} \right)^{1/2} a \; c^{1/2}$

and a = distance of closest approach.

B. B. Owen and S. R. Brinkley, *Ann. N.Y. Acad. Sci.*, 1949, **51**, 753.

TABLE III, 3

LIMITING SLOPES(A_f) FOR ACTIVITY COEFFICIENTS IN DIOXAN-WATER MIXTURES
OF DIELECTRIC CONSTANT ε

X = weight percent of Dioxan.

$t \, °C.$	$X = 20$		$X = 45$	
	ε	A_f	ε	A_f
0	69·16	0·6989	44·28	1·364
5	67·39	0·7072	43·05	1·385
10	65·68	0·7156	41·86	1·406
15	64·01	0·7245	40·70	1·429
20	62·38	0·7339	39·57	1·453
25	60·79	0·7437	38·48	1·477
30	59·94	0·7540	37·41	1·503
35	57·73	0·7648	36·37	1·530
40	56·26	0·7760	35·37	1·557
45	54·83	0·7877	34·39	1·586
50	53·43	0·7999	33·43	1·616

TABLE III, 3 *(Continued)*

$t\,°C.$	$X = 70$		$X = 82$	
	ε	A_f	ε	A_f
0	20·37	4·373	—	—
5	19·81	4·437	10·52	11·47
10	19·25	4·510	10·27	11·58
15	18·72	4·581	10·01	11·72
20	18·20	4·657	9·77	11·85
25	17·69	4·738	9·53	11·98
30	17·20	4·820	9·29	12·16
35	16·72	4·907	9·06	12·30
40	16·26	4·995	8·84	12·46
45	15·80	5·092	8·62	12·64
50	15·37	5·185	—	—

H. S. HARNED and B. B. OWEN, *The Physical Chemistry of Electrolytic Solutions,* Reinhold Publ. Corp., New York, 1950.

TABLE III, 4

VALUES OF THE PARAMETER a IN THE DEBYE-HÜCKEL THEORY.

DISTANCES OF CLOSEST APPROACH IN NON-AQUEOUS SOLUTIONS

$K =$ dissociation constant of the electrolyte in the solvent. Values of the distances of closest approach are calculated by the method of R. M. FUOSS and C. A. KRAUS (*J. Am. Chem. Soc.,* 1933, **55,** 1019).

1. MeOH 25 °C.		2. EtOH 25 °C.	
	From K		From K
$AgNO_3$	2·36 Å.	$KEtCO_3$	2·47 Å.
Et_4NClO_4	2·66	Et_4NClO_4	2·57
Et_4NBr	4·86	Et_4N Picrate	3·65
$KMeCO_3$	4·98	KOEt	5·32
Et_4N Picrate	5·15	KI	5·87
KCl	7·54	LiI	10·03

A. G. OGSTON, *Trans. Faraday Soc.,* 1936, **32,** 1679.

TABLE III, 5

VALUES OF THE PARAMETER a IN THE DEBYE-HÜCKEL THEORY.

DISTANCES OF CLOSEST APPROACH OF IONS IN AQUEOUS SOLUTIONS

Salt	Molality range fitted	a in Ångstrom	Salt	Molality range fitted	a in Ångstrom
HCl	0·01 - 1·0	4·47	$MgCl_2$	0·1 - 1·4	5·02
HBr	0·1 - 1·0	5·18	$MgBr_2$	0·1 - 1·0	5·46
HI	0·1 - 0·7	5·69	MgI_2	0·1 - 0·7	6·18
$HClO_4$	0·1 - 2·0	5·09	$CaCl_2$	0·01 - 1·4	4·73
LiCl	0·1 - 1·0	4·32	$CaBr_2$	0·1 - 1·0	5·02
LiBr	0·1 - 1·5	4·56	CaI_2	0·1 - 0·7	5·69
LiI	0·1 - 1·0	5·60	$SrCl_2$	0·1 - 1·8	4·61
$LiClO_4$	0·2 - 1·0	5·63	$SrBr_2$	0·01 - 1·4	4·89
NaCl	0·1 - 5·0	3·97	SrI_2	0·1 - 1·0	5·58
NaBr	0·1 - 4·0	4·24	$BaCl_2$	0·1 - 1·8	4·45
NaI	0·1 - 1·5	4·47	$BaBr_2$	0·1 - 1·5	4·68
$NaClO_4$	0·2 - 4·0	4·04	BaI_2	0·1 - 1·0	5·44
KCl	0·1 - 4·0	3·63	$MnCl_2$	0·1 - 1·4	4·74
KBr	0·1 - 4·0	3·85	$FeCl_2$	0·1 - 1·4	4·80
KI	0·1 - 4·0	4·16	$CoCl_2$	0·1 - 1·0	4·81
RbCl	0·1 - 1·5	3·49	$NiCl_2$	0·1 - 1·4	4·86
RbBr	0·1 - 1·5	3·48	$Zn(ClO_4)_2$	0·1 - 0·7	6·18
RbI	0·1 - 1·5	3·56			

From R. H. STOKES and R. A. ROBINSON, *J. Am. Chem. Soc.*, 1949, **70**, 1870. The data of J. H. JONES, *J. Phys. Chem.*, 1947, **51**, 516, have been used for lithium and sodium.

TABLE III, 6

MEAN ACTIVITY COEFFICIENTS OF ELECTROLYTES IN DILUTE AQUEOUS SOLUTION

(VALUES GIVEN AS $-\log_{10} f_\pm$)

Salt	Temp. °C.	Ref.	Molalities						
			0·0005	0·001	0·002	0·005	0·01	0·02	0·05
LiCl	Freezing point of the solution ,,	3	—	—	—	0·0343	0·0463	0·0605	0·0830
LiBr		3	—	—	—	0·0298	0·0400	0·0525	0·0720
$LiNO_3$		1	—	—	—	0·0304	0·0412	0·0543	0·0760
$LiClO_3$		4	—	—	—	0·0302	0·0406	0·0537	0·0745
$LiClO_4$		4	—	—	—	0·0290	0·0386	0·0506	0·0692

TABLE III, 6 (*Continued*)

MEAN ACTIVITY COEFFICIENTS OF ELECTROLYTES IN DILUTE AQUEOUS SOLUTION

(VALUES GIVEN AS $-\log_{10} f_{\pm}$)

Salt	Temp. °C.	Ref.	Molalities						
			0·0005	0·001	0·002	0·005	0·01	0·02	0·05
LiOOC.H	Freezing	5	—	—	—	0·0311	0·0424	0·0573	0·0836
LiOOC.CH$_3$	point	5	—	—	—	0·0309	0·0421	0·0564	0·0799
	of the								
NaCl	solution	3	—	—	—	0·0306	0·0416	0·0557	0·0804
NaBr	,,	3	—	—	—	0·0282	0·0377	0·0503	0·0721
NaNO$_3$	,,	1	—	—	—	0·0311	0·0428	0·0584	0·0870
NaClO$_3$	,,	4	—	—	—	0·0316	0·0433	0·0588	0·0865
NaClO$_4$	,,	4	—	—	—	0·0321	0·0439	0·0588	0·0857
NaOOC.H	,,	5	—	—	—	0·0308	0·0416	0·0557	0·0794
NaOOC.CH$_3$	,,	5	—	—	—	0·0306	0·0412	0·0544	0·0754
KCl	,,	3	—	—	—	0·0317	0·0434	0·0587	0·0857
KBr	,,	3	—	—	—	0·0313	0·0428	0·0578	0·0839
KNO$_3$	,,	1	—	—	—	0·0329	0·0461	0·0645	0·1001
KClO$_3$	,,	4	—	—	—	0·0301	0·0418	0·0583	0·0913
KClO$_4$	,,	4	—	—	—	0·0347	0·0492	0·0697	—
KOOC.H	,,	5	—	—	—	0·0362	0·0406	0·0543	0·0774
KOOC.CH$_3$	,,	5	—	—	—	0·0306	0·0411	0·0544	0·0750
NH$_4$Cl	,,	2	—	—	—	0·0405	0·0555	0·0732	0·1025
NH$_4$Br	,,	2	—	—	—	0·0451	0·0605	0·0786	0·1082
NH$_4$I	,,	2	—	—	—	0·0375	0·0509	0·0674	0·0947
NH$_4$NO$_3$	,,	2	—	—	—	0·0401	0·0547	0·0736	0·1064
(NH$_4$)$_2$SO$_4$	,,	2	—	—	—	0·1308	0·1749	0·2294	0·3194

MEAN ACTIVITY COEFFICIENTS $f_{\pm}$ OF ELECTROLYTES IN DILUTE AQUEOUS SOLUTIONS

Salt	Temp. °C.	Ref.	0·0005	0·001	0·002	0·005	0·01	0·02	0·05
NaCl	25	6	—	—	—	0·9283	0·9032	0·8724	0·8215
LiOH	25	7	—	—	—	—	—	—	0·803
NaOH	25	8	—	—	—	—	—	—	0·818
KOH	25	9	—	—	—	—	—	—	0·824
CsOH	25	10	—	—	—	—	—	—	0·831
Na$_2$SO$_4$	0	11	—	—	—	—	0·719	—	0·537
H$_2$SO$_4$	0	12	0·908	0·873	0·825	0·734	0·649	0·554	0·426
H$_2$SO$_4$	25	12	0·885	0·830	0·757	0·639	0·544	0·453	0·340
SrCl$_2$	25	13	—	—	—	—	0·729	—	0·571
BaCl$_2$	25	13	—	—	—	—	0·723	—	0·554

TABLE III, 6 (*Continued*)

MEAN ACTIVITY COEFFICIENTS $(f_{\pm})$ OF ELECTROLYTES IN DILUTE AQUEOUS SOLUTIONS

Salt	Temp.° C.	Ref.	Molalities						
			0·0005	0·001	0·002	0·005	0·01	0·02	0·05
Ba(OH)$_2$	25	27	—	—	—	0·773	0·712	0·628	0·526
ZnCl$_2$	25	15	—	—	—	0·789	0·731	0·607	0·628
ZnBr$_2$	25	16	—	—	—	—	—	0·685	0·605
ZnI$_2$	25	17	—	—	0·851	0·799	0·746	0·690	0·621
ZnSO$_4$	25	22	0·780	0·700	0·608	0·477	0·387	0·298	0·202
CdCl$_2$	25	18	0·880	0·819	0·743	0·623	0·524	0·456	0·304
CdBr$_2$	25	19	0·855	0·787	0·699	0·570	0·468	0·370	0·259
CdI$_2$	25	20	—	—	—	0·490	0·379	0·281	0·167
CdSO$_4$	25	21	0·774	0·697	—	0·476	0·383	—	0·199
PbCl$_2$	25	14	0·902	0·859	0·803	0·704	0·612	0·497	—
AlCl$_3$	25	25/26	—	—	—	—	—	—	0·447
ScCl$_3$	25	25/26	—	—	—	—	—	—	0·447
LaCl$_3$	25	23	—	0·853	—	0·717	0·637	0·552	0·447
In$_2$(SO$_4$)$_3$	25	24	—	—	—	—	0·142	0·095	0·054
YCl$_3$	25	25/26	—	—	—	—	—	—	0·447
CeCl$_3$	25	25/26	—	—	—	—	—	—	0·447
PrCl$_3$	25	25/26	—	—	—	—	—	—	0·447
NdCl$_3$	25	25/26	—	—	—	—	—	—	0·447
SmCl$_3$	25	25/26	—	—	—	—	—	—	0·447
EuCl$_3$	25	25/26	—	—	—	—	—	—	0·447

References:

[1] G. SCATCHARD, G. JONES and S. S. PRENTISS, *J. Am. Chem. Soc.*, 1932, 54, 2690.

[2] G. SCATCHARD and S. S. PRENTISS, *ibid.*, 1932, 54, 2696.

[3] *Ibid.*, 1933, 55, 4355.

[4] G. SCATCHARD, S. S. PRENTISS and G. JONES, *ibid.*, 1934, 56, 805.

[5] G. SCATCHARD and S. S. PRENTISS, *ibid.*, 1934, 56, 807.

[6] A. S. BROWN and D. A. MACINNES, *ibid.*, 1935, 57, 1356.

[7] H. S. HARNED and F. E. SWINDELLS, *ibid.*, 1926, 48, 126.

[8] H. S. HARNED and J. C. HECKER, *ibid.*, 1933, 55, 4838.

[9] H. S. HARNED and M. A. COOK, *ibid.*, 1937, 59, 496.

[10] H. S. HARNED and O. E. SCHUPP, *ibid.*, 1930, 52, 3886.

[11] H. S. HARNED and J. C. HECKER, *ibid.*, 1934, 56, 650.

[12] H. S. HARNED and W. J. HAMER, *ibid.*, 1935, 57, 27.

[13] H. S. HARNED, *ibid.*, 1926, 48, 326.

[14] W. R. CARMODY, *ibid.*, 1929, 51, 2905.

[15] R. A. ROBINSON and R. H. STOKES, *Trans. Faraday Soc.*, 1940, 36, 740.

[16] H. N. Parton and J. W. Mitchell, *ibid.*, 1939, **35**, 758.

[17] R. G. Bates, *J. Am. Chem. Soc.*, 1938, **60**, 2983.

[18] H. S. Harned and M. E. Fitzgerald, *ibid.*, 1936, **58**, 2624.

[19] R. G. Bates, *ibid.*, 1939, **61**, 308.

[20] R. G. Bates and W. C. Vosburgh, *ibid.*, 1937, **59**, 1583.

[21] V. K. LaMer and W. G. Parks, *ibid.*, 1931, **53**, 2040.

[22] H. S. Harned and B. B. Owen, *Physical Chemistry of Electrolytic Solutions*, p. 426, Reinhold Publishing Corp., New York, 1943.

[23] R. A. Robinson, *Trans. Faraday Soc.*, 1939, **35**, 1229.

[24] H. M. Hattox and T. de Vries, *J. Am. Chem. Soc.*, 1936, **58**, 2126.

[25] C. M. Mason, *ibid.*, 1938, **60**, 1638; 1941, **63**, 220.

[26] T. Shedlovsky and D. A. MacInnes, *ibid.*, 1939, **61**, 200.

[27] R. A. Robinson and H. S. Harned, *Chem. Rev.*, 1941, **28**, 419.

TABLES III, 7, 8 and 9

OSMOTIC AND ACTIVITY COEFFICIENTS OF ELECTROLYTES †

Osmotic and Activity Coefficients. The following tables * give practical osmotic and activity coefficients at 25°. Data have been included for one non-electrolyte, sucrose, [10], [11], [12] which should be useful as a reference solute for isopiestic measurements on other non-electrolytes, but data derived from isopiestic work on glycerol and urea [12] and an interesting series of measurements on 18 amino-acids [13] have been omitted**. Some recent determinations on sodium and potassium acid sulphate [14] have also been omitted because, whilst the isopiestic data enable the vapour pressures to be calculated, the dissociation of the bisulphate ion makes f_0 and $f_\pm$ values of little use. In addition, reference only is made to measurements [15] on a series of sodium salts of fatty acids up to the caprate. (But see Table III, 12.)

The following notes will enable some estimate of the reliability of the data given in the tables to be made.

Some of the data depend on isopiestic measurements only and no confirmation is available from other techniques. This holds for the following salts: lithium iodide, perchlorate, nitrate, acetate and toluenesulphonate; sodium chlorate, perchlorate, bromate, nitrate, acetate, toluenesulphonate, thiocyanate and phosphate; potassium fluoride, chlorate, bromate, nitrate, acetate, toluenesulphonate, thiocyanate and phosphate; the five rubidium salts; caesium bromide, iodide, nitrate and acetate; silver nitrate; the three thallium salts, magnesium, manganese and nickel sulphate; all the trivalent metal salts (for lanthanum chloride independent isopiestic measurements are in good agreement); potassium ferrocyanide and ferricyanide; aluminium and chromium sulphate and thorium nitrate.

---

† This compilation of values is taken from R. H. Stokes and R. A. Robinson, *Trans. Faraday Soc.*, 1949, **45**, 612.

* For previous tabulations see refs. 5, 6 and 7.

** See Tables III, 34, 35.

TABLES III, 7, 8 and 9 (*Continued*)

With some it is possible to compare the osmotic and activity coefficients with those derived from freezing point measurements but there are seldom sufficient heat content data available to estimate the temperature correction exactly; nevertheless, it is found that the activity coefficients at $0 \cdot 1m$ usually agree within 1% at the two temperatures; only in the case of lithium nitrate, potassium nitrate, potassium chlorate and sodium acetate do differences of up to 2% appear but the heat content data available are not sufficient to indicate if this difference is real or due to error in the activity coefficients at either temperature.

Hydrochloric Acid. The values of $f_\pm$ between $0 \cdot 1$ and $4m$ are taken from the very careful work of HARNED and EHLERS [16], interpolated at some concentrations by means of the DEBYE-HÜCKEL constants given by HARNED and EHLERS. Osmotic coefficients have been calculated by the method outlined by STOKES [9]. RANDALL and YOUNG [17] quote values of $f_\pm$ between $1 \cdot 2$ and $4m$ which are, on the average, $0 \cdot 35\%$ higher (*i.e.* a difference equivalent to $0 \cdot 18$ mv.). The data in the tables for concentrations above $4m$ are taken from the paper of RANDALL and YOUNG, some intermediate values being obtained by BESSELIAN interpolation. The values above $4m$ are supported by the data of ÅKERLÖF and TEARE [18] whose $f_\pm$ values exhibit an average deviation of 1% from those of RANDALL and YOUNG.

Hydrobromic Acid. The f_0 values are from HARNED, KESTON and DONELSON [19]; interpolation has been made at some concentrations by the use of their DEBYE-HÜCKEL constants and $f_\pm$ has been calculated by the procedure of STOKES [9].

Hydriodic Acid. The values depend on isopiestic data only [20].

Perchloric Acid. The isopiestic f_0 values agree within 1% with those derived from the direct vapour pressure measurements of PEARCE and NELSON [21]. Their $f_\pm$ values are, however, very different.

Nitric Acid. The $f_\pm$ values are those obtained from freezing point measurements by HARTMAN and ROSENFELD [42] with some interpolations added. The f_0 values are computed from these.

Lithium Hydroxide. $f_\pm$ values are from the e.m.f. measurements of HARNED and SWINDELLS [22] with interpolations at some concentrations.

Lithium Chloride and Bromide. The isopiestic data are confirmed up to $2m$ by the e.m.f. values of HARNED [23] which agree within $0 \cdot 8\%$ with the isopiestic values; above $2m$, however, there are considerable differences and, because the lithium amalgam electrode is known to be erratic, the isopiestic data are to be preferred.

Sodium Hydroxide. Up to $2m, f_\pm$ values interpolated from the e.m.f. measurements of HARNED [24] and of HARNED and HECKER [25] have been used; above $2m$ the isopiestic measurements of STOKES have been used [26]: it should be noted that the values of $f_\pm$ due to ÅKERLÖF and KEGELES [27] are considerably different (by about 3%).

Sodium Fluoride. Attention should be drawn to the e.m.f. measurements of IVETT and DE VRIES [28] which do not agree well with the $f_\pm$ values tabulated from isopiestic data.

Sodium Chloride. HARNED's [23] e.m.f. values of $f_\pm$ (extending up to $4m$) do not differ from those in the tables by more than $0 \cdot 004$ in $f_\pm$ at any concentration and

TABLES III, 7, 8 and 9 (*Continued*)

only differ on the average by 0·3%. Similar data by HARNED and NIMS [30] give an average difference of 0·5%, there being a difference of 0·009 in $f_{\pm}$ at $4m$. The $f_{\pm}$ values of OLYNYK and GORDON [31] between 1·5 and $6m$ agree within 0·3% whilst f_0 values calculated from the direct vapour pressure measurements of NEGUS [31a] agree within 0·2% from 1 to $5m$.

Sodium Bromide. The isopiestic data quoted in the tables agree within 0·2% with the e.m.f. data of HARNED and CRAWFORD [32] up to $2m$; between 2·5 and $4m$ their data are higher by about 1·5%.

Sodium Iodide. The isopiestic data are in good agreement with the values quoted by HARNED [23], the average difference being 0·3% in $f_{\pm}$ up to $1m$ (the highest concentration at which e.m.f. measurements were made).

Potassium Hydroxide. Up to $4m$ values calculated from the e.m.f. measurements of HARNED and COOK [33] have been used and above $4m$ those of ÅKERLÖF and BENDER [34].

Potassium Chloride. The values quoted in the tables agree with those of HARNED [23] and of HARNED and COOK [35] with an average deviation of 0·4%. Moreover, the direct vapour pressure measurements of LOVELACE, FRAZER, and SEASE [35a] can be corrected from 20° to 25° to give values of f_0 which agree within 0·3%.

Potassium Bromide and Iodide. The values in the tables for the bromide, taken from isopiestic data, are within 0·3% of those given from e.m.f. data by HARNED [23]. Similarly, the data for the iodide agree within 0·3% up to $1m$ above which the e.m.f. values are 2% higher.

Caesium Hydroxide. The data quoted are derived from the e.m.f. measurements of HARNED and SCHUPP [36].

Caesium Chloride. The data in the tables, from isopiestic measurements, exhibit an average deviation of only 0·5% from the e.m.f. data of HARNED and SCHUPP.

Copper Sulphate. The e.m.f. data of NIELSEN and BROWN [37] are within 2% of the isopiestic $f_{\pm}$ values whilst the values of WETMORE and GORDON [38] are within 1·5%.

Zinc Sulphate. BRAY [39] has made measurements which yield activity coefficients which differ, on the average, by less than 2% from the isopiestic values quoted.

Cadmium Sulphate. The e.m.f. data of LAMER and PARKS [40] do not agree with the isopiestic values that have been used, there being differences of the order of 13%. Values at low molalities, enclosed in brackets, are subject to revision.

TABLE III, 7

OSMOTIC COEFFICIENTS AT 25 °C.

m	HCl	HBr	HI	HClO$_4$	HNO$_3$	LiOH	LiCl	LiBr	LiI	LiClO$_4$	LiNO$_3$
0·1	0·943	0·948	0·953	0·947	0·940	0·920	0·939	0·943	0·952	0·951	0·938
0·2	0·945	0·954	0·969	0·951	0·935	0·902	0·939	0·944	0·966	0·959	0·935
0·3	0·952	0·964	0·984	0·958	0·936	0·890	0·945	0·952	0·980	0·971	0·940
0·4	0·963	0·978	1·001	0·966	0·940	0·881	0·954	0·960	0·995	0·985	0·946
0·5	0·974	0·993	1·019	0·976	0·944	0·875	0·963	0·970	1·008	0·999	0·954
0·6	0·986	1·007	1·038	0·988	0·950	0·869	0·973	0·981	1·022	1·013	0·962
0·7	0·998	1·023	1·057	1·000	0·957	0·866	0·984	0·993	1·034	1·027	0·970
0·8	1·011	1·038	1·075	1·013	0·964	0·863	0·995	1·007	1·049	1·043	0·978
0·9	1·025	1·054	1·094	1·026	0·971	0·861	1·006	1·021	1·063	1·058	0·987
1·0	1·039	1·072	1·113	1·041	0·979	0·860	1·018	1·035	1·080	1·072	0·997
1·2	1·067	—	1·153	1·072	0·994	0·863	1·041	1·067	1·111	1·104	1·015
1·4	1·096	—	1·193	1·106	1·009	0·866	1·066	1·098	1·143	1·137	1·033
1·6	1·126	—	1·233	1·141	1·025	0·870	1·091	1·130	1·176	1·170	1·052
1·8	1·157	—	1·273	1·175	1·042	0·872	1·116	1·163	1·212	1·204	1·070
2·0	1·188	—	1·315	1·210	1·060	0·875	1·142	1·196	1·250	1·238	1·088
2·5	1·266	—	1·424	1·305	1·106	0·882	1·212	1·278	1·351	1·328	1·134
3·0	1·348	—	1·535	1·406	1·154	0·886	1·286	1·364	1·467	1·419	1·181
3·5	1·431	—	—	1·511	—	0·889	1·366	1·467	—	1·512	1·227
4·0	1·517	—	—	1·622	—	0·892	1·449	1·578	—	1·595	1·270
4·5	1·598	—	—	1·738	—	—	1·533	1·687	—	—	1·312
5·0	1·680	—	—	1·860	—	—	1·619	1·793	—	—	1·352
5·5	1·763	—	—	1·981	—	—	1·705	1·891	—	—	1·387
6·0	1·845	—	—	2·106	—	—	1·791	1·989	—	—	1·420
Ref.	16	19	20	41	42	22	10, 43	44, 45	10	46	47, 48

References:

[1] R. H. STOKES, *Trans. Faraday Soc.*, 1948, **44**, 295.
[2] R. A. ROBINSON, *Trans. Roy. Soc. N.Z.*, 1945, **75**, 203.
[3] S. SHANKMAN and A. R. GORDON, *J. Am. Chem. Soc.*, 1939, **61**, 2370.
[4] R. H. STOKES, *ibid.*, 1947, **69**, 1291.

TABLE III, 7 (*Continued*)

OSMOTIC COEFFICIENTS AT 25 °C.

m	$\overline{\text{LiAc}}$	$\overline{\text{LiTol}}$	NaOH	NaF	NaCl	NaBr	NaI	Na-ClO_3	Na-ClO_4	Na-BrO_3	Na-NO_3
0·1	0·935	0·928	0·925	0·924	0·932	0·934	0·938	0·927	0·930	0·918	0·921
0·2	0·928	0·917	0·925	0·908	0·925	0·928	0·936	0·913	0·920	0·896	0·902
0·3	0·929	0·912	0·929	0·898	0·922	0·928	0·939	0·904	0·915	0·883	0·890
0·4	0·931	0·908	0·933	0·891	0·920	0·929	0·945	0·897	0·912	0·873	0·881
0·5	0·935	0·906	0·937	0·886	0·921	0·933	0·952	0·892	0·910	0·865	0·873
0·6	0·940	0·906	0·941	0·882	0·923	0·937	0·959	0·888	0·909	0·857	0·867
0·7	0·945	0·905	0·945	0·879	0·926	0·942	0·967	0·885	0·910	0·851	0·862
0·8	0·951	0·905	0·949	0·876	0·929	0·947	0·975	0·883	0·911	0·845	0·858
0·9	0·956	0·905	0·953	0·874	0·932	0·953	0·983	0·882	0·912	0·839	0·854
1·0	0·962	0·905	0·958	0·872	0·936	0·958	0·991	0·880	0·913	0·833	0·851
1·2	0·975	0·904	0·969	—	0·943	0·969	1·007	0·878	0·916	0·824	0·845
1·4	0·988	0·902	0·980	—	0·951	0·983	1·025	0·876	0·920	0·815	0·839
1·6	1·001	0·899	0·991	—	0·962	0·997	1·043	0·874	0·925	0·808	0·835
1·8	1·014	0·894	1·002	—	0·972	1·012	1·061	0·875	0·930	0·804	0·830
2·0	1·027	0·893	1·015	—	0·983	1·028	1·079	0·876	0·934	0·800	0·826
2·5	1·061	0·899	1·054	—	1·013	1·067	1·129	0·879	0·947	0·792	0·817
3·0	1·093	0·912	1·094	—	1·045	1·107	1·188	0·881	0·960	—	0·810
3·5	1·123	0·930	1·139	—	1·080	1·150	1·243	0·886	0·975	—	0·804
4·0	1·153	0·951	1·195	—	1·116	1·199	—	—	0·991	—	0·797
4·5	—	0·972	1·255	—	1·153	—	—	—	1·008	—	0·792
5·0	—	—	1·314	—	1·192	—	—	—	1·025	—	0·788
5·5	—	—	1·374	—	1·231	—	—	—	1·042	—	0·787
6·0	—	—	1·434	—	1·271	—	—	—	1·060	—	0·788
Ref.	47	47	24, 25, 26, 27	29	2	44, 49	44	50	46	51	47

$\overline{\text{Ac}}$ = Acetate. $\overline{\text{Tol}}$ = Toluenesulphonate.

[5] G. N. LEWIS and M. RANDALL, *Thermodynamics* (McGraw-Hill Book Co. Inc., New York, 1923).

[6] E. A. GUGGENHEIM, *Phil. Mag.*, 1935, **19**, (7), 588; 1936, **22**, (7), 322.

[7] H. S. HARNED and B. B. OWEN, *Physical Chemistry of Electrolytic Solutions*, Reinhold Publishing Corp., New York, 1943.

TABLE III, 7 (Continued)
OSMOTIC COEFFICIENTS AT 25 °C.

m	$\overline{\text{NaAc}}$	Na-$\overline{\text{Tol}}$	Na-CNS	NaH$_2$-PO$_4$	KOH	KF	KCl	KBr	KI	K-ClO$_3$	K-BrO$_3$	K-NO$_3$
0·1	0·940	0·924	0·937	0·911	0·944	0·930	0·927	0·928	0·932	0·913	0·910	0·906
0·2	0·939	0·907	0·934	0·884	0·936	0·919	0·913	0·916	0·922	0·887	0·881	0·873
0·3	0·945	0·897	0·935	0·864	0·938	0·915	0·906	0·910	0·918	0·867	0·858	0·851
0·4	0·951	0·887	0·938	0·847	0·944	0·914	0·902	0·906	0·917	0·849	0·837	0 833
0·5	0·959	0·880	0·943	0·832	0·953	0·915	0·899	0·904	0·917	0·832	0·816	0·817
0·6	0·967	0·874	0·948	0·819	0·962	0·916	0·898	0·904	0·918	0·816	—	0·802
0·7	0·977	0·867	0·953	0·808	0·972	0·919	0·897	0·904	0·919	0·802	—	0·790
0·8	0·986	0·861	0·958	0·798	0·983	0·923	0·897	0·905	0·922	—	—	0·778
0·9	0·994	0·855	0·963	0·789	0·993	0·926	0·897	0·906	0·924	—	—	0·767
1·0	1·002	0·849	0·969	0·780	1·003	0·931	0·897	0·907	0·926	—	—	0·756
1·2	1·018	0·837	0·979	0·765	1·026	0·941	0·899	0·910	0·931	—	—	0·736
1·4	1·038	0·824	0·990	0·751	1·051	0·951	0·901	0·914	0·937	—	—	0·718
1·6	1·057	0·811	1·002	0·739	1·076	0·962	0·904	0·917	0·943	—	—	0·700
1·8	1·074	0 799	1·014	0·729	1·100	0·973	0·908	0·922	0·950	—	—	0·684
2·0	1·092	0·787	1·025	0·721	1·125	0·984	0·912	0·927	0·957	—	—	0·669
2·5	1·137	0·763	1·055	0·705	1·183	1·014	0·924	0·941	0·974	—	—	0·631
3·0	1·181	0·748	1·086	0·696	1·248	1·048	0·937	0·955	0·990	—	—	0·602
3·5	1·223	0·738	1·118	0·691	1·317	1·084	0·950	0·969	1·006	—	—	0·577
4·0	—	0·733	1·150	0·691	1·387	1·124	0·965	0·984	1·021	—	—	—
4·5	—	—	—	0·694	1·459	—	0·980	1·000	1·032	—	—	—
5·0	—	—	—	0·699	1·524	—	—	1·015	—	—	—	—
5·5	—	—	—	0·706	1·594	—	—	—	—	—	—	—
6·0	—	—	—	0·713	1·661	—	—	—	—	—	—	—
Ref.	47	47	52	53	33, 34	29	2	44, 49	44, 54	51	55	47

$\overline{\text{Ac}}$ = Acetate.　$\overline{\text{Tol}}$ = Toluenesulphonate.

[8] M. RANDALL and A. M. WHITE, *J. Am. Chem. Soc.*, 1926, **48**, 2514.

[9] R. H. STOKES, *ibid.*, 1945, **67**, 1686.

[10] R. A. ROBINSON and P. A. SINCLAIR, *ibid.*, 1934, **56**, 1830.

[11] R. A. ROBINSON, P. K. SMITH and E. R. B. SMITH, *Trans. Faraday Soc.*, 1942, **38**, 63.

[12] G. SCATCHARD, W. J. HAMER and S. E. WOOD, *J. Am. Chem. Soc.*, 1938, **60**, 3061.

TABLE III, 7 *(Continued)*

OSMOTIC COEFFICIENTS AT 25 °C

m	$\overline{\text{KAc}}$	$\overline{\text{KTol}}$	K-CNS	KH_2-PO_4	RbCl	RbBr	RbI	Rb NO_3	$\overline{\text{RbAc}}$	CsOH	CsCl	CsBr
0·1	0·943	0·921	0·926	0·901	0·923	0·922	0·921	0·903	0·943	0·942	0·917	0·917
0·2	0·944	0·901	0·911	0·868	0·907	0·905	0·904	0·871	0·945	0·939	0·897	0·896
0·3	0·951	0·886	0·904	0·843	0·898	0·897	0·896	0·847	0·952	0·940	0·885	0·882
0·4	0·958	0·873	0·900	0·823	0·893	0·892	0·890	0·826	0·961	0·949	0·875	0·873
0·5	0·968	0·860	0·897	0·805	0·889	0·888	0·886	0·809	0·971	0·960	0·869	0·865
0·6	0·977	0·847	0·896	0·789	0·887	0·886	0·884	0·794	0·981	0·970	0·864	0·861
0·7	0·987	0·834	0·895	0·773	0·886	0·884	0·881	0·781	0·992	0·982	0·861	0·857
0·8	0·997	0·822	0·895	0·760	0·886	0·882	0·880	0·768	1·002	0·992	0·859	0·854
0·9	1·007	0·809	0·894	0·747	0·885	0·881	0·879	0·756	1·013	1·003	0·858	0·852
1·0	1·017	0·798	0·894	0·736	0·885	0·881	0·878	0·745	1·023	1·014	0·857	0·850
1·2	1·038	0·775	0·893	0·716	0·886	0·880	0·878	0·725	1·046	—	0·856	0·849
1·4	1·060	0·751	0·892	0·698	0·888	0·881	0·878	0·706	1·068	—	0·856	0·848
1·6	1·081	0·732	0·892	0·683	0·890	0·882	0·880	0·689	1·091	—	0·857	0·848
1·8	1·103	0·715	0·893	0·669	0·893	0·884	0·882	0·673	1·114	—	0·859	0·850
2·0	1·123	0·700	0·894	—	0·896	0·887	0·886	0·656	1·137	—	0·862	0·852
2·5	1·177	0·664	0·898	—	0·905	0·893	0·893	0·620	1·192	—	0·869	0·859
3·0	1·228	0·637	0·903	—	0·916	0·899	0·901	0.588	1·248	—	0·879	0·866
3·5	1·274	0·615	0·908	—	0·928	0·907	0·911	0·561	1·302	—	0·889	0·874
4·0	—	—	0·912	—	0·941	0·916	0·921	0·538	—	—	0·900	0·884
4·5	—	—	0·917	—	0·952	0·924	0·931	0·516	—	—	0·912	0·892
5·0	—	—	0·921	—	0·966	0·934	0·940	—	—	—	0·924	0·901
5·5	—	—	—	—	—	—	—	—	—	—	—	—
6·0	—	—	—	—	—	—	—	—	—	—	—	—
Ref.	47	47	52	53	10, 56	44, 56	44, 56	47, 56	47, 56	36	10, 36	44, 56

$\overline{\text{Ac}}$ = Acetate. $\overline{\text{Tol}}$ = Toluenesulphonate.

[13] E. R. B. SMITH and P. K. SMITH, *J. Biol. Chem.*, 1937, **117**, 209; **121**, 607; 1940, **132**, 47, 57.
[14] R. H. STOKES, *J. Am. Chem. Soc.*, 1948, **70**, 874.
[15] P. K. SMITH and R. A. ROBINSON, *Trans. Faraday Soc.*, 1942, **38**, 70.
[16] H. S. HARNED and R. W. EHLERS, *J. Am. Chem. Soc.*, 1933, **55**, 2179.
[17] M. RANDALL and L. E. YOUNG, *ibid.*, 1928, **50**, 989.

TABLE III, 7 (Continued)

OSMOTIC COEFFICIENTS AT 25 °C.

m	CsI	$CsNO_3$	$\overline{CsAc}$	Ag-NO_3	Tl-ClO_4	Tl-NO_3	$\overline{TlAc}$	$CuSO_4$	Mg-SO_4	$ZnSO_4$	$CdSO_4$
0·1	0·916	0·902	0·945	0·903	0·900	0·881	0·913	0·561	0·606	0·590	0·565
0·2	0·895	0·869	0·947	0·870	0·867	0·833	0·891	0·515	0·562	0·533	0·513
0·3	0·880	0·842	0·954	0·847	0·842	0·800	0·876	0·494	0·540	0·506	0·490
0·4	0·870	0·820	0·964	0·827	0·821	0·775	0·865	0·478	0·529	0·492	0·476
0·5	0·863	0·802	0·975	0·811	0·804	—	0·855	0·469	0·522	0·483	0·466
0·6	0·858	0·787	0·986	0·795	—	—	0·849	0·462	0·518	0·476	0·458
0·7	0·855	0·774	0·996	0·779	—	—	0·843	0·458	0·517	0·473	0·452
0·8	0·852	0·761	1·006	0·766	—	—	0·838	0·457	0·518	0·473	0·450
0·9	0·849	0·748	1·016	0·754	—	—	0·833	0·458	0·520	0·474	0·449
1.0	0·846	0·736	1·026	0·742	—	—	0·829	0·461	0·525	0·478	0·452
1·2	0·842	0·715	1·049	0·720	—	—	0·823	0·473	0·542	0·489	0·461
1·4	0·839	0·695	1·072	0·699	—	—	0·818	0·491	0·567	0·508	0·476
1·6	0·836	—	1·095	0·680	—	—	0·814	—	0·597	0·533	0·496
1·8	0·834	—	1·119	0·662	—	—	0·810	—	0·630	0·566	0·522
2·0	0·832	—	1·142	0·646	—	—	0·807	—	0·666	0·602	0·551
2·5	0·827	—	1·196	0·609	—	—	0·801	—	0·780	0·717	0·632
3·0	0·822	—	1·251	0·576	—	—	0·796	—	0·922	0·861	0·726
3·5	—	—	1·306	0·550	—	—	0·789	—	—	1·033	0·832
4·0	—	—	—	0·523	—	—	0·783	—	—	—	—
4·5	—	—	—	0·502	—	—	0·777	—	—	—	—
5·0	—	—	—	0·483	—	—	0·772	—	—	—	—
5·5	—	—	—	0·467	—	—	0·766	—	—	—	—
6·0	—	—	—	0·452	—	—	0·760	—	—	—	—
Ref.	44, 56	47, 56	47, 56	57	56	56	56	58	58	58	58

$\overline{Ac}$ = Acetate.

[18] G. Åkerlöf and J. W. Teare, ibid., 1937, 59, 1855.

[19] H. S. Harned, A. S. Keston and J. G. Donelson, ibid., 1936, 58, 989.

[20] H. S. Harned and R. A. Robinson, Trans. Faraday Soc., 1941, 37, 302.

[21] J. N. Pearce and A. F. Nelson, J. Am. Chem. Soc., 1933, 55, 3075.

[22] H. S. Harned and F. E. Swindells, ibid., 1926, 48, 126.

TABLE III, 7 (*Continued*)

OSMOTIC COEFFICIENTS AT 25 °C.

m	Mn-SO$_4$	NiSO$_4$	AlCl$_3$	ScCl$_3$	CrCl$_3$	YCl$_3$	LaCl$_3$	CeCl$_3$	PrCl$_3$	NdCl$_3$	SmCl$_3$
0·1	0·587	0·581	0·819	0·797	0·811	0·789	0·788	0·782	0·784	0·783	0·789
0·2	0·538	0·533	0·841	0·827	0·833	0·810	0·800	0·805	0·801	0·801	0·809
0·3	0·516	0·508	0·889	0·868	0·875	0·847	0·833	0·835	0·830	0·832	0·841
0·4	0·501	0·488	0·947	0·917	0·926	0·892	0·871	0·872	0·866	0·871	0·879
0·5	0·490	0·475	1·008	0·969	0·983	0·939	0·912	0·914	0·905	0·913	0·921
0·6	0·481	0·465	1·074	1·027	1·045	0·989	0·955	0·955	0·945	0·954	0·964
0·7	0·475	0·458	1·145	1·090	1·111	1·042	0·998	1·007	0·996	1·006	1·019
0·8	0·472	0·456	1·220	1·156	1·181	1·100	1·052	1·057	1·046	1·056	1·074
0·9	0·472	0·456	1·299	1·222	1·250	1·161	1·102	1·107	1·100	1·110	1·128
1·0	0·475	0·459	1·382	1·291	1·319	1·223	1·154	1·158	1·154	1·165	1·186
1·2	0·485	0·472	1·560	1·430	1·443	1·354	1·266	1·264	1·271	1·283	1·302
1·4	0·504	0·492	1·749	1·572	—	1·491	1·384	1·387	1·388	1·404	1·427
1·6	0·527	0·517	1·951	1·718	—	1·631	1·502	1·504	1·507	1·527	1·554
1·8	0·556	0·551	2·175	1·869	—	1·780	1·623	1·638	1·631	1·656	1·686
2·0	0·588	0·589	—	—	—	1·940	1·748	1·777	1·759	1·789	1·824
2·5	0·677	0·708	—	—	—	—	—	—	—	—	—
3·0	0·782	—	—	—	—	—	—	—	—	—	—
3·5	0·909	—	—	—	—	—	—	—	—	—	—
4·0	1·048	—	—	—	—	—	—	—	—	—	—
Ref.	58	58	59	59	60	59	59, 61	59	59	59	62

[23] H. S. HARNED, *ibid.*, 1929, **51**, 416.

[24] H. S. HARNED, *ibid.*, 1925, **47**, 676.

[25] H. S. HARNED and J. C. HECKER, *ibid.*, 1933, **55**, 4838.

[26] R. H. STOKES, *ibid.*, 1945, **67**, 1689.

[27] G. ÅKERLÖF and G. KEGELES, *ibid.*, 1940, **62**, 620.

TABLE III, 7 *(Continued)*
OSMOTIC COEFFICIENTS AT 25 °C.

m	$EuCl_3$	$Cr(NO_3)_3$	$K_3Fe(CN)_6$	$K_4Fe(CN)_6$	$Al_2(SO_4)_3$	$Cr_2(SO_4)_3$	$Th(NO_3)_4$
0·1	0·794	0·795	0·727	0·595	0·420	0·414	0·675
0·2	0·812	0·818	0·695	0·556	0·390	0·401	0·685
0·3	0·842	0·860	0·682	0·535	0·391	0·412	0·705
0·4	0·882	0·906	0·678	0·518	0·421	0·437	0·734
0·5	0·926	0·953	0·676	0·506	0·477	0·473	0·770
0·6	0·971	1·003	0·676	0·498	0·545	0·524	0·807
0·7	1·027	1·055	0·679	0·494	0·625	0·585	0·846
0·8	1·082	1·111	0·685	0·494	0·718	0·657	0·885
0·9	1·137	1·168	0·694	0·501	0·809	0·740	0·925
1·0	1·193	1·227	0·705	—	0·922	0·832	0·965
1·2	1·310	1·343	0·727	—	—	1·031	1·044
1·4	1·438	1·456	0·750	—	—	—	1·120
1·6	1·570	—	—	—	—	—	1·192
1·8	1·707	—	—	—	—	—	1·259
2·0	1·853	—	—	—	—	—	1·325
2·5	—	—	—	—	—	—	1·455
3·0	—	—	—	—	—	—	1·546
3·5	—	—	—	—	—	—	1·616
4·0	—	—	—	—	—	—	1·659
4·5	—	—	—	—	—	—	1·688
5·0	—	—	—	—	—	—	1·706
Ref.	62	60	63	56	56	60	63

[28] R. W. IVETT and T. DE VRIES, *ibid.*, 1941, **63**, 2821.
[29] R. A. ROBINSON, *ibid.*, 1941, **63**, 628.
[30] H. S. HARNED and N. F. NIMS, *ibid.*, 1932, **54**, 423; H. S. HARNED and M. A. COOK, *ibid.*, 1939, **61**, 495.
[31] F. OLYNYK and A. R. GORDON, *ibid.*, 1943, **65**, 224.
[31a] NEGUS, *Thesis*, Johns Hopkins University, 1922.

TABLE III, 8

ACTIVITY COEFFICIENTS AT 25 °C.

m	HCl	HBr	HI	H-ClO₄	H-NO₃	LiOH	LiCl	LiBr	LiI	Li-ClO₄	Li-NO₃	$\overline{\text{LiAc}}$
0·1	0·796	0·805	0·818	0·803	0·791	0·760	0·790	0·796	0·815	0·812	0·788	0·784
0·2	0·767	0·782	0·807	0·778	0·754	0·702	0·757	0 766	0·802	0·794	0·752	0·742
0·3	0·756	0·777	0·811	0·768	0·735	0·665	0·744	0·756	0·804	0·792	0·736	0·721
0·4	0·755	0·781	0·823	0·766	0·725	0·638	0·740	0·752	0·813	0·798	0·728	0·709
0·5	0·757	0·789	0·839	0·769	0·720	0·617	0·739	0·753	0·824	0·808	0·726	0·700
0·6	0·763	0·801	0·860	0·776	0·717	0·599	0·743	0·758	0·838	0·820	0·727	0·691
0·7	0·772	0·815	0·883	0·785	0·717	0·585	0·748	0·767	0·852	0·834	0·729	0·689
0·8	0·783	0·832	0·908	0·795	0·718	0·573	0·755	0·777	0·870	0·852	0·733	0·688
0·9	0·795	0·850	0·935	0·808	0·721	0·563	0·764	0·789	0·888	0·869	0·737	0·688
1·0	0·809	0·871	0·963	0·823	0·724	0·554	0·774	0·803	0·910	0·887	0·743	0·689
1·2	0·840	—	1·027	0·858	0·734	0·542	0·796	0·837	0·955	0·931	0·757	0·693
1·4	0·876	—	1·098	0·900	0·745	0·532	0·823	0·874	1·007	0·979	0·774	0·700
1·6	0·916	—	1·175	0·947	0·758	0·525	0·853	0·917	1·063	1·034	0·792	0·709
1·8	0·960	—	1·260	0·998	0·775	0·518	0·885	0·964	1·127	1·093	0·812	0·719
2·0	1·009	—	1·356	1·055	0·793	0·513	0·921	1·015	1·198	1·158	0·835	0·729
2·5	1·147	—	1·641	1·227	0·846	0·503	1·026	1·161	1·418	1·350	0·896	0·762
3·0	1·316	—	2·015	1·448	0·909	0·494	1·156	1·341	1·715	1·582	0·966	0·798
3·5	1·518	—	—	1·726	—	0·487	1·317	1·584	—	1·866	1·044	0·837
4·0	1·762	—	—	2·08	—	0·481	1·510	1·897	—	2·18	1·125	0·877
4·5	2·04	—	—	2·53	—	—	1·741	2·28	—	—	1·215	—
5·0	2·38	—	—	3·11	—	—	2·02	2·74	—	—	1·310	—
5·5	2·77	—	—	3·83	—	—	2·34	3·27	—	—	1·407	—
6·0	3·22	—	—	4·76	—	—	2·72	3·92	—	—	1·506	—
Ref.	16	19	20	41	42	22	10, 43	44, 45	10	46	47, 48	47

$\overline{\text{Ac}}$ = Acetate.

[32] H. S. HARNED and C. C. CRAWFORD, *J. Am. Chem. Soc.*, 1937, **59**, 1903.
[33] H. S. HARNED and M. A. COOK, *ibid.*, 1937, **59**, 496.
[34] G. ÅKERLÖF and P. BENDER, *ibid.*, 1948, **70**, 2366.
[35] H. S. HARNED and M. A. COOK, *ibid.*, 1937, **59**, 1290.
[35a] B. F. LOVELACE, J. C. W. FRAZER and V. B. SEASE, *ibid.*, 1921, **43**, 102.

TABLE III, 8 (*Continued*)
ACTIVITY COEFFICIENTS AT 25 °C.

m	$\overline{\text{LiTol}}$	NaOH	NaF	NaCl	NaBr	NaI	Na-ClO$_3$	Na-ClO$_4$	Na-BrO$_3$	Na-NO$_3$	$\overline{\text{NaAc}}$
0·1	0·772	0·766	0·765	0·778	0·782	0·787	0·772	0·775	0·758	0·762	0·791
0·2	0·723	0·727	0·710	0·735	0·741	0·751	0·720	0·729	0·696	0·703	0·757
0·3	0·695	0·708	0·676	0·710	0·719	0·735	0·688	0·701	0·657	0·666	0·744
0·4	0·674	0·697	0·651	0·693	0·704	0·727	0·664	0·683	0·628	0·638	0·737
0·5	0·659	0·690	0·632	0·681	0·697	0·723	0·645	0·668	0·605	0·617	0·735
0·6	0·647	0·685	0·616	0·673	0·692	0·723	0·630	0·656	0·585	0·599	0·736
0·7	0·638	0·681	0·603	0·667	0·689	0·724	0·617	0·648	0·569	0·583	0·740
0·8	0·630	0·679	0·592	0·662	0·687	0·727	0·606	0·641	0·554	0·570	0·745
0·9	0·623	0·678	0·582	0·659	0·687	0·731	0·597	0·635	0·541	0·558	0·752
1·0	0·617	0·678	0·573	0·657	0·687	0·736	0·589	0·629	0·528	0·548	0·757
1·2	0·605	0·681	—	0·654	0·692	0·747	0·575	0·622	0·507	0·530	0·769
1·4	0·595	0·686	—	0·655	0·699	0·763	0·563	0·616	0·489	0·514	0·789
1·6	0·586	0·692	—	0·657	0·706	0·780	0·553	0·613	0·473	0·501	0·809
1·8	0·575	0·700	—	0·662	0·718	0·799	0·545	0·611	0·461	0·489	0·829
2·0	0·568	0·709	—	0·668	0·731	0·820	0·538	0·609	0·450	0·478	0·851
2·5	0·558	0·743	—	0·688	0·768	0·883	0·525	0·609	0·426	0·455	0·914
3·0	0·556	0·784	—	0·714	0·812	0·963	0·515	0·611	—	0·437	0·982
3·5	0·559	0·835	—	0·746	0·865	1·053	0·508	0·617	—	0·422	1·057
4·0	0·566	0·903	—	0·783	0·929	—	—	0·626	—	0·408	—
4·5	0·575	0·985	—	0·826	—	—	—	0·637	—	0·396	—
5·0	—	1·077	—	0·874	—	—	—	0·649	—	0·386	—
5·5	—	1·181	—	0·928	—	—	—	0·662	—	0·378	—
6·0	—	1.299	—	0·986	—	—	—	0·677	—	0·371	—
Ref.	47	24,25 26,27	29	2	44, 49	44	50	46	51	47	47

$\overline{\text{Ac}}$ = Acetate. $\overline{\text{Tol}}$ = Toluenesulphonate.

[36] H. S. HARNED and O. E. SCHUPP, *ibid.*, 1930, **52**, 3886.
[37] R. F. NIELSEN and D. J. BROWN, *ibid.*, 1927, **49**, 2423.
[38] F. E. W. WETMORE and A. R. GORDON, *J. Chem. Physics*, 1937, **5**, 60.
[39] U. B. BRAY, *J. Am. Chem. Soc.*, 1927, **49**, 2372.
[40] V. K. LAMER and W. G. PARKS, *ibid.*, 1931, **53**, 2040.

TABLE III, 8 (*Continued*)

ACTIVITY COEFFICIENTS AT 25 °C.

m	$\overline{\text{NaTol}}$	Na-CNS	Na-H_2PO_4	KOH	KF	KCl	KBr	KI	$KClO_3$	K-BrO_3	KNO_3
0·1	0·765	0·787	0·744	0·798	0·775	0·770	0·772	0·778	0·749	0·745	0·739
0·2	0·709	0·750	0·675	0·760	0·727	0·718	0·722	0·733	0·681	0·674	0·663
0·3	0·674	0·731	0·629	0·742	0·700	0·688	0·693	0·707	0·635	0·625	0·614
0·4	0·648	0·720	0·593	0·734	0·682	0·666	0·673	0·689	0·599	0·585	0·576
0·5	0·627	0·715	0·563	0·732	0·670	0·649	0·657	0·676	0·568	0·552	0·545
0·6	0·609	0·712	0·539	0·733	0·661	0·637	0·646	0·667	0·541	—	0·519
0·7	0·593	0·710	0·517	0·736	0·654	0·626	0·636	0·660	0·518	—	0·496
0·8	0·579	0·710	0·499	0·742	0·650	0·618	0·629	0·654	—	—	0·476
0·9	0·566	0·711	0·483	0·749	0·646	0·610	0·622	0·649	—	—	0·459
1·0	0·554	0·712	0·468	0.756	0·645	0·604	0·617	0·645	—	—	0·443
1·2	0·532	0·716	0·442	0·776	0·643	0·593	0·608	0·640	—	—	0·414
1·4	0·511	0·723	0·420	0·800	0·644	0·586	0·602	0·637	—	—	0·390
1·6	0·493	0·730	0·401	0·827	0·647	0·580	0·598	0·636	—	—	0·369
1·8	0·476	0·737	0·385	0·856	0·652	0·576	0·595	0·636	—	—	0·350
2·0	0·460	0·744	0·371	0·888	0·658	0·573	0·593	0·637	—	—	0·333
2·5	0·427	0·779	0·343	0·974	0·678	0·569	0·593	0·644	—	—	0·297
3·0	0·402	0·804	0·320	1·081	0·705	0·569	0·595	0·652	—	—	0·269
3·5	0·383	0·854	0·305	1·215	0·738	0·572	0·600	0·662	—	—	0·246
4·0	0·368	0·897	0·293	1·352	0·779	0·577	0·608	0·673	—	—	—
4·5	—	—	0·283	1·53	—	0·583	0·616	0·683	—	—	—
5·0	—	—	0·276	1·72	—	—	0·626	—	—	—	—
5·5	—	—	0·270	1·95	—	—	—	—	—	—	—
6·0	—	—	0·265	2·20	—	—	—	—	—	—	—
Ref.	47	52	53	33, 34	29	2	44, 49	44, 54	51	55	47

$\overline{\text{Tol}}$ = Toluensulphonate.

[41] R. A. ROBINSON and O. J. BAKER, *Trans. Roy. Soc. N.Z.*, 1946, **76**, 250.
[42] F. HARTMAN and P. ROSENFELD, *Z. physik. Chem.*, 1933, **164**, 377.
[43] R. A. ROBINSON, *Trans. Faraday Soc.*, 1945, **41**, 756.
[44] R. A. ROBINSON, *J. Am. Chem. Soc.*, 1935, **57**, 1161.
[45] R. A. ROBINSON and H. J. McCOACH, *ibid.*, 1947, **69**, 2244.

TABLE III, 8 (*Continued*)

ACTIVITY COEFFICIENTS AT 25 °C.

m	$\overline{KAc}$	$\overline{KTol}$	K-CNS	KH_2 -PO_4	RbCl	RbBr	RbI	Rb-NO_3	$\overline{RbAc}$	CsOH	CsCl	CsBr
0·1	0·796	0·762	0·769	0·731	0·764	0·763	0·762	0·734	0·796	0·795	0·756	0·754
0·2	0·766	0·702	0·716	0·653	0·709	0·706	0·705	0·658	0·767	0·761	0·694	0·694
0·3	0·754	0·662	0·685	0·602	0·675	0·673	0·671	0·606	0·756	0·744	0·656	0·654
0·4	0·750	0·632	0·663	0·561	0·652	0·650	0·647	0·565	0·753	0·739	0·628	0·626
0·5	0·751	0·605	0·646	0·529	0·634	0·632	0·629	0·534	0·755	0·739	0·606	0·603
0·6	0·754	0·582	0·633	0·501	0·620	0·617	0·614	0·508	0·759	0·742	0·589	0·586
0·7	0·759	0·560	0·623	0·477	0·608	0·605	0·602	0·485	0·766	0·748	0·575	0·571
0·8	0·766	0·541	0·614	0·456	0·599	0·595	0·591	0·465	0·773	0·754	0·563	0·558
0·9	0·774	0·523	0·606	0·438	0·590	0·586	0·583	0·446	0·782	0·762	0·553	0·547
1·0	0·783	0·506	0·599	0·421	0·583	0·578	0·575	0·430	0·792	0·771	0·544	0·538
1·2	0·803	0·476	0·587	0·393	0·572	0·565	0·562	0·402	0·815	—	0·529	0·523
1·4	0·827	0·448	0·577	0·369	0·563	0·556	0·551	0·377	0·840	—	0·518	0·510
1·6	0·854	0·424	0·569	0·348	0·556	0·547	0·544	0·356	0·869	—	0·509	0·500
1·8	0·881	0·404	0·562	0·332	0·551	0·541	0·537	0·338	0·900	—	0·501	0·493
2·0	0·910	0·386	0·556	—	0·546	0·536	0·533	0·321	0·933	—	0·495	0·486
2·5	0·995	0·347	0·546	—	0·539	0·526	0·524	0·285	1·023	—	0·484	0·474
3·0	1·086	0·317	0·538	—	0·536	0·520	0·518	0·257	1·126	—	0·478	0·465
3·5	1·181	0·292	0·533	—	0·536	0·516	0·516	0·234	1·240	—	0·474	0·460
4·0	—	—	0·529	—	0·538	0·514	0·515	0·216	—	—	0·473	0·457
4·5	—	—	0·526	—	0·541	0·514	0·516	0·200	—	—	0·473	0·455
5·0	—	—	0·524	—	0·546	0·515	0·517	—	—	—	0·474	0·453
5·5	—	—	—	—	—	—	—	—	—	—	—	—
6·0	—	—	—	—	—	—	—	—	—	—	—	—
Ref.	47	47	52	53	10, 56	44, 56	44, 56	47, 56	47, 56	36	10, 36	44, 56

$\overline{Ac}$ = Acetate. $\overline{Tol}$ = Toluenesulphonate.

[46] J. H. JONES, *J. Phys. Chem.*, 1947, **51**, 516.
[47] R. A. ROBINSON, *J. Am. Chem. Soc.*, 1935, **57**, 1165.
[48] R. A. ROBINSON, *ibid.*, 1946, **68**, 2402.
[49] R. A. ROBINSON, *Trans. Faraday Soc.*, 1939, **35**, 1217.
[50] J. H. JONES, *J. Am. Chem. Soc.*, 1943, **65**, 1353.

TABLE III, 8 (*Continued*)

ACTIVITY COEFFICIENTS AT 25 °C.

m	CsI	$CsNO_3$	CsAc	$AgNO_3$	$TlClO_4$	$TlNO_3$	TlAc	$CuSO_4$	$MgSO_4$
0·1	0·754	0·733	0·799	0·734	0·730	0·702	0·750	(0·150)	(0·150)
0·2	0·692	0·655	0·771	0·657	0·652	0·606	0·686	0·104	0·108
0·3	0·651	0·602	0·761	0·606	0·599	0·545	0·644	0·083	0·088
0·4	0·621	0·561	0·759	0·567	0·559	0·500	0·614	0·071	0·076
0·5	0·599	0·528	0·762	0·536	0·527	—	0·589	0·062	0·068
0·6	0·581	0·501	0·768	0·509	—	—	0·570	0·056	0·062
0·7	0·567	0·478	0·776	0·485	—	—	0·553	0·052	0·057
0·8	0·554	0·458	0·783	0·464	—	—	0·539	0·048	0·054
0·9	0·543	0·439	0·792	0·446	—	—	0·526	0·045	0·051
1·0	0·533	0·422	0·802	0·429	—	—	0·515	0·043	0·049
1·2	0·516	0·393	0·826	0·399	—	—	0·496	0·039	0·045
1·4	0·501	0·368	0·853	0·374	—	—	0·480	0·037	0·044
1·6	0·489	—	0·883	0.352	—	—	0·466	—	0·042
1·8	0·479	—	0·916	0.333	—	—	0·454	—	0·042
2·0	0·470	—	0·950	0.316	—	—	0·444	—	0·042
2·5	0·450	—	1·041	0·280	—	—	0·422	—	0·044
3·0	0·434	—	1·145	0·252	—	—	0·405	—	0·049
3·5	—	—	1·263	0·229	—	—	0·389	—	—
4·0	—	—	—	0·210	—	—	0·376	—	—
4·5	—	—	—	0·194	—	—	0·364	—	—
5·0	—	—	—	0·181	—	—	0·354	—	—
5·5	—	—	—	0·169	—	—	0·344	—	—
6·0	—	—	—	0·159	—	—	0·335	—	—
Ref.	44, 56	47, 56	47, 56	57	56	56	56	58	58

$\overline{Ac}$ = Acetate.

[51] J. H. JONES and H. R. FRONING, *ibid.*, 1944, **66**, 1672.

[52] R. A. ROBINSON, *ibid.*, 1940, **62**, 3131.

[53] R. H. STOKES, *Trans. Faraday Soc.*, 1945, **41**, 685.

[54] R. A. ROBINSON and J. M. WILSON, *ibid.*, 1940, **36**, 738.

[55] J. H. JONES, *J. Am. Chem. Soc.*, 1947, **69**, 2066.

TABLE III, 8 *(Continued)*

ACTIVITY COEFFICIENTS AT 25° C.

m	Zn-SO$_4$	Cd-SO$_4$	Mn-SO$_4$	Ni-SO$_4$	AlCl$_3$	ScCl$_3$	CrCl$_3$	YCl$_3$	LaCl$_3$	CeCl$_3$	PrCl$_3$	NdCl$_3$
0·1	(·150)	(·150)	(·150)	(·150)	(·337)	(·320)	(·331)	(·314)	(·314)	(·309)	(·311)	(·310)
0·2	0·104	0·102	0·106	0·105	0·305	0·288	0·298	0·278	0·274	0·273	0·273	0·272
0·3	0·083	0·082	0·085	0·084	0·302	0·282	0·294	0·269	0·263	0·261	0·260	0·261
0·4	0·071	0·069	0·073	0·071	0·313	0·287	0·300	0·271	0·261	0·260	0·258	0·259
0·5	0·063	0·061	0·064	0·063	0·331	0·298	0·314	0·278	0·266	0·264	0·262	0·264
0·6	0·057	0·055	0·058	0·056	0·356	0·316	0·335	0·291	0·274	0·272	0·268	0·272
0·7	0·052	0·050	0·053	0·052	0·388	0·339	0·362	0·307	0·285	0·286	0·281	0·284
0·8	0·048	0·046	0·049	0·047	0·429	0·369	0·397	0·329	0·302	0·302	0·297	0·301
0·9	0·046	0·043	0·046	0·044	0·479	0·403	0·436	0·355	0·321	0·320	0·316	0·321
1·0	0·043	0·041	0·044	0·042	0·539	0·443	0·481	0·385	0·342	0·342	0·338	0·344
1·2	0·040	0·038	0·040	0·039	0·701	0·544	0·584	0·462	0·398	0·395	0·395	0·403
1·4	0·038	0·035	0·038	0·036	0·936	0·677	—	0·566	0·470	0·469	0·467	0·480
1·6	0·036	0·034	0·037	0·035	1·284	0·853	—	0·701	0·561	0·559	0·558	0·577
1·8	0·035	0·032	0·036	0·034	1·819	1·089	—	0·884	0·677	0·684	0·675	0·704
2·0	0·035	0·032	0·035	0·034	—	—	—	1·136	0·825	0·847	0·825	0·867
2·5	0·037	0·032	0·035	0·035	—	—	—	—	—	—	—	—
3·0	0·041	0·033	0·038	—	—	—	—	—	—	—	—	—
3·5	0·048	0·035	0·042	—	—	—	—	—	—	—	—	—
4·0	—	—	0·048	—	—	—	—	—	—	—	—	—
Ref.	58	58	58	58	59	59	60	59	59, 61	59	59	59

[56] R. A. ROBINSON, *ibid.*, 1937, **59**, 84.
[57] R. A. ROBINSON and D. A. TAIT, *Trans. Faraday Soc.*, 1941, **37**, 569.
[58] R. A. ROBINSON and J. H. JONES, *J. Am. Chem. Soc.*, 1936, **58**, 959.
[59] C. M. MASON, *ibid.*, 1938, **60**, 1638.
[60] N. O. SMITH, *ibid.*, 1947, **69**, 91.

TABLE III, 8 *(Continued)*

ACTIVITY COEFFICIENTS AT 25 °C.

m	$SmCl_3$	$EuCl_3$	$Cr(NO_3)_3$	$K_3Fe(CN)_6$	$K_4Fe(CN)_6$	$Al_2(SO_4)_3$	$Cr_2(SO_4)_3$	$Th(NO_3)_4$
0·1	(0·314)	(0·318)	(0·319)	(0·268)	(0·139)	(0·0350)	(0·0458)	(0·279)
0·2	0·278	0·282	0·285	0·212	0·100	0·0225	0·0300	0·225
0·3	0·267	0·270	0·279	0·184	0·081	0·0176	0·0238	0·203
0·4	0·266	0·270	0·281	0·167	0·070	0·0153	0·0207	0·192
0·5	0·271	0·276	0·291	0·155	0·062	0·0143	0·0190	0·189
0·6	0·280	0·286	0·304	0·146	0·056	0·0140	0·0182	0·188
0·7	0·296	0·303	0·322	0·140	0·052	0·0142	0·0181	0·191
0·8	0·314	0·322	0·344	0·135	0·048	0·0149	0·0185	0·195
0·9	0·336	0·345	0·371	0·131	0·046	0·0159	0·0194	0·201
1·0	0·362	0·371	0·401	0·128	—	0·0175	0·0208	0·207
1·2	0·424	0·436	0·474	0·124	—	—	0·0250	0·224
1·4	0·509	0·525	0·565	0·122	—	—	—	0·246
1·6	0·616	0·641	—	—	—	—	—	0·269
1·8	0·756	0·792	—	—	—	—	—	0·296
2·0	0·940	0·995	—	—	—	—	—	0·326
2·5	—	—	—	—	—	—	—	0·405
3·0	—	—	—	—	—	—	—	0·486
3·5	—	—	—	—	—	—	—	0·568
4·0	—	—	—	—	—	—	—	0·647
4·5	—	—	—	—	—	—	—	0·722
5·0	—	—	—	—	—	—	—	0·791
Ref.	62	62	60	63	56	56	60	63

[61] R. A. ROBINSON, *Trans. Faraday Soc.*, 1939, **35**, 1229.
[62] C. M. MASON, *J. Am. Chem. Soc.*, 1941, **63**, 220.
[63] R. A. ROBINSON and B. J. LEVIEN, *Trans. Roy. Soc. N.Z.*, 1946, **76**, 295.

TABLE III, 9

OSMOTIC AND ACTIVITY COEFFICIENTS AT 25 °C. FOR HIGH CONCENTRATIONS ($m > 6$)

	HCl		HClO$_3$		LiCl		LiBr		LiNO$_3$	
m	f_0	$f_\pm$	f_0	$f_\pm$	f_0	$f_\pm$	f_0	$f_\pm$	f_0	$f_\pm$
7	2·008	4·37	2·365	7·44	1·965	3·71	2·206	5·76	1·485	1·723
8	2·163	5·90	2·629	11·83	2·143	5.10	2·432	8·61	1·541	1·952
9	2·315	7·94	2·901	19·11	2·310	6.96	2.656	12·92	1·591	2·19
10	2·444	10·44	3·167	30·9	2·464	9·40	2·902	19·92	1·633	2·44
11	2·559	13·51	3·433	50·1	2·607	12·55	3·150	31.0	1·668	2·69
12	2·663	17·25	3·688	80·8	2·730	16·41	3·356	46·3	1·700	2·95
13	2·760	21·8	3·935	129·5	2·830	20·9	3·581	70·6	1·727	3·20
14	2·853	27·3	4·166	205·0	2·915	26·2	3·776	104·7	—	—
15	2·944	34·1	4·393	322·0	2·978	31·9	3·912	146·0	—	—
16	3·033	42·4	4·608	500·0	3·023	37·9	4·025	198·0	—	—
17	—	—	—	—	3·044	43·8	4·110	260·0	—	—
18	—	—	—	—	3·057	49·9	4·173	331·0	—	—
19	—	—	—	—	3·066	56·3	4·216	411·0	—	—
20	—	—	—	—	3·063	62·4	4·217	485·0	—	—

	KOH		NaOH		AgNO$_3$	
m	f_0	$f_\pm$	f_0	$f_\pm$	f_0	$f_\pm$
7	1·81	2·88	1·567	1·603	0·426	0·142
8	1·96	3·77	1·707	2·01	0·408	0·129
9	2·09	4·86	1·853	2·55	0·393	0·118
10	2·22	6·22	1·993	3·23	0·378	0·109
11	2·36	8·10	2·131	4·10	0·371	0·102
12	2·50	10·5	2·262	5·19	0·363	0·096
13	2·60	13·2	2·382	6·50	0·356	0·090
14	2·66	15·8	2·488	8·04	—	—
15	2·76	19·6	2·574	9·74	—	—
16	2·87	24·6	2·643	11·58	—	—
17	—	—	2·694	13.47	—	—
18	—	—	2·730	15·41	—	—
19	—	—	2·756	17·38	—	—
20	—	—	2·772	19·33	—	—

NaOH (*contd.*)

m	21·0	22·0	23·0	24·0	25·0	26·0	27·0	28·0	29·0
f_0	2·780	2·780	2·773	2·764	2·749	2·731	2·712	2·693	2·678
$f_\pm$	21·3	23·1	24·8	26·5	28·0	29·5	30·9	32·2	33·7

R. A. ROBINSON and R. H. STOKES, *Trans. Faraday Soc.*, 1949, 45, 612.

TABLE III, 9 (*Continued*)

	Osmotic Coefficients f_0				Activity Coefficients $f_\pm$			
m	$UO_2(NO_3)_2$	UO_2Cl_2	$UO_2(ClO_4)_2$	$Ca(ClO_4)_2$	$UO_2(NO_3)_2$	UO_2Cl_2	$UO_2(ClO_4)_2$	$Ca(ClO_4)_2$
0·1	0·875	0·870	0·921	0·883	0·551	0·544	0·626	0·565
0·2	0·899	0·890	0·972	0·911	0·520	0·510	0·634	0·540
0·3	0·928	0·914	1·028	0·942	0·518	0·502	0·669	0·540
0·4	0·960	0·942	1·089	0·976	0·526	0·505	0·723	0·552
0·5	0·996	0·975	1·152	1·014	0·542	0·517	0·790	0·573
0·6	1·031	1·005	1·216	1·051	0·563	0·532	0·871	0·598
0·7	1·067	1·034	1·284	1·089	0·587	0·549	0·969	0·627
0·8	1·105	1·066	1·356	1·131	0·617	0·571	1·087	0·664
0·9	1·143	1·097	1·430	1·175	0·651	0·595	1·226	0·706
1·0	1·182	1·128	1·507	1·219	0·689	0·620	1·390	0·754
1·2	1·258	1·188	1·661	1·310	0·773	0·678	1·804	0·866
1·4	1·330	1·247	1·823	1·405	0·868	0·744	2·38	1·007
1·6	1·398	1·303	1·990	1·503	0·975	0·816	3·17	1·179
1·8	1·466	1·356	2·165	1·605	1·099	0·894	4·29	1·393
2·0	1·532	1·406	2·354	1·710	1·237	0·978	5·91	1·659
2·5	1·673	1·530	2·818	1·992	1·626	1·228	13·37	2·66
3·0	1·764	1·655	3·284	2·261	2·03	1·551	30·9	4·27
3·5	1·807	—	3·721	2·521	2·41	—	70·4	6·86
4·0	1·809	—	4·152	2·769	2·68	—	160·2	10·93
4·5	1·790	—	4·561	3·005	2·89	—	358	17·28
5·0	1·765	—	4·907	3·233	3·06	—	750	27·1
5·5	1·753	—	5·220	3·454	3·25	—	1510	42·3
6·0	—	—	—	3·655	—	—	—	64·7
6·5	—	—	—	3·828	—	—	—	95·7
7·0	—	—	—	3·989	—	—	—	139·3

R. A. ROBINSON, private communication, 1951; also *J. Chem. Soc.*, in course of publication.

TABLE III, 10

OSMOTIC AND ACTIVITY COEFFICIENTS OF SODIUM SALTS OF FUMARIC AND MALEIC ACID
AT 25 °C.

m	Na-Fumarate		Na-Maleate	
	f_0	$f_\pm$	f_0	$f_\pm$
0·1	0·812	0·465	0·770	0·430
0·2	0·801	0·402	0·744	0·354
0·3	0·797	0·369	0·732	0·314
0·5	0·805	0·335	0·727	0·272
0·7	0·833	0·325	0·734	0·250
1·0	0·875	0·322	0·751	0·232
1·5	0·937	0·330	0·782	0·217
2·0	0·994	0·345	0·822	0·211
2·5	—	—	0·866	0·215
3·0	—	—	0·915	0·221

R. A. ROBINSON, P. K. SMITH and E. R. B. SMITH, *Trans. Faraday Soc.*, 1942, **38**, 63.

TABLE III, 11

OSMOTIC COEFFICIENTS OF SUCCINIC, MALEIC, MALIC, d-TARTARIC AND
$meso$-TARTARIC ACIDS AT 25 °C.

m	Maleic	Malic	d-Tartaric	$meso$-Tartaric
0·5	1·109	1·023	1·072	1·068
1·0	1·042	1·020	1·085	1·088
1·5	1·006	1·023	1·108	1·115
2·0	0·983	1·029	1·135	1·144
2·5	0·970	1·038	1·165	1·175
3·0	0·964	1·048	1·195	1·207
3·5	—	1·059	1·227	1·238
4·0	—	1·072	1·256	1·267
4·5	—	1·085	1·287	1·299
5·0	—	1·098	1·313	1·325
5·5	—	1·113	1·339	1·351
6·0	—	1·113	1·364	1·376

For succinic acid at $0·517m$, $f_0 = 0·958$.

R. A. ROBINSON, P. K. SMITH and E. R. B. SMITH, *Trans. Faraday Soc.*, 1942, **38**, 63.

OSMOTIC COEFFICIENTS OF FATTY ACID SODIUM SALTS AT 25 °C.

m	Formate	Acetate	Propionate	Butyrate	Valerate	Caproate	Heptylate	Caprylate	Pelargonate	Caprate
0·1	0·931	0·939	0·944	0·944	0·944	0·946	0·946	0·947	—	—
0·2	0·924	0·939	0·947	0·949	0·951	0·952	0·953	0·955	—	—
0·3	0·922	0·943	0·955	0·961	0·963	0·964	0·966	0·968	0·812	0·448
0·4	—	—	—	—	—	—	—	—	0·607	0·370
0·5	0·925	0·957	0·975	0·991	0·998	0·999	0·987	0·882	0·521	0·326
0·6	—	—	—	—	—	—	—	0·802	0·458	0·293
0·7	0·929	0·974	0·997	1·027	1·028	1·034	0·982	0·722	0·416	0·270
0·8	—	—	—	—	—	1·046	0·958	0·644	0·385	0·251
0·9	—	—	—	—	—	1·052	0·892	0·568	0·362	0·235
1·0	0·939	1·000	1·032	1·076	1·071	1·054	0·833	0·535	0·343	0·231
1·1	—	—	—	—	—	—	—	0·509	0·328	0·230
1·2	—	—	—	—	—	—	—	0·486	0·316	—
1·25	—	—	—	—	—	1·050	0·725	—	—	—
1·4	—	—	—	—	—	1·020	0·659	0·448	0·304	0·231
1·5	0·953	1·044	1·093	1·146	1·134	—	—	—	—	—
1·6	—	—	—	—	—	—	—	0·420	0·300	0·234
1·75	—	—	—	—	—	0·974	0·607	—	—	—
1·8	—	—	—	—	—	—	—	0·394	0·298	0·236
2·0	0·970	1·092	1·151	1·203	1·159	0·925	0·562	0·386	0·296	—
2·25	—	—	—	—	—	0·869	0·527	—	—	—
2·5	0·988	1·138	1·205	1·241	1·124	0·827	0·505	0·387	0·289	—
2·75	—	—	—	—	—	0·795	0·498	—	—	—
3·0	1·005	1·182	1·252	1·272	1·065	0·770	0·492	0·394	—	—
3·5	1·022	—	—	1·297	0·980	0·746	0·495	—	—	—
4·0	—	—	—	—	—	0·745	0·502	—	—	—
4·5	—	—	—	—	—	0·761	0·511	—	—	—
5·0	—	—	—	—	—	—	0·523	—	—	—

E. R. B. SMITH and R. A. ROBINSON, Trans. Faraday Soc., 1942, 38, 74.

TABLE III, 13

ACTIVITY COEFFICIENTS $(f_\pm)$ AT ROUND LOW CONCENTRATIONS AT 25 °C.

molality m	$f_\pm$				
	HCl	NaCl	KCl	CaCl$_2$	LaCl$_3$
0·001	0·9653	0·9651	0·9650	0·8893	0·7902
0·002	0·9525	0·9519	0·9516	0·8519	0·7294
0·005	0·9287	0·9273	0·9270	0·7888	0·6361
0·01	0·9049	0·9022	0·9015	0·7314	0·5597
0·02	0·8757	0·8707	0·8694	0·6681	0·4831
0·05	0·8301	0·8192	0·8164	0·5825	0·3881
0·10	0·7938	0·7744	0·7692	0·5232	0·3252

Compare data in Table III, 6 and III, 22.

Accuracy: $\pm 0 \cdot 0005$. Agreement with other workers is considerably less than this.

T. SHEDLOVSKY, *J. Am. Chem. Soc.*, 1950, **72**, 3680.

TABLE III, 14

MEAN ACTIVITY COEFFICIENT OF POTASSIUM CHLORIDE IN AQUEOUS SOLUTION

molality m	0°	5°	10°	15°	20°	25°	30°	35°	40°
0·1	0·768	0·769	0·769	0·769	0·770	0·769	0·768	0·767	0·765
0·2	·717	·718	·718	·719	·718	·719	·718	·717	·715
0·3	·683	·685	·687	·687	·688	·688	·687	·685	·682
0·5	·642	·646	·648	·650	·651	·651	·651	·648	·646
0·7	·613	·619	·623	·624	·627	·628	·629	·627	·626
1·0	·588	·595	·598	·601	·604	·606	·604	·604	·603
1·5	·563	·570	·576	·579	·582	·585	·585	·585	·585
2·0	·547	·554	·562	·568	·573	·576	·578	·579	·578
2·5	·540	·549	·556	·562	·568	·572	·574	·575	·575
3·0	·539	·549	·556	·562	·567	·571	·573	·574	·573
3·5	·540	·550	·558	·565	·571	·574	·577	·578	·578
4·0	—	—	·563	·569	·574	·579	·582	·584	·585

H. S. HARNED and M. A. COOK, *J. Am. Chem. Soc.*, 1937, **59**, 1290.

TABLE III, 15

MEAN ACTIVITY COEFFICIENT OF SODIUM BROMIDE IN AQUEOUS SOLUTION

molality m	0°	5°	10°	15°	20°	25°	30°	35°	40°
0·2	·738	·739	·741	·740	·741	·740	·739	·737	·734
0·3	·713	·716	·718	·720	·718	·718	·717	·715	·712
0·5	·685	·689	·693	·693	·695	·695	·694	·692	·689
0·7	·670	·675	·681	·684	·683	·687	·686	·685	·685
1·0	·659	·667	·675	·680	·684	·686	·687	·686	·686
1·5	·664	·673	·686	·693	·699	·703	·706	·708	·707
2·0	·679	·693	·708	·719	·727	·734	·739	·741	·743
2·5	·708	·727	·745	·733	·769	·773	·784	·789	·791
3·0	·745	·766	·787	·802	·815	·826	·834	·839	·842
3·5	·787	·811	·834	·852	·866	·878	·887	·893	·896
4·0	·832	·858	·885	·905	·921	·934	·945	·951	·954

Accuracy: Agreement with SMITH [1] and SPENCER [2] to $\pm 0·001$ (see below).
H. S. HARNED and C. C. CRAWFORD, J. Am. Chem. Soc., 1937, 59, 1903.

TABLE III, 16

MEAN ACTIVITY COEFFICIENT OF POTASSIUM HYDROXIDE IN AQUEOUS SOLUTION

molality m	0°	5°	10°	15°	20°	25°	30°	35°
0·1	·795	·796	·798	·798	·798	·798	·796	·793
0·15	·778	·778	·778	·777	·776	·774	·773	·771
0·25	·758	·757	·759	·758	·757	·757	·753	·751
0·35	·738	·740	·740	·739	·739	·739	·736	·733
0·5	·737	·736	·735	·734	·732	·728	·725	·725
0·75	·742	·742	·743	·743	·741	·740	·740	·736
1·0	·755	·756	·758	·757	·756	·756	·755	·752
1·5	·809	·812	·815	·815	·814	·814	·812	·809
2·0	·889	·886	·890	·890	·889	·888	·884	·879
2·5	·974	·978	·981	·982	·980	·974	·972	·965
3·0	1·088	1·091	1·094	1·003	1·087	1·081	1·072	1·065
3·5	1·219	1·229	1·231	1·229	1·219	1·215	1·199	1·195
4·0	1·391	1·395	1·389	1·381	1·361	1·352	1·334	1·314

Accuracy: Observed $f_\pm$ and calculated values agree to $\pm 0·25\%$
H. S. HARNED and M. A. COOK, J. Am. Chem. Soc., 1937, 59, 496.

[1] R. P. SMITH, ibid., 1933, 55, 3279.
[2] H. M. SPENCER, ibid., 1932, 54, 4490.

TABLE III, 17

MEAN ACTIVITY COEFFICIENT OF SODIUM HYDROXIDE IN AQUEOUS SOLUTION

molality m (¹)	0°	5°	10°	15°	20°	25°	30°	35°
0·05	0·820	0·821	0·820	0·820	0·819	0·818	0·818	0·816
0·1	·767	·768	·768	·767	·766	·766	·765	·764
0·25	·713	·715	·716	·717	·714	·713	·712	·712
0·5	·648	·688	·690	·692	·693	·693	·693	·694
1·0	·660	·668	·672	·676	·678	·679	·680	·678
1·5	·661	·669	·673	·681	·682	·683	·685	·683

Accuracy: (¹) ±0·25%

---

¹ 0·05 to 1·5m, H. S. HARNED and J. C. HECKER, *J. Am. Chem. Soc.*, 1933, **55**, 4838.

TABLE III, 17 (*Continued*)

molality m (¹)	0°	10°	20°	30°	40°	50°	60°	70°
1·5	0·657	0·679	0·685	0·688	0·684	0·674	0·657	0·635
2·0	·682	·702	·709	·712	·707	·696	·677	·652
3·0	·763	·766	·789	·781	·783	·767	·742	·711
4·0	·900	·920	·916	·911	·895	·872	·839	·800
5·0	1·100	1·109	1·098	1·081	1·053	1·017	·971	·822
6·0	1·39	1·40	1·35	1·32	1·27	1·21	1·14	1·07
8·0	2·35	2·31	2·17	2·06	1·93	1·78	1·63	1·48
10·0	4·12	4·00	3·61	3·31	3·00	2·67	2·34	2·03
12·0	7·16	6·67	5·80	5·11	4·43	3·79	3·19	2·65
14·0	11·4	10·00	8·68	7·43	6·26	5·20	4·26	3·43
17·0	22·5	19·0	15·82	13·00	10·52	8·39	6·60	5·11

¹ 1·5 to 17m, G. ÅKERLÖF and G. KEGELES, *J. Am. Chem. Soc.*, 1940, **62**, 620.

TABLE III, 18

ACTIVITY COEFFICIENTS OF $Ba(NO_3)_2$ IN SUPERSATURATED SOLUTION
IN THE PRESENCE OF OTHER ELECTROLYTES AT 25 °C.

Ionic Strength	$\log f_\pm$ $Ba(NO_3)_2$
1·1	—0·60
1·5	—0·68
2·0	—0·75
2·5	—0·82
3·0	—0·88
3·5	—0·91
4·0	—0·97

Calculated values from solubility data of $Ba(NO_3)_2$ in $BaCl_2$, K-, Na-, NH_4- and Ca-nitrates and HNO_3.

E. GLÜCKAUF, *Nature*, 1939, **163**, 414.

TABLE III, 19

ACTIVITY COEFFICIENTS OF TETRAMETHYL- AND TETRAETHYL-AMMONIUM IODIDES

IN AQUEOUS SOLUTION AT 25 °C.

$(Me_4)NI$ molality	KCl reference electrolyte, molality	$f_\pm$
0·10	0·0990	0·757
0·12	0·1156	0·723
0·14	0·1308	0·689
0·16	0·1437	0·651
0·18	0·1551	0·615
0·20	0·1657	0·582
0·225	0·1790	0·547
0·25	0·1925	0·519

TABLE III, 19 (*Continued*)

(Et₄)NI molality	KCl reference electrolyte, molality	$f_\pm$
0·20	0·167	0·495
0·40	0·309	0·385
0·60	0·440	0·326
0·80	0·560	0·285
1·00	0·666	0·253
1·20	0·758	0·227
1·40	0·835	0·206
1·60	0·896	0·187

Accuracy: ±0·005.

J. BOWLER REED, Ph. D. *Thesis*, London, 1950.

TABLE III, 20

ACTIVITIES OF WATER IN ELECTROLYTE SOLUTIONS AT 25 °C.

From e.m.f. data for the cell Pt H₂ | H₂SO₄ | PbSO₄ | PbO₂ Pt accurate to
±0·0005 v. c

Aq. KCl *solution*			
c (g.equiv./l.)	—log a_w	c (g.equiv./l.)	—log a_w
0·05	0·000733	1·0	0·014061
0·1	0·001450	2·0	0·02860
0·2	0·002863	3·0	0·04393
0·3	0·004256	4·0	0·06042
0·5	0·002051		

Aq. H₂SO₄ *solution*			
c	a_w	c	a_w
0·01	0·99951	2·0	0·9136
0·02	0·99912	5·0	0·6981
0·05	0·99801	7·0	0·5453
0·1	0·99628	11·0	0·3171
0·2	0·99278	15·0	0·1763
0·5	0·98205	17·0	0·1289
1·0	0·96217		

R. H. STOKES, *J. Am. Chem. Soc.*, 1945, **67**, 1686.
H. S. HARNED and W. J. HAMER, *J. Am. Chem. Soc.*, 1935, **57**, 27.
S. SHANKMAN and A. R. GORDON, *J. Am. Chem. Soc.*, 1939, **61**, 2370.

TABLE III, 21

MEAN ACTIVITY COEFFICIENT OF SULPHURIC ACID

IN AQUEOUS SOLUTIONS FROM ELECTROMOTIVE FORCE MEASUREMENTS

m	0°	10°	20°	25°	30°	40°	50°	60 °C.
0·0005	0·912	0·901	0·890	0·885	0·880	0·869	0·859	0·848
0·0007	0·896	0·880	0·867	0·857	0·854	0·841	0·828	0·814
0·001	0·876	0·857	0·839	0·830	0·823	0·806	0·790	0·775
0·002	0·825	0·796	0·769	0·757	0·746	0·722	0·701	0·680
0·003	0·788	0·754	0·723	0·709	0·695	0·669	0·645	0·622
0·005	0·734	0·693	0·656	0·639	0·623	0·593	0·566	0·533
0·007	0·691	0·647	0·608	0·591	0·574	0·543	0·515	0·489
0·01	0·649	0·603	0·562	0·544	0·527	0·495	0·467	0·441
0·02	0·554	0·509	0·470	0·453	0·437	0·407	0·380	0·356
0·03	0·495	0·453	0·417	0·401	0·386	0·358	0·333	0·311
0·05	0·426	0·387	0·354	0·340	0·326	0·301	0·279	0·260
0·07	0·383	0·346	0·315	0·301	0·290	0·266	0·246	0·228
0·1	0·341	0·307	0·278	0·265	0·254	0·227	0·214	0·197
0·2	0·271	0·243	0·219	0·209	0·199	0·161	0·166	0·153
0·5	0·202	0·181	0·162	0·154	0·147	0·133	0·122	0·107
1·0	0·173	0·153	0·137	0·130	0·123	0·111	0·101	0·0922
1·5	0·167	0·147	0·131	0·124	0·117	0·106	0·0956	0·0869
2·0	0·170	0·149	0·132	0·124	0·118	0·105	0·0949	0·0859
3·0	0·201	0·173	0·151	0·141	0·132	0·117	0·104	0·0926
4·0	0·254	0·215	0·184	0·171	0·159	0·138	0·121	0·106
5·0	0·330	0·275	0·231	0·212	0·196	0·168	0·145	0·126
6·0	0·427	0·350	0·289	0·264	0·242	0·205	0·174	0·150
7·0	0·546	0·440	0·359	0·326	0·297	0·247	0·208	0·177
8·0	0·686	0·545	0·439	0·397	0·358	0·296	0·246	0·206
9·0	0·843	0·662	0·527	0·470	0·425	0·346	0·285	0·237
10·0	1·012	0·785	0·618	0·553	0·493	0·398	0·325	0·268
11·0	1·212	0·930	0·725	0·643	0·573	0·458	0·370	0·302
12·0	1·431	1·088	0·840	0·742	0·656	0·521	0·418	0·339
13·0	1·676	1·261	0·965	0·851	0·750	0·590	0·471	0·379
14·0	1·958	1·458	1·104	0·967	0·850	0·664	0·525	0·420
15·0	2·271	1·671	1·254	1·093	0·957	0·741	0·583	0·462
16·0	2·612	1·907	1·420	1·234	1·076	0·828	0·647	0·511
17·0	3·015	2·176	1·604	1·387	1·204	0·919	0·712	0·559
17·5	3·217	2·316	1·703	1·471	1·275	0·972	0·752	0·589

Accuracy: $\pm 0·003$.

H. S. HARNED and W. J. HAMER, *J. Am. Chem. Soc.*, 1935, **57**, 27. (Regions of confirmed validity 0 to 4m and 9 to 11m inclusive.)

T

MEAN ACTIVITY COEFFICI|

From observed electromotive forces. Results at concentrations less than $m =$
are based on the data of H. S. HARNED and R. W. EHLERS (*J. Am. Chem*
made a careful study of the hydrogen silver-silver chloride cell con|
were made for the solubi|

molality m	0°	5°	10°	15°	20°	2|
0·0001	(0·9890)	(0·9886)	(0·9890)	(0·9890)	(0·9892)	(0.9|
·0002	(·9848)	(·9847)	(·9846)	(·9844)	(·9844)	(·9|
·0005	(·9756)	(·9756)	(·9756)	(·9757)	(·9759)	(·9|
·001	(·9668)	(·9662)	(·9666)	(·9661)	(·9661)	(·9|
·002	·9541	·9539	·9544	·9530	·9527	·9|
·005	·9303	·9300	·9300	·9297	·9294	·9|
·01	·9065	·9056	·9055	·9055	·9052	·9|
·02	·8774	·8768	·8773	·8770	·8768	·8|
·05	·8346	·8344	·8338	·8329	·8317	·8|
·1	·8027	·8023	·8016	·8000	·7985	·7|
·2	·7756	·7756	·7740	·7717	·7694	·7|
·5	·7761	·7730	·7694	·7658	·7616	·7|
1·0	·8419	·8363	·8295	·8229	·8162	·8|
1·5	·9452	·9365	·9270	·9154	·9065	·8|
2·0	1·078	1·068	1·053	1·039	1·024	1·0|
3·0	1·452	1·427	1·401	1·373	1·345	1·3|
4·0	2·006	1·960	1·911	1·862	1·812	1·7|

See also Table III, 13.
Accuracy: $\pm 0·06\%$

T

MEAN ACTIVITY COEFFICIE|

molality m	0°	5°	10°	15°	20°	2|
0·001	0·967	0·967	0·967	0·966	0·966	0·9|
·005	·932	·932	·932	·930	·930	·9|
·01	·910	·910	·909	·908	·907	·9|
·02	·883	·883	·883	·882	·879	·8|
·05	·843	·843	·843	·842	·838	·8|
·1	·812	·812	·811	·808	·807	·8|
·2	·793	·791	·790	·787	·785	·7|
·5	·806	·803	·800	·797	·793	·7|
1·0	·900	·894	·889	·888	·877	·8|

Accuracy: Agreement between observed and calculated values to within $\pm 0·25\%$,
experimental accuracy: probably $\pm 0·1\%$.

CHLORIC ACID IN WATER

btained from plots used for extrapolation (values in brackets). These values
55, 2179). N. J. ANDERSON, *Dissertation*, University of Chicago (1934), has
hloric acid at concentrations between 0·00002 and 0·003*m*. Corrections
chloride and for other effects.

0°	35°	40°	45°	50°	55°	60°
890)	(0·9886)	(0·9885)	(0·9883)	(0·9879)	(0·9879)	(0·9879)
835)	(·9838)	(·9833)	(·9835)	(·9831)	(·9833)	(·9831)
747)	(·9745)	(·9741)	(·9741)	(·9738)	(·9735)	(·9734)
650)	(·9647)	(·9643)	(·9644)	(·9639)	(·9636)	(·9632)
515	·9513	·9505	·9504	·9500	·9497	·9491
275	·9268	·9265	·9261	·9250	·9240	·9235
034	·9025	·9016	·9008	·9000	·8990	·8987
741	·8731	·8715	·8704	·8690	·8680	·8666
285	·8265	·8246	·8232	·8211	·8195	·8168
940	·7918	·7891	·7872	·7850	·7829	·7813
630	·7604	·7569	·7538	·7508	·7474	·7437
526	·7477	·7432	·7387	·7344	·7292	·7237
018	·7942	·7865	·7790	·7697	·7628	·7541
849	·8740	·8601	·8517	·8404	·8276	·8178
929	·9755	·9602	·9481	·9327	·9186	·9072
—	—	—	—	—	—	—
—	—	—	—	—	—	—

BROMIC ACID IN AQUEOUS SOLUTION [1]

0°	35°	40°	45°	50°	55°	60°
066	0·965	0·964	0·964	0·964	0·963	0·963
029	·928	·928	·927	·926	·924	·924
006	·905	·904	·904	·902	·900	·898
879	·878	·877	·875	·873	·871	·869
837	·834	·833	·831	·830	·827	·826
804	·802	·800	·797	·795	·791	·788
780	·777	·774	·772	·769	·765	·758
784	·781	·776	·772	·767	·764	·760
864	·856	·850	·844	·838	·831	·823

[1] H. S. HARNED, A. S. KESTON and J. G. DONELSON, *J. Am. Chem. Soc.*, 1937, **58**, 989.

TABLE III, 24

MEAN ACTIVITY COEFFICIENT OF HYDROCHLORIC ACID IN ORGANIC SOLVENTS AND
ORGANIC SOLVENT-WATER MIXTURES

$N_2 =$ mol. fraction of organic solvent. (Figures in brackets refer to references.)

I. Methanol

molality of HCl m	$N_2 = 0.0588$ [1]			$N_2 = 0.1233$ [1]		
	0°	25°	40°	0°	25°	40°
0·001	0·964	0·962	0·961	0·961	0·959	0·957
·002	·951	·948	·946	·946	·943	·941
·005	·926	·922	·919	·919	·915	·912
·01	·901	·897	·893	·893	·888	·884
·02	·872	·866	·861	·862	·856	·850
·05	·825	·819	·812	·814	·806	·798
·1	·790	·780	·772	·771	·762	·751
·2	·762	·747	·736	·741	·727	·715
·5	·754	·737	·718	·726	·703	·693
1·0	·809	·783	·756	·772	·747	·722
1·5	·898	·861	·827	·855	·814	·781
2·0	1·020	·966	·917	·965	·911	·860

$N_2 = 1$ [2]

molality of HCl m	25°	m	25°	m	25°
0·00236	0·826	0·01444	0·658	0·0733	0·470
·002683	·817	·01722	·638	·0751	·468
·002980	·809	·01986	·621	·0947	·443
·003161	·804	·02363	·601	·1155	·423
·00494	·766	·02549	·592	·4802	·325
·00542	·758	·04261	·532	·5574	·322
·00711	·732	·04356	·530	—	—
·00986	·699	·05312	·507	—	—

[1] H. S. HARNED and C. H. THOMAS, *J. Am. Chem. Soc.*, 1936, **58**, 761.
[2] G. NONHEBEL and H. HARTLEY, *Phil. Mag.*, 1925, **50**, (6), 298, 729.

TABLE III, 24 (*Continued*)

II. Ethanol

$N_2 = 0\cdot0417$ [3]		$N_2 = 0\cdot0891$ [3]		$N_2 = 0\cdot5$ [4, 5]		$N_2 = 1$ [4, 5]	
m	25°	m	25°	m	25°	m	25°
0·00631	0·914	0·00470	0·915	0·005	0·815	0·005	0·728
·00758	·907	·00787	·894	·01	·757	·01	·632
·01088	·891	·01015	·883	·02	·676	·02	·544
·01987	·864	·01983	·850	·05	·586	·0249	·514
·04210	·824	·04150	·809	·1	·521	·0423	·445
·05100	·814	·05166	·794	·2	·471	·05	·426
·07085	·795	·07123	·775	·5	·432	·1	·352
·0800	·788	·0816	·770	·1·0	·449	·1242	·327
·0885	·783	·0924	·761	1·5	.510	·1782	·300
·1091	·773	·1042	·751	2·0	·582	·2	·286
·1990	·744	·3038	·699	2·5	·697	·4437	·218
·2999	·731	·4751	·698	—	—	1·0	·177
·5050	·730	·7309	·709	—	—	1·050	·168
·7014	·743	1·0216	·741	—	—	1·481	·159
·9946	·776	1·549	·819	—	—	3·62	·150
1·499	·856	2·079	·930	—	—	—	—
1·994	·954	—	—	—	—	—	—

III. Isopropanol [3]
$N_2 = 0\cdot0323$

m	25°	m	25°	m	25°
0·001862	0·948	0·03558	0·830	0·2990	0·726
·004019	·927	·04855	·813	·4451	·723
·006356	·911	·06685	·795	·6993	·737
·008616	·899	·07947	·785	·8863	·757
·00892	·898	·1119	·766	1·0	·770
·02089	·858	·1921	·740	—	—

[3] H. S. HARNED and C. CALMON, *J. Am. Chem. Soc.*, 1939, **61**, 1491.
[4] H. S. HARNED and M. H. FLEYSHER, *ibid.*, 1925, **47**, 82.
[5] W. W. LUCASSE, *Z. physik. Chem.*, 1926, **121**, 254.

TABLE III, 24 (*Continued*)

IV. Glycerol ([5])

m	$N_2 = 0.01$ 25°	$N_2 = 0.05$ 25°	m	$N_2 = 0.01$ 25°	$N_2 = 0.05$ 25°
0·002	0·951	—	0·5	0·755	0·737
·005	·924	0·898	0·7	·772	·760
·01	·902	·885	1·0	·810	·801
·02	·873	·858	1·5	·901	·901
·05	·826	·810	2·0	1·019	1·030
·1	·798	·775	2·5	1·161	1·190
·2	·764	·744	3·0	1·345	1·385
·28	·756	·738	4·0	1·792	1·914
·38	·753	·738	—	—	—

Accuracy: Agreement between observed and calculated $f_{\pm}$ is ± 0.001 - 0.002. Accuracy of basic e.m.f. data is ± 0.05 mv.

TABLE III, 25

ACTIVITY COEFFICIENTS OF SALTS IN ANHYDROUS AMMONIA AT —50 °C.

$f_{\pm}(NH_4NO_3)$		$f_{\pm}(NH_4Cl)$	
c mol/l.	$f_{\pm}$	c mol/l.	$f_{\pm}$
0·0001	0·953	0·005	0·423
0·0002	0·935	0·01	0·341
0·0005	0·883	0·02	0·266
0·001	0·824	0·05	0·188
0·005	0·578	0·1	0·143
0·01	0·466	0·2	0·106
0·05	0·282	0·5	0·070
0·1	0·216		
0·5	0·122		
1·0	0·104		

V. A. PLESKOV and A. M. MONOSSOHN, *Acta Physicochim.*, *U.R.S.S.*, 1934, **1**, 713.

TABLE III, 26

MEAN MOLAL ACTIVITY COEFFICIENTS OF HCl IN METHANOL-WATER MIXTURES AT 25 °C.

m	wt.% CH₃OH				
	43·3	64·0	84·2	94·2	100
2	0·773	—	—	—	—
1·5	0·732	—	—	—	—
1·0	0·666	0·597	0·499	—	—
0·5	0·636	0·578	0·476	—	—
0·25	0·652	—	0·504	—	—
0·20	—	0·605	—	—	—
0·10	0·702	0·653	0·563	—	—
0·05	0·752	0·706	0·617	—	0·522
0·02	0·817	0·773	0·708	0·662	0·629
0·01	0·857	0·821	0·764	0·732	0·701
0·008	0·871	—	0·787	—	0·722
0·005	0·891	0·861	0·820	0·791	0·762
0·003	0·915	—	0·852	0·827	0·804
0·002	0·928	0·900	0·878	0·855	0·833
0·001	0·947	0·934	0·911	0·895	0·876

Note discrepancy between values for 100% CH₃OH and those of NONHEBEL and HARTLEY, *Phil. Mag.*, 1925, **50**, (6), 729. These modern data are more reliable. J. M. AUSTIN, A. H. HUNT, F. A. JOHNSON and H. N. PARTON, in course of publication.

TABLE III, 27

MEAN ACTIVITY COEFFICIENTS OF HYDROCHLORIC ACID IN DIOXAN-WATER MIXTURES
$(X = \text{wt.}\% \text{ DIOXAN})$

			$X = 20$				
m	$0°$	$10°$	$20°$	$25°$	$30°$	$40°$	$50°$
0·005	0·902	0·900	0·898	0·896	0·895	0·892	0·889
·007	·889	·886	·883	·880	·880	·876	·871
·01	·872	·869	·865	·862	·861	·857	·851
·02	·835	·830	·825	·821	·820	·814	·808
·03	·811	·805	·800	·796	·795	·788	·781
·05	·780	·774	·768	·763	·762	·755	·748
·07	·759	·753	·746	·740	·740	·732	·725
·1	·736	·729	·722	·720	·716	·708	·701
·2	·696	·688	·681	·676	·673	·665	·656
·3	·682	·675	·667	·661	·658	·649	·639
·5	·684	·675	·666	·660	·656	·646	·633
·7	·649	·690	·679	·672	·667	·655	·641
1·0	·736	·725	·712	·704	·698	·683	·666
1·5	·830	·815	·797	·786	·777	·755	·732
2·0	·959	·938	·913	·898	·885	·855	·823
3·0	1·337	1·293	1·245	1·219	1·195	1·141	1·085

			$X = 45$				
0·003	0·849	0·846	0·844	0·842	0·839	0·834	0·828
·005	·824	·817	·811	·808	·803	·795	·786
·007	·802	·793	·786	·782	·777	·767	·757
·01	·776	·766	·758	·753	·747	·737	·725
·02	·720	·707	·697	·692	·686	·673	·660
·03	·683	·671	·661	·654	·649	·635	·622
·05	·637	·624	·613	·607	·600	·586	·573
·07	·605	·593	·583	·577	·570	·557	·545
·1	·579	·566	·553	·547	·540	·525	·512
·2	·529	·514	·503	·496	·488	·474	·459
·3	·511	·496	·484	·476	·466	·453	·438
·5	·503	·487	·473	·465	·456	·440	·423
·7	·513	·495	·480	·471	·461	·443	·424
1·0	·547	·526	·508	·497	·485	·463	·442
1·5	·640	·612	·585	·570	·555	·524	·496
2·0	·773	·733	·695	·676	·655	·614	·575
3·0	1·191	1·112	1·037	1·001	·962	·887	·818

TABLE III, 27 (*Continued*)

$X = 70$							
m	0°	10°	20°	25°	30°	40°	50°
0·001	0·719	0·713	0·705	0·700	0·696	0·686	0·675
·0015	·672	·665	·656	·651	·647	·636	·624
·002	·641	·633	·623	·618	·613	·601	·589
·003	·589	·582	·573	·568	·563	·552	·540
·005	·530	·521	·510	·505	·499	·487	·473
·007	·488	·479	·468	·462	·457	·444	·431
·01	·446	·436	·425	·418	·413	·401	·388
·02	·369	·359	·348	·342	·336	·324	·312
·03	·328	·318	·308	·303	·297	·286	·275
·05	·283	·274	·264	·258	·253	·243	·232
·07	·259	·249	·239	·234	·229	·219	·208
·1	·236	·226	·217	·212	·207	·197	·188
·2	·204	·194	·185	·180	·175	·165	·156
·3	·193	·182	·173	·168	·163	·154	·144
·5	·191	·179	·169	·163	·158	·147	·137
·7	·200	·187	·175	·168	·162	·150	·139
1·0	·227	·211	·195	·187	·179	·165	·151
1·5	·303	·277	·252	·240	·228	·207	·187

$X = 82$					
m	5°	15°	25°	35°	45°
0·001	0·4242	0·4129	0·3979	0·3795	0·3592
·0015	·3725	·3627	·3488	·3318	·3129
·002	·3369	·3277	·3147	·2990	·2810
·003	·2862	·2781	·2682	·2553	·2378
·005	·2319	·2267	·2181	·2062	·1916
·007	·2019	·1977	·1900	·1791	·1654
·01	·1744	·1707	·1629	·1529	·1412
·025	·1472	·1440	·1371	·1282	·1176
·02	·1311	·1274	·1213	·1131	·1035
·03	·1112	·1076	·1020	·0946	·0869
·05	·0912	·0876	·0826	·0766	·0698
·07	·0780	·0756	·0713	·0659	·0596
·1	·0701	·0675	·0634	·0582	·0525
·15	·0627	·0597	·0560	·0513	·0460
·2	·0589	·0560	·0521	·0476	·0425
·3	·0563	·0532	·0490	·0443	·0392
·5	·0595	·0554	·0504	·0445	·0386

H. S. HARNED and J. O. MORRISON, *Am. J. Sci.*, 1937, 33, 161; *J. Am. Chem. Soc.*, 1936, 58, 1908.

TABLE III, 28

STOICHIOMETRIC ACTIVITY COEFFICIENTS FOR DILUTE SOLUTIONS
OF SULPHURIC ACID IN METHANOL

Molality of H_2SO_4	Stoichiometric activity coefficient γ			
	20°	25°	30°	35°
0·0005	0·924	0·912	0·905	0·894
0·001	0·894	0·879	0·867	0·854
0·002	0·855	0·835	0·821	0·803
0·005	0·783	0·757	0·738	0·712
0·010	0·712	0·682	0·659	0·627
0·020	0·626	0·594	0·568	0·531
0·050	0·494	0·465	0·438	0·397
0·100	0·393	0·369	0·344	0·304
0·200	0·301	0·282	0·263	0·230
0·400	0·236	0·209	0·199	0·181

Accuracy: $\pm 0·002$.

E. W. KANNING and W. G. BOWMAN, *J. Am. Chem. Soc.*, 1946, **68**, 2042.

TABLE III, 29

ACTIVITY COEFFICIENTS $(f_{\pm})$ OF LEAD CHLORIDE IN DIOXAN-WATER MIXTURES AT
ROUNDED VALUES OF IONIC STRENGTH, $I_{(m)}$.

$I_{(m)}$	wt.% Dioxan		
	20%	40%	60%
0·0005	0·919	0·870	0·662
0·001	0·887	0·818	0·562
0·004	0·782	0·661	0·318
0·008	0·705	0·561	0·202
0·01	0·678	0·527	0·173
0·04	0·471	0·301	0·060
0·08	0·356	0·198	0·039
0·1	0·323	0·171	0·035
0·3	0·176	0·084	0·020
0·5	0·117	0·064	—
0·7	0·080	0·055	—
0·9	0·053	0·046	—
1·0	0·045	—	—

Accuracy of $f_{\pm}$, $\pm 0·005$.

Values of $f_{\pm}$ are computed from experimental e.m.f. and solubility data.

M. V. NOBLE and A. B. GARRETT, *J. Am. Chem. Soc.*, 1944, **66**, 231.

TABLE III, 30

ACTIVITY COEFFICIENTS OF LEAD CHLORIDE OF IONIC STRENGTH $I_{(m)}$ IN ETHYLENE GLYCOL-WATER MIXTURES AT 25 °C.

$I_{(m)}$	100% H_2O	78·25% H_2O	57·43% H_2O	37·56% H_2O	19·30% H_2O	0% H_2O
0·001	0·912	0·910	0·895	0·866	0·823	0·793
0·003	0·847	0·844	0·820	0·775	0·715	0·677
0·006	0·791	0·786	0·755	0·701	0·637	0·591
0·008	0·764	0·758	0·724	0·666	0·594	0·553
0·01	0·740	0·732	0·697	0·635	0·562	0·520
0·03	0·604	0·593	0·551	0·483	0·407	0·364
0·06	0·505	0·494	0·450	0·385	0·316	0·273
0·08	0·464	0·452	0·410	0·348	0·282	0·241
0·1146	0·413	0·402	0·363	0·305	0·243	0·202
0·1397	0·385	0·372	0·336	0·283	0·226	0·182
0·2	0·335	0·320	0·290	0·248	0·196	0·144
0·4	—	0·236	0·217	0·193	0·166	—
0·8	—	0·166	0.160	0.148	—	—

Solvent composition is given as wt.% H_2O.

ACTIVITY COEFFICIENTS OF THALLOUS CHLORIDE OF IONIC STRENGTH $I_{(m)}$ IN ETHYLENE GLYCOL-WATER MIXTURES AT 25 °C.

$I_{(m)}$	100% H_2O	80% H_2O	60% H_2O	40% H_2O	20% H_2O	0% H_2O
0·001	0·957	0·953	0·950	0·917	0·890	0·827
0·004	0·921	0·911	0·895	0·848	0·807	0·721
0·007	0·897	0·880	0·861	0·808	0·763	0·668
0·010	0·881	0·862	0·833	0·780	0·732	0·635
0·040	0·777	0·739	0·695	0·642	0·605	0·503
0·100	0·680	0·615	0·576	0·544	0·518	0·427
0·300	0·529	0·470	0·441	0·430	—	—
0·500	0·450	0·414	0·387	0·379	—	—
1·000	0·345	0·349	0·332	0·326	—	—

Accuracy of $f_{\pm}$ is better than ± 0.005 for all values of concentration.

A. B. GARRETT et al., J. Am. Chem. Soc., 1943, 65, 1406.

T

INDIVIDUAL ACTIVITY COEFFICIENTS OF IONS IN WA

These values have been calculated from the equation: $\log f_i = \dfrac{-0\cdot358\ z_i}{1 + 10^8\ a'_i 0\cdot2}$

hydrated ion and $\Gamma = 2I_{(m)}$.

Values of a'_i are derived by various methods (see KIELLAND, *loc. cit.*). T

Inorganic Ions	$10^8\ a'_i$	0·0(
H·	9	0·9?
Li·	6	·9?
Rb·, Cs·, NH₄·, Tl·, Ag·	2·5	·9?
K·, Cl′, Br′, I′, CN′, NO₂′, NO₃′	3	·9?
OH′. F′, NCS′, NCO′, HS′, ClO₃′, ClO₄′, BrO₃′, IO₄′, MnO₄′	3·5	·9?
Na·, CdCl·, ClO₂′, IO₃′, HCO₃′, H₂PO₄′, HSO₃′, H₂AsO₄·, [Co(NH₃)₄(NO₂)₂]·	4·5	·9?
Hg₂··, SO₄″, S₂O₃″, S₂O₆″, S₂O₈″, SeO₄″, CrO₄″, HPO₄″ .	4	·9(
Pb··, CO₃″, SO₃″, MoO₄″, [Co(NH₃)₅Cl]··, [Fe(CN)₅NO]″	4·5	·9(
Sr··, Ba··, Ra··, Cd··, Hg··, S″, S₂O₄″, WO₄″	5	·9(
Ca··, Cu··, Zn··, Sn··, Mn··, Fe··, Ni··, Co··	6	·9(
Mg··, Be··	8	·9(
PO₄‴,[Fe(CN)₆]‴, [Cr(NH₃)₆]···, [Co(NH₃)₆]···, [Co(NH₃)₅H₂O]···	4	·7?
[Co(ethylenediamine)₃]···	6	·7?
Al···, Fe···, Cr···, Sc···, Y···, La···, In···, Ce···, Pr···, Nd···, Sm···	9	·8(
[Fe(CN)₆]⁗	5	·6(
[Co(S₂O₃)(CN)₅]⁗	6	·6?
Th····, Zr····, Ce····, Sn····	11	·6?
[Co(SO₃)₂(CN)₄]⁗′	9	·5?

Organic Ions

HCOO′, citrate′, CH₃NH₃·, (CH₃)₂NH₂·	3·5	0·9?
NH₃·. CH₂COOH, (CH₃). NH·, C₂H₅NH₃·	4	·9?
CH₃COO′, CH₂ClCOO′, (CH₃)₄N·, (C₂H₅)₂NH₂·, NH₂CH₂COO′	4·5	·9?
CHCl₂COO′, CCl₃COO′, (C₂H₅)₃NH·, (C₃H₇)NH₃· . . .	5	·9?
C₆H₅COO′, C₆H₄OHCOO′, C₆H₄ClCOO′, C₆H₅CH₂COO′, CH₂= =CHCH₂COO′, (CH₃)₂C=CHCOO′, (C₂H₅)₄N·, (C₃H₇)₂ NH₂· .	6	·9?
(C₆H₂)(NO₂)₃O′, (C₃H₇)₃NH·, CH₃OC₆H₄COO′	7	·9?
(C₆H₅)₂CHCOO′, (C₃H₇)₄N·	8	·9?
(COO)₂″, citrate″	4·5	·9(
H₂C(COO)₂″, (CH₂COO)₂″, (CHOHCOO)₂″	5	·9(
C₆H₄(COO)₂″, H₂C(CH₂COO)₂″, (CH₂CH₂COO)₂″	6	·9(
OOC(CH₂)₅COO″, OOC(CH₂)₆COO″, Congo red anion″ . .	7	·9(
Citrate‴	5	·7?

J. KIELLAND, *J. Am. Chem. Soc.*, 1937, **59**, 1675.

31

C. CALCULATED FROM THE DEBYE-HÜCKEL THEORY

e f_i is the rational activity coefficient, a'_i is the effective diameter of the

grouped according to their effective diameters of hydration, a'_i.

·002	0·005	0·01	0·02	0·05	0·1	0·2
			total ionic concentration			
·967	0·950	0·933	0·914	0·88	0·86	0·83
·965	·948	·929	·907	·87	·835	·80
·964	·945	·924	·898	·85	·80	·75
·964	·945	·925	·899	·85	·805	·755
·964	·946	·926	·900	·855	·81	·76
·964	·947	·928	·902	·86	·82	·775
·867	·803	·740	·660	·545	·445	·355
·868	·805	·742	·665	·55	·455	·37
·868	·805	·744	·67	·555	·465	·38
·870	·809	·749	·675	·57	·485	·405
·872	·813	·755	·69	·595	·52	·45
·725	·612	·505	·395	·25	·16	·095
·731	·620	·52	·415	·28	·195	·13
·738	·632	·54	·445	·325	·245	·18
·57	·425	·31	·20	·10	·048	·021
·575	·43	·315	·21	·105	·055	·027
·588	·455	·35	·255	·155	·10	·065
·43	·28	·18	·105	·045	·020	·009
·964	0·946	0·926	0·900	0·855	0·81	0·76
·964	·947	·927	·901	·855	·815	·77
·964	·947	·928	·902	·86	·82	·775
·964	·947	·928	·904	·865	·83	·79
·965	·948	·929	·907	·87	·835	·80
·965	·948	·930	·909	·875	·845	·81
·966	·949	·931	·912	·880	·85	·82
·867	·804	·741	·662	·55	·45	·36
·868	·805	·744	·67	·555	·465	·38
·870	·809	·749	·675	·57	·485	·405
·872	·812	·755	·685	·58	·50	·425
·728	·616	·51	·405	·27	·18	115

TABLE III, 32

MEAN IONIC ACTIVITY COEFFICIENTS FOR SALTS IN ANHYDROUS AMMONIA AT 25 °C. These activity coefficients $(f_{\pm}')$ are derived with reference to an arbitrary unit activity at molality of salt = 1.

NH$_4$NO$_3$		NH$_4$Cl		NH$_4$Br		NH$_4$I	
Molality	$f_{\pm}'$	Molality	$f_{\pm}'$	Molality	$f_{\pm}'$	Molality	$f_{\pm}'$
48·9	1·17	24·4	0·239	24·8	1·26	25·4	11·5
34·5	1·19	18·9	0·192	17·3	0·714	18·0	5·66
22·8	1·05	10·7	0·176	10·5	0·401	14·3	2·96
15·2	0·779	5·49	0·255	5·23	0·380	9·32	1·13
8·63	0·510	4·00	0·324	2·39	0·577	5·21	0·676
4·19	0·483	1·96	0·580	1·28	0·857	3·19	0·644
1·97	0·677	1·06	0·958	0·979	1·01	1·33	0·869
1·40	0·825	0·850	1·14	0·587	1·42	1·07	0·966
1·14	0·930	0·506	1·68	0·369	1·93	0·883	1·06
0·917	1·05			0·280	2·19	0·675	1·21
0·508	1·49					0·309	1·87
0·411	1·69						

W. E. LARSON and H. HUNT, *J. Phys. Chem.*, 1935, **39**, 877.

T'

ACTIVITY COEFFICIENTS $(f_{\pm})$ OF α-AMINO AC

Molality m	DL-α-Alanine	Sarcosine	DL-Serine	DL-α-Amino -n-butyric acid	DL-Three
0·2	0·002	0·002	—0·016	0·009	—0·0
0·3	0·003	0·003	—0·025	0·012	—0·0
0·4	0·004	—	—	0·017	—
0·5	0·005	0·005	—0·042	0·020	—0·0
0·65	0·006	—		0·026	—
0·7	—	0·009		—	—0·0
0·8	0·008	—		0·032	—
1·0	0·010	0·014		0·040	—0·0
1·2	0·012	0·018		0·047	—0·0
1·5	0·015	0·025		0·057	—0·0
1·7	0·017	—		0·064	—
1·9	0·020	—		0·071	—
2·0	—	0·038		—	—0·0
Approx. Saturated Solution	1·9m 0·020	7·0m 0·211	0·5m —0·043	2·1m 0·077	2·0n —0·0

From isopiestic measurements at 25 °C.
Values of $\log_{10} f_{\pm}$ are accurate to approximately ± 0.002.

TABLE III, 33

ACTIVITY COEFFICIENTS OF HYDROGEN CHLORIDE IN ANHYDROUS ACETIC ACID AT 25 °C.

c (mol/l.)	$f_\pm$ (HCl)	c (mol/l.)	$f_\pm$ (HCl)
0·0004	2·81	0·0400	20·41
0·0016	4·87	0·0625	25·01
0·0036	7·06	0·0900	30·20
0·0064	9·08	0·1215	34·78
0·0100	13·80	0·1600	40·74
0·0225	15·80		

Accuracy: These values of $f_\pm$ are calculated from e.m.f. data accurate to $\pm 0·001$ v. The corresponding accuracy of $f_\pm$ is c. $\pm 0·005$.

Note: the values of $f_\pm$ obtained from the e.m.f. data do not agree with those derived from the plot of activity v. mol fraction of HCl, given by these authors.

B. O. HESTON and N. F. HALL, *J. Am. Chem. Soc.*, 1934, **56**, 1463.

US SOLUTIONS AT 25 °C. (VALUES GIVEN ARE $\log_{10} f_\pm$)

Amino butyric acid	DL-α-Amino n-valeric acid	DL-Valine	Betaine	Proline	L-Hydroxy proline
·011	0·009	0·013	0·030	0·008	0·000
·016	0·014	0·019	0·044	0·012	0·000
·021	0·019	0·025	—	—	—
·026	0·023	0·032	0·074	0·020	0·001
·033	0·030	0·042	—	—	—
—			0·104	0·029	0·001
·041			—	—	—
·050			0·147	0·040	0·003
·058			0·176	—	0·004
·071			0·219	0·060	0·006
—			—	—	—
—			—	—	—
—			0·289	0·081	0·011
·5m	0·65m	0·65m	5·0m	7·3m	2·3m
·071	0·030	0·042	0·595	0·301	0·015

References: E. R. SMITH and P. K. SMITH, *J. Biol. Chem.*, 1937, **117**, 209; *ibid.*, 1937, **121**, 607; *ibid.*, 1940, **132**, 47, 57; *ibid.*, 1940, **135**, 273.

ACTIVITY COEFFICIENTS, $(f_{\pm})$ OF AMINO ACIDS AND PI

Molality m	DL-β-Alanine	DL-β-Amino butyric acid	DL-β-Amino valeric acid	γ-Amino butyric acid	DL-γ-A valeric
0·1	—	—	—	—	—
0·2	—0·003	0·003	0·007	—0·007	0·00
0·3	—	—	—	—	—
0·5	—0·005	0·008	0·019	—0·015	0·00
0·7	—0·006	0·012	0·027	—0·017	0·00
1·0	—0·005	0·021	0·040	—0·018	0·01
1·2	—0·004	0·027	0·048	—0·016	—
1·5	0·000	0·037	0·062	—0·011	0·03
1·7	—	—	—	—	—
2·0	0·007	0·056	0·086	0·003	0·05

Values of $\log_{10} f_{\pm}$ are accurate to approximately ± 0.002.

TABLE III, 36

ACTIVITIES OF METALS IN ALLOYS IN 60% LiCl - 40% KCl EUTECTIC

1. Thallium (1) — Tin (2) Alloys

	N_1	$\log f_I$	a_I
352 °C.	0·0	0·4443	0·0000
	0·2	0·2843	0·2291
	0·4	0·1599	0·5781
	0·6	0·0711	0·7067
	0·8	0·0178	0·8335
	1·0	0·0000	1·0000

35

QUEOUS SOLUTION AT 25 °C. (VALUES GIVEN ARE $\log_{10} f_{\pm}$)

-Amino-proic acid	Glycyl-glycine	Glycyl-alanine	Analyl-glycine	Alanyl-alanine	Triglycine
—	—	—	—	—	—0·041
—0·013	—0·040	—0·029	—0·032	—0·008	—0·070
—	—0·056	—0·040	—0·043	—0·009	—0·095
—0·022	—0·082	—0·054	—0·056	—0·007	
—0·024	—0·102	—0·061	—0·063	—0·001	
—0·026	—0·128	—0·068	—0·068	—0·015	
—0·016	—0·141	—0·073	—		
0·001	—0·157	—	—		
—	—0·164	—	—		
0·030	—	—	—		

E. R. SMITH and P. K. SMITH *(loc. cit.)* see Table III, 34.

TABLE III, 36 *(Continued)*

	N_1	log. f_I	a_I
414 °C.	0·0	0·3823	0·0000
	0·2	0·2447	0·3514
	0·4	0·1376	0·5492
	0·6	0·0612	0·6909
	0·8	0·0153	0·8287
	1·0	0·0000	1·0000
478 °C.	0·0	0·3183	0·0000
	0·2	0·2037	0·3197
	0·4	0·1146	0·5207
	0·6	0·0509	0·6746
	0·8	0·0127	0·8238
	1·0	0·0000	1·0000

TABLE III, 36 (*Continued*)

2. Thallium (1) — Lead (2) Alloys

N_1	Activities						
	438 °C.		500 °C.		563 °C.		
	a_1	a_2	a_1	a_2	a_1	a_2	
0·0	0·000	1·000	0·000	1·000	0·000	1·000	
0·1	0·080	0·919	0·084	0·918	0·087	0·912	
0·2	0·152	0·823	0·157	0·828	0·163	0·829	
0·3	0·232	0·716	0·240	0·720	0·247	0·723	
0·4	0·320	0·604	0·328	0·610	0·336	0·611	
0·5	0·419	0·488	0·428	0·495	0·436	0·495	
0·6	0·529	0·367	0·538	0·373	0·545	0·373	
0·7	0·656	0·243	0·665	0·248	0·672	0·251	
0·8	0·790	0·132	0·801	0·139	0·810	0·148	
0·9	0·935	0·055	0·929	0·062	0·923	0·069	
1·0	1·000	0·000	1·000	0·000	1·000	0·000	

J. H. Hildebrand and J. N. Sharma, *J. Am. Chem. Soc.*, 1929, **51**, 462.

a_1 = activity of metal 1.

a_2 = activity of metal 2.

N_1 = mol fraction of 1.

f = activity coefficient of metal in the alloy.

3. Cadmium (1) — Tin (2) Alloys

N_1	Activities							
	431 °C.		483 °C.		544 °C.		585 °C.	
	a_1	a_2	a_1	a_2	a_1	a_2	a_1	a_2
0·0	0·000	1·000	0·000	1·000	0·000	1·000	0·00	1·00
0·2	0·32	0·82	0·31	0·82	0·29	0·82	0·28	0·82
0·4	0·53	0·67	0·51	0·66	0·50	0·66	0·48	0·65
0·6	0·68	0·52	0·68	0·50	0·67	0·49	0·66	0·48
0·8	0·83	0·32	0·83	0·31	0·83	0·29	0·82	0·28
0·1	1·00	0·00	1·00	0·00	1·00	0·00	1·00	0·00

TABLE III, 36 (*Continued*)

4. Cadmium (1) — Lead (2) Alloys

N_1	432 °C.		480 °C.		544 °C.		572 °C.	
	a_1	a_2	a_1	a_2	a_1	a_2	a_1	a_2
0·00	0·000	1·000	0·000	1·000	0·000	1·000	0·000	1·000
0·2	0·500	0·835	0·470	0·840	0·430	0·830	0·420	0·830
0·4	0·700	0·730	0·675	0·725	0·635	0·710	0·630	0·710
0·6	0·800	0·640	0·790	0·620	0·760	0·595	0·750	0·590
0·8	0·875	0·510	0·875	0·485	0·865	0·435	0·865	0·415
1·0	1·000	0·000	1·000	0·000	1·000	0·000	1·000	0·000

Activities

5. Cadmium (1) — Bismuth (2) Alloys

N_1	431 °C.		477 °C.		533 °C.	
	a_1	a_2	a_1	a_2	a_1	a_2
0·0	0·000	1·000	0·000	1·000	0·000	1·000
0·2	0·183	0·806	0·178	0·806	0·174	0·806
0·4	0·358	0·609	0·354	0·605	0·348	0·604
0·6	0·581	0·373	0·572	0·371	0·563	0·369
0·8	0·820	0·168	0·818	0·161	0·816	0·155
1·0	1·000	0·000	1·000	0·000	1·000	0·000

Activities

6. Zinc (1) — Cadmium (2) Alloys

N_1	435 °C.		466 °C.		540 °C.	
	a_1	a_2	a_1	a_2	a_1	a_2
0·0	0·000	1·000	0·000	1·000	0·000	1·000
0·2	0·497	0·838	0·483	0·835	0·440	0·830
0·4	0·695	0·740	0·684	0·725	0·660	0·705
0·6	0·811	0·635	0·805	0·620	0·785	0·590
0·8	0·910	0·480	0·900	0·470	0·890	0·440
1·0	1·000	0·000	1·000	0·000	1·000	0·000

Activities

TABLE III, 36 (Continued)

7. Zinc (1) — Tin (2) Alloys

N_1	Activities							
	431 °C.		466 °C.		539 °C.		570 °C.	
	a_1	a_2	a_1	a_2	a_1	a_2	a_1	a_2
0·0	0·000	1·000	0·000	1·000	0·000	1·000	0·000	1·000
0·2	0·380	0·815	0·355	0·810	0·318	0·808	0·303	0·806
0·4	0·655	0·655	0·620	0·645	0·575	0·635	0·555	0·630
0·6	0·821	0·524	0·800	0·505	0·760	0·480	0·740	0·475
0·8	0·914	0·405	0·905	0·375	0·885	0·333	0·875	0·315
1·0	1·000	0·000	1·000	0·000	1·000	0·000	1·000	0·000

All in 60% LiCl — 40% KCl containing a little $ZnCl_2$ or $CdCl_2$ (potential of the cell is not affected by this addition).

Activities accurate to $\pm 0·005$.

TABLE III, 36 (Continued)

ACTIVITY COEFFICIENTS IN THE VARIOUS ALLOYS

1. log (a/N) for Cd

Alloy	t °C.	$N_{Cd} = 0·0$	$N_{Cd} = 0·1$	$N_{Cd} = 0·2$
Cd — Sn	483	0·28	0·228	0·185
Cd — Pb	480	0·55	0·455	0·369
Cd — Zn	466	0·80	0·540	0·373

2. log (a/N) for Sn

Alloy	t °C.	$N_{Sn} = 0·0$	$N_{Sn} = 0·1$	$N_{Sn} = 0·2$
Sn — Zn	466	0·72	0·459	0·274
Sn — Cd	483	0·33	0·250	0·184

From e.m.f. measurements with the system M_1 | eutectic | $M_1 M_2$ alloy.

N. W. TAYLOR, J. Am. Chem. Soc., 1923, 45, 2865.

TABLE III, 37

RELATIVE APPARENT MOLAL HEAT CONTENTS (H_m^A) IN DILUTE AQUEOUS SOLUTIONS AT 25 °C. IN cal./mol.

Salt	Ref.	Values of $\sqrt{m}$									
		0·01	0·02	0·04	0·06	0·08	0·10	0·15	0·20	0·25	0·30
HCl	1	4·8	9·6	19·2	29	38	48	71	93	114	134
LiCl	2	4·3	8·4	16·6	25	33	40	60	78	96	114
LiBr	3,16	4·2	8·2	16·2	24	32	39	59	76	93	110
NaCl	4	4·5	8·5	17·0	25	33	40	55	67	77	83
NaBr	5,9	4·2	8·4	16·4	24	31	38	52	62	69	73
NaNO$_3$	7	4·3	8·5	16·5	23	29	34	43	44	40	31[a]
NaClO$_3$	7	4·2	8·4	17·0	24	30	35	43	49	48	43[a]
NaBrO$_3$	7	4·3	8·5	16·7	24	30	34	39	38	34	26[a]
NaIO$_3$	7	4·0	7·5	14·0	19	21	21	16	–20	–24	–57[a]
NaOH	8	4·8	9·5	19·0	28	36	44	62	77	90	99
KF	9,10, 12	4·5	8·5	16·0	24	31	38	54	65	72	77
KBr	5,9	4·2	8·2	15·6	23	29	36	47	55	61	64
KNO$_3$	12	4·1	8·0	15·1	20	23	24	22	12	–6	–29[b]
KClO$_3$	13	4·2	8·2	15·5	21	26	29	28	19	4	–19[a]
KClO$_4$	13	4·3	8·0	13·0	16	16	14	–3	–28	–59	–109[a]
RbF	12	4	8	14	20	26	31	44	57	69	80[c]
CsCl	16	4	8	15	21	27	32	43	49	51	51[d]
NH$_4$Cl	11	4·4	8·6	17	25	33	39	53	66	78	88[e]
Li$_2$SO$_4$	15	24	47	91	135	177	218	307	377	438	488
Na$_2$SO$_4$	15	23	44	84	119	150	175	216	237	243	237
K$_2$SO$_4$	15	22	42	81	116	146	171	214	238	249	250
Rb$_2$SO$_4$	15	21	41	79	114	143	166	200	215	226	219
Cs$_2$SO$_4$	15	20	39	71	99	121	139	160	161	152	137
MgCl$_2$	14	24	47	89	129	167	202	280	350	415	471
MgBr$_2$	14	23	45	86	124	161	196	271	334	389	437
Mg(NO$_3$)$_2$	15	23	44	81	119	155	187	254	304	344	376
CaCl$_2$	14	24	47	88	127	165	199	275	340	398	445
CaBr$_2$	14	23	44	83	120	154	186	252	308	355	394
Ca(NO$_3$)$_2$	15	22	43	79	111	136	158	200	222	230	224
SrCl$_2$	14	23	46	86	124	161	195	270	332	381	420
SrBr$_2$	14	23	44	82	120	152	182	244	293	333	366
Sr(NO$_3$)$_2$	15	21	40	72	99	122	140	166	169	159	135
BaCl$_2$	14	23	46	86	124	160	194	268	329	375	412
BaBr$_2$	14	22	43	81	117	150	180	240	287	325	356
Ba(NO$_3$)$_2$	15	19	36	59	70	72	66	20	–46	–128	–223

TABLE III, 37 (*Continued*)

Salt	Ref.	Values of $\sqrt{m}$									
		0·01	0·02	0·04	0·06	0·08	0·10	0·15	0·20	0·25	0·30
MgSO$_4$	15	44	118	154	369	463	542	685	784	842	—
CaSO$_4$	12	47	125	283	415	523	611	700	—	—	—
ZnSO$_4$	17	51	127	273	396	501	581	731	826	896	953
CdSO$_4$	17	70	180	386	554	693	807	1018	1150	1246	1324
CuSO$_4$	17	62	159	345	501	618	713	885	1012	1109	1183

Notes:

[a] at $\sqrt{m} = 0·3162$.

[b] at $\sqrt{m} = 0·35$, $H_m^A = -55$.

[c] at $\sqrt{m} = 0·35$, 0·40, 0·45 and 0·50, $H_m^A = 91$, 101, 111, and 120 respectively.

[d] at $\sqrt{m} = 0·35$ and 0·40, $H_m^A = 49$ and 44 respectively.

[e] at $\sqrt{m} = 0·4$, 0·5, 0·6, 0·72, 0·88 and 1, $H_m^A = 101$, 111, 127, 136, 142 and 143, respectively.

[f] at $\sqrt{m} = 0·125$.

[1] J. M. STURTEVANT, *J. Am. Chem. Soc.*, 1940, **62**, 584, corrections *ibid.*, p. 3265.

[2] E. LANGE and F. DÜRR, *Z. physik. Chem.*, 1926, **121**, 361.

[3] E. LANGE and E. SCHWARTZ, *ibid.*, 1928, **133**, 129.

[4] A. L. ROBINSON, *J. Am. Chem. Soc.*, 1932, **54**, 1311.

[5] H. HAMMERSCHMID and A. L. ROBINSON, *ibid.*, 1932, **54**, 3120.

[6] E. LANGE and A. EICHLER, *Z. physik. Chem.*, 1927, **129**, 285.

[7] E. LANGE and A. L. ROBINSON, *ibid.*, 1930, **148A**, 97.

[8] J. M. STURTEVANT, *J. Am. Chem. Soc.*, 1940, **62**, 2276.

[9] J. WÜST and E. LANGE, *Z. physik. Chem.*, 1925, **116**, 161.

[10] E. LANGE and P. A. LEIGHTON, *Z. Elektrochem.*, 1928, **34**, 566.

[11] H. STREECK, *Z. physik. Chem.*, 1934, **169A**, 103, data for the methyl-ammonium chlorides are also given.

[12] E. LANGE and J. MONHEIM, *ibid.*, 1930, **150A**, 349.

[13] M. ANDAUER and E. LANGE, *ibid.*, 1933, **165A**, 89.

[14] E. LANGE and H. STREECK, *ibid.*, 1931, **152A**, 1.

[15] E. LANGE and H. STREECK, *ibid.*, 1931, **157A**, 1.

[16] E. LANGE and J. MESSNER, *Z. Elektrochem.*, 1927, **33**, 431.

[17] E. LANGE, J. MONHEIM and A. L. ROBINSON, *J. Am. Chem. Soc.*, 1933, **55**, 4733.

TABLE III, 38

RELATIVE PARTIAL MOLAL HEAT CONTENTS IN DILUTE $(\overline{L}_2)$ AQUEOUS SOLUTIONS AT 25 °C. IN cal./mol.

Salt	Ref.	Values of $\sqrt{m}$									
		0·01	0·02	0·04	0·06	0·08	0·10	0·15	0·20	0·25	0·30
HCl	*	7·2	14·3	28·6	43	57	71	105	136	165	193
LiCl		6·4	12·3	24·7	37	49	60	89	115	141	165
LiBr		6·3	12·2	24·0	35	47	59	86	111	136	159
NaCl		6·5	12·5	24·0	35	46	57	77	92	100	104
NaBr		6·3	12·2	24·2	35	45	54	70	79	83	82
NaNO$_3$		6·0	11·5	22·5	31	40	46	51	40	27	13[a]
NaClO$_3$		6·6	12·9	24·4	34	41	47	55	55	45	27[a]
NaBrO$_3$		6·5	12·7	24·2	33	39	43	42	33	22	8[a]
NaIO$_3$		5·8	11·0	19·8	24	24	20	0	—41	—88	—143[a]
NaOH		7·1	14·0	28·0	42	54	65	89	104	117	125
KF		7·0	13·8	27·4	41	54	66	94	117	136	151
KCl		6·5	12·5	24·0	36	46	55	71	82	88	91
KBr		6·1	12·1	23·0	33	41	48	62	69	71	68
KNO$_3$		5·7	11·0	20·3	26	29	28	12	—17	—57	—103[b]
KClO$_3$		6·7	12·3	21·7	28	32	32	20	—6	—37	—77[a]
KClO$_4$		6·2	11·3	16·6	17	13	4	—34	—86	—148	—228[a]
NH$_4$Cl		6·7	13	25	37	47	56	75	91	105	121[a]
Li$_2$SO$_4$		35	69	135	200	260	317	424	508	578	620
Na$_2$SO$_4$		33	64	122	170	206	229	261	264	241	287
K$_2$SO$_4$		32	62	119	164	200	226	262	272	266	233
Rb$_2$SO$_4$		31	61	115	162	195	216	233	233	225	201
Cs$_2$SO$_4$		29	57	102	136	161	176	172	152	124	87
MgCl$_2$		36	70	130	187	240	287	388	484	567	626
MgBr$_2$		34	67	125	181	233	278	372	453	519	564
Mg(NO$_3$)$_2$		32	62	121	175	224	264	339	393	437	465
CaCl$_2$		35	68	127	185	237	282	378	463	530	576
CaBr$_2$		34	65	120	172	219	260	340	410	462	498
Ca(NO$_3$)$_2$		31	62	114	152	183	212	245	250	234	191
SrCl$_2$		34	66	125	180	232	277	372	443	492	528
SrBr$_2$		33	64	119	170	216	254	324	383	423	452
Sr(NO$_3$)$_2$		30	58	102	137	159	180	185	161	116	46
BaCl$_2$		34	66	124	180	231	275	369	435	480	513
BaBr$_2$		33	64	118	169	214	251	317	372	412	439
Ba(NO$_3$)$_2$		27	51	75	80	68	37	—65	–195	–352	–528
MgSO$_4$		79	191	380	525	631	715	865	937	951	—
CaSO$_4$		80	208	418	588	712	802	882[c]	—	—	—
ZnSO$_4$		86	202	415	595	698	765	893	989	1064	1120

TABLE III, 38 (*Continued*)

Salt	Ref.	Values of $\sqrt{m}$									
		0·01	0·02	0·04	0·06	0·08	0·10	0·15	0·20	0·25	0·30
CdSO$_4$	*	119	290	567	785	939	1071	1266	1380	1467	1542
CuSO$_4$		106	256	518	711	826	930	1115	1242	1321	1375

* For references see Table III, 37 for the corresponding compounds.

ᵃ at $\sqrt{m} = 0\cdot3162$,   ᵇ at $\sqrt{m} = 0\cdot35$, $\overline{L}_2 = -149$,   ᶜ at $\sqrt{m} = 0\cdot125$.

TABLE III, 39

RELATIVE APPARENT MOLAL HEAT CONTENTS (H_m^A) IN WATER AT 25 °C. *
IN cal./mol.

m	HCl	LiCl	LiBr	NaCl	NaBr	NaOH	KF	KCl	KBr
0·1	140	119	117	83	73	102	117	78	64
0·2	191	162	156	90	72	117	143	81	70
0·3	229	194	185	84	63	121	155	76	46
0·4	261	220	210	72	53	119	163	63	29
0·5	290	242	232	58	41	114	169	48	9
0·6	317	263	252	42	27	108	174	33	—13
0·7	342	283	271	26	13	101	179	18	—35
0·8	368	300	289	9	—3	94	183	3	—58
0·9	391	318	306	—7	—20	86	186	—12	—81
1·0	414	334	322	—23	—37	78	190	—26	—104
1·2	460	365	353	—57	—72	61	198	—55	—148
1·5	526	410	394	—105	—124	38	209	—99	—212
1·7	569	438	421	—136	—160	25	215	—128	—251
2·0	633	479	460	—177	—212	8	223	—169	—306
2·5	739	547	524	—224	—294	—10	234	—236	—394
3·0	847	615	588	—304	—364	—17	246	—300	—480
3·5	954ᵃ	683	652	—355	—424	—12	260	—355	—559
4·0	—	758	716	—395	—482	3	279	—405	—631
4·5	—	838	780	—427	—533	36ᵃ	305	—448	—697
5·0	—	921	849	—453	—578	—	334	—472ᶜ	—760
5·5	—	1007	920	—470	—617	—	368	—	—819
6·0	—	1098	994	—483ᵇ	—648	—	404	—	—839ᵈ

* For references see Table III, 37 for the corresponding compounds.

TABLE III, 39 *(Continued)*

^{a} extrapolated
^{b} for sat. soln., $m = 6 \cdot 12$
^{c} for sat. soln., $m = 4 \cdot 82$
^{d} for sat. soln., $m = 5 \cdot 68$

TABLE III, 40
RELATIVE PARTIAL MOLAL HEAT CONTENTS $(\overline{L_2})$ IN WATER AT 25 °C. *
IN cal./mol.

m	HCl	LiCl	LiBr	NaCl	NaBr	NaOH	KF	KCl	KBr
0·1	202	173	166	102	78	127	155	91	70
0·2	273	234	223	90	58	133	179	72	39
0·3	332	279	267	62	31	122	190	44	1
0·4	383	318	305	28	2	105	197	12	—42
0·5	430	352	339	—10	—30	89	203	—21	—89
0·6	475	384	371	—48	—66	69	209	—55	—136
0·7	518	313	400	—85	—100	51	215	—85	—180
0·8	560	440	424	—120	—136	33	220	—115	—224
0·9	604	467	448	—156	—173	13	226	—146	—268
1·0	645	491	471	—188	—206	—4	231	—176	—309
1·2	728	540	515	—252	—280	—37	240	—233	—390
1·5	853	614	580	—343	—382	—70	254	—316	—507
1·7	934	665	625	—398	—448	—81	262	—370	—579
2·0	1055	744	696	—466	—538	—86	274	—446	—678
2·5	1269	885	821	—556	—654	—73	291	—558	—823
3·0	1484	1044	960	—626	—751	—24	318	—648	—956
3·5	1690^d	1205	1097	—671	—832	57	376	—721	—1076
4·0	—	1375	1237	—688	—897	180	456	—782	—1181
4·5	—	1524	1386	—683	—945	—	546	—828	—1269
5·0	—	1743	1544	—656	—981	—	643	—853^e	—1345
5·5	—	1947	1700	—620	—1001	—	754	—	—1392
6·0	—	2163	1865	—570^b	—992	—	884	—	—1412^d

* For references see Table III, 37 for the corresponding compounds.
^{a} extrapolated
^{b} for sat. soln., $m = 6 \cdot 12$
^{c} for sat. soln., $m = 4 \cdot 82$
^{d} for sat. soln., $m = 5 \cdot 68$

TABLE III, 41

RELATIVE PARTIAL MOLAL HEAT CONTENT $(\overline{L_2})$ OF SODIUM CHLORIDE IN cal./mol.

m	0°	10°	20°	25°	30°	40°	60°	70°	80°	90°	100 °C.
0·5	—330	—185	—90	—45	15	170	300	400	500	600	700
1·0	—630	—440	—250	—180	—100	30	310	430	550	670	760
1·5	—860	—680	—430	—330	—260	—60	240	420	580	720	800
2·0	—1120	—840	—560	—450	—330	—130	280	450	650	820	1020
2·5	—1300	—1070	—710	—560	—380	—140	290	480	700	890	1040
3·0	—1650	—1190	—770	—580	—400	—150	300	500	730	910	1040
3·5	—1800	—1230	—800	—590	—420	—170	310	520	820	960	1120
4·0	—1850	—1380	—850	—620	—440	—150	360	590	890	1100	1300

Accuracy: approximately $\pm 1\%$.

Combined calorimetric, electromotive force and boiling point data.

R. P. SMITH and D. S. HIRTLE, *J. Am. Chem. Soc.*, 1939, **61**, 1123.

TABLE III, 42

RELATIVE PARTIAL MOLAL HEAT CONTENT $(\overline{L_2})$ AND HEAT CAPACITY $(\overline{J_2})$
OF POTASSIUM CHLORIDE IN AQUEOUS SOLUTION

Constants of equations: $\overline{L_2} = \overline{L_2}_{(0°)} + at + \beta t^2$; $\overline{J_2} = a + 2\beta t$;
Valid from $t = 0$ to 40 °C.

m	$\overline{L_2}_{(0°)}$ cal./mol.	a	β
0·05	(34) *	2·0	0·014
0·1	— 15	3·5	0·025
0·2	— 80	5·1	0·030
0·3	— 190	7·5	0·034
0·5	— 280	9·4	0·037
0·7	— 430	12·0	0·040
1·0	— 570	14·4	0·045
1·5	— 760	18·4	0·049
2·0	— 920	22·2	0·055
2·5	—1000	23·0	0·060
3·0	—1025	25·4	0·066
3·5	—1200	27·7	0·072
4·0	—1270	29·6	0·079

* Extrapolated value.

H. S. HARNED and M. A. COOK, *J. Am. Chem. Soc.*, 1937, **59**, 1290.

TABLE III, 43

RELATIVE PARTIAL MOLAL HEAT CONTENT AND HEAT CAPACITY OF SODIUM BROMIDE
IN AQUEOUS SOLUTION

Constants of equations: $\overline{L_2} = \overline{L_2}_{(0°)} + at + \beta t^2$; $\overline{J_2} = a + 2\beta t$;
Valid from $t = 0$ to 40 °C.

m	$\overline{L_2}_{(0°)}$ cal./mol.	a	β
0·1	— 23	4·6	0·015
0·2	— 140	8·2	0·023
0·3	— 210	11·8	0·027
0·5	— 400	15·5	0·036
0·7	— 580	21·8	0·044
1·0	— 830	23·5	0·049
1·5	—1140	27·4	0·055
2·0	—1390	30·6	0·061
2·5	—1600	33·6	0·066
3·0	—1790	37·0	0·073
3·5	—1940	41·4	0·079
4·0	—2020	43·2	0·086

H. S. HARNED and C. C. CRAWFORD, J. Am. Chem. Soc., 1937, 59, 1903.

TABLE III, 44

RELATIVE PARTIAL MOLAL HEAT CONTENT ($\overline{L_2}$) AND HEAT CAPACITY ($\overline{J_2}$)
OF SODIUM HYDROXIDE IN AQUEOUS SOLUTION

Constants of equations: $\overline{L_2} = \overline{L_2}_{(0°)} + at$; $\overline{J_2} = a$; t in °C. Valid from 0 — 35 °C.

m	$-\overline{L_2}_{(0°)}$ cal./mol.	a
0·05	7	6
0·1	70	9·5
0·25	200	15
0·5	400	20
1·0	680	27
1·5	820	30·5
2·0	940	35

Extensive tables of $\overline{L_2}$ and $\overline{J_2}$ from 0 to 70°, and to 17M sodium hydroxyde are given by G. AKERLÖF and G. KEGELES, J. Am. Chem. Soc., 1940, 62, 620.

H. S. HARNED and J. C. HECKER, J. Am. Chem. Soc., 1933, 55, 4838.

TABLE III, 48

RELATIVE PARTIAL MOLAL HEAT CONTENT ($\overline{L_2}$) AND HEAT CAPACITY ($\overline{J_2}$)

OF SULPHURIC ACID

Constants of Equation: $\overline{L_2} = \overline{L_2}_{(0°)} + at + \beta t^2; \quad t$ in °C.

m	$\overline{L_2}_{(0°)}$ cal./mol.	a	$\beta \cdot 10^2$	$\overline{L_2}_{(25°)}$ cal./mol.	$\overline{J_2}_{(25°)}$* cal./mol./ °C.	$\overline{J_2}_{(25°)}$** cal./mol./ °C.
0·0005	397	7·228	6·748	620	11	—
0·001	858	7·678	6·706	1092	11	—
0·002	1481	7·038	6·664	1699	10	—
0·005	2503	6·948	6·676	2719	10	—
0·01	3244	7·538	6·691	3474	11	6
0·02	3729	7·328	6·713	3954	11	7
0·05	4192	7·128	6·628	4411	10	8
0·1	4672	7·748	6·712	4908	11	9
0·2	4903	8·008	6·798	5145	11	11
0·5	5063	8·268	6·828	5313	12	15
1·0	5310	10·168	7·118	5608	14	21
2·0	5766	11·068	7·658	6091	15	27
3·0	6607	11·528	7·488	6942	15	25
4·0	7464	11·908	7·458	7908	15	21
6·0	9059	12·578	7·638	9421	16	16
8·0	10399	13·898	7·098	10795	18	13
10·0	11474	16·768	8·518	11946	21	20
12·0	12434	18·218	8·748	12944	23	24
14·0	13402	16·168	8·308	13858	20	26
16·0	14320	12·438	7·388	14677	16	28
17·5	14961	11·508	7·488	15296	15	29

* From e.m.f. measurements.

** From calorimetric measurements.

H. S. HARNED and W. J. HAMER, *J. Am. Chem. Soc.*, 1935, **57**, 27.

TABLE III, 49

PARAMETERS AND LIMITING SLOPES FOR PARTIAL MOLAL VOLUMES AND HEAT CAPACITIES

OF SOME AMINO ACIDS AND AMIDES

Parameter	Glycine	β-Alanine	α-Alanine	Glycolamide	Lactamide
$\mu \cdot 10^{18}$ e.s.u.	15·3	18·9	15·3	2	2
$a \cdot 10$ Å	5·28	5·84	5·82	5·54	6·00

TABLE III, 52

SALTING-IN BY TETRA-ALKYL AMMONIUM SALTS

System	$\dfrac{\Delta s}{s_0\,m} = k$ †
Et$_4$NI — glycol — benzoic acid	+0·26
Me$_4$NB$_2$ — water — benzene *	+0·72
Me$_4$NI — water — benzoic acid	+0·80
Et$_4$NI — water — benzoic acid	+2·66
Pr$_4$NI — water — benzoic acid	+8·3
Bu$_4$NI — water — benzoic acid	+2·0

* TAYLOR and WHITENFISH (unpublished communication).
† For definitions see table III, 51; m = molality of salt.

J. O'M. BOCKRIS, J. BOWLER REED and J. A. KITCHENER, *Trans. Faraday Soc.*, 1951, 47, 184.

TABLE III, 53

HYDRATION NUMBERS OF UNIVALENT IONS IN AQUEOUS SOLUTION AT 25 °C.

Method Ion	Activity (1)	Density (2)	Compressibility (3) **	Entropy (4)	Mobility (5)	Calcd. (6)
Li·	6	6	3	5	5	6
Na·	—	4	4	4	4	4·5
K·	0	4	3	2	4 *	2·9
Rb·	—	0	—	2	—	2·3
Cs·	—	0	—	—	—	0
F′	—	4	5	5	—	4·7
Cl′	2·6	0	3	2	4 *	2·9
Br′	—	0	—	1·5	—	2·4
I′	—	0	2	0·5	0·7 *	0

* Extrapolated from some results in alcoholic solutions. STOKES' law is not applicable for these ions in aqueous solutions.
** Calculated for individual ions on the approximate assumption that K· and Cl′ are equally hydrated in aq. solutions of KCl.

1 N. BJERRUM, *Z. anorg. Chem.*, 1920, 109, 275.
2 J. D. BERNAL and R. H. FOWLER, *J. Chem. Phys.*, 1933, 1, 515.
3 A. PASSYNSKI, *Acta Physicochim. U.R.S.S.*, 1938, 8, 385.
4 H. ULICH, *Z. Elektrochem.*, 1930, 36, 497; *Z. physik. Chem.*, 1934, 168, 141.
5 H. ULICH, *Trans. Faraday Soc.*, 1927, 23, 392.
6 J. O'M. BOCKRIS, *Quarterly Reviews*, 1949, III, 173.

TABLE III, 54

HEATS OF HYDRATION OF IONS IN k.cal./g.ion

Ion	BERNAL & FOWLER (1)		WEBB (2)	LATIMER (3)	VERWEY (4)
	calc.	obs. *			
H·	276				
Li·	136	131		114·6	112·5
Na·	114	116	99	89·7	88·5
K·	94	92	81·9	73·5	72
Rb·	87	87	76·9	67·5	66·5
Cs·	80	79	71·5	60·8	59
Tl·	140	107	78·6		
Ag·	174	162	95·5		108
NH₄·	87	87			
Be··	608	600			
Mg··	490	495			
Ca··	410	410			
Sr··	376	370			
Ba··	346	350			
Zn··	626	528	525		
Fe··	561	500			
Cd··	596	462	473		
Co··	580	500			
Ni··	594	516			
Cu··	645	536			
Mn··	534	479			
Hg··	672	480	486		
Al···	1149	1149			
F′	97	94	87	113·9	114
Cl′	65	67	70·1	84·2	86
Br′	57	63	66·2	78	80·5
I′	47	49	61·5	70	72·5

* Calculated using experimental values for KF as reference compound.

[1] *J. Chem. Phys.*, 1933, **1**, 515. See original paper for discussion of assignment of relative hydration numbers on which the above comparison of observed and calculated heats is made.

[2] *J. Am. Chem. Soc.*, 1926, **48**, 2589.

[3] *J. Chem. Phys.*, 1939, **7**, 108.

[4] *Rec. Trav. Chim.*, 1941, **60**, 887.

TABLE III, 55

FREE ENERGIES, HEATS AND ENTROPIES OF HYDRATION OF ORGANIC COMPOUNDS
AT 25 °C.

Compound		$-\Delta G$	ΔH	ΔS
Aliphatic Alcohols	Methyl	3·09	11·24	48·2
	Ethyl	3·19	12·88	54·0
	n-Propyl	3·38	14·42	59·7
	iso-Propyl	3·45	13·45	56·7
	n-Butyl	3·49	15·94	65·2
	iso-Butyl	3·68	15·24	63·6
	sec-Butyl	3·59	15·06	62·6
	tert-Butyl	3·69	14·44	60·8
	n-Amyl	3·73	17·50	71·2
	iso-Amyl	3·78	—	—
	sec-Amyl	3·81	—	—
	tert-Amyl	3·77	15·69	65·3
	n-Hexyl	3·84	—	—
	n-Heptyl	3·96	—	—
	n-Octyl	4·11	—	—
Other Compounds	Methane	10·23	3·18	45·0
	Ethane	10·05	4·43	48·6
	Butane	10·46	—	—
	Ethylamine	3·58	12·91	55·4
	n-Propylamine	3·72	—	—
	n-Butylamine	3·83	—	—
	Methyl acetate	4·89	—	—
	Ethyl acetate	5·11	—	—
	Propyl acetate	5·35	11·71	56·3
	Di-ethyl ether	6·24	—	—
	Ethyl-propyl ether	6·39	12·76	63·7
	Di-propyl ether	7·05	—	—
	n-Propionitrile	4·36	—	—
	n-Butyronitrile	4·56	—	—
	Acetic acid	1·50	—	—
	Propionic acid	1·73	—	—
	n-Butyric acid	1·85	—	—
	Acetone	4·29	10·09	48·3
	Glycol	5·50	—	—
	Glycerol	1·01	24·73	80·0
	Chloroform	7·14	9·8	57·0

ΔG and ΔH in k.cal./g.mol. ΔS in cal./g.mol/ °C.

J. A. V. BUTLER, *Trans. Faraday Soc.*, 1937, **33**, 229.

TABLE III, 56

HEATS OF SOLVATION ΔH_S IN WATER, METHANOL AND ETHANOL

Salt	ΔH_S (H$_2$O)	ΔH_S (CH$_3$OH)	ΔH_S (C$_2$H$_5$OH)
LiCl	—213	—216	—217
NaCl	—186	—189	—
NaBr	—175	—179	—178
NaI	—164	—170	—169
KI	—144	—	—148

FREE ENERGIES OF SOLVATION $(-\Delta G_S)$

Ion	From BORN Equation for Solvation			From BJERRUM Equation for Solvation		
	H$_2$O	CH$_3$OH	C$_2$H$_5$OH	H$_2$O	CH$_3$OH	C$_2$H$_5$OH
Li˙	236	231	229	240	243	246
Na˙	169	165	163	171	174	176
K˙	122	120	119	124	126	128
Cl′	87	86	85	89	90	91
Br′	83	82	81	84	86	87
I′	75	73	72	76	77	78

Ion	From the Thermochemical Data Solvation Heats (ΔH_S)		
	ΔH_S (H$_2$O)	ΔH_S (CH$_3$OH)	ΔH_S (C$_2$H$_5$OH)
Li˙	—125	—127	—127
Na˙	—98	—100	—99
K˙	—78	—	—79
Cl′	—88	—89	—90
Br′	—77	—79	—78
I′	—66	—70	—69

ΔH_S in k.cal./g.mol.

Derivation of these thermodynamic data for solvation involve certain assumptions and no definite accuracy can be specified.

K. MISCENKO, *Acta Physicochim.*, *U.R.S.S.*, 1935, 3, 693.

TABLE III, 57

RELATIVE MOLAR SURFACE TENSION OF STRONG ELECTROLYTE SOLUTIONS

γ = surface tension of solution, γ_0 = surface tension of solvent (pure H_2O),
C = molar concentration, $\varDelta = 100\ (\gamma - \gamma_0)/C\gamma_0$.

NaCl		KCl		$\frac{1}{2}MgCl_2$		$\frac{1}{2}Na_2SO_4$	
C	$\varDelta$	C	$\varDelta$	C	$\varDelta$	C	$\varDelta$
0·020	2·61	0·025	2·55	0·269	2·00	0·210	2·46
0·059	2·33						
0·093	2·30	0·090	2·38	0·336	1·97	0·321	2·16
0·123	2·30						
0·251	2·13	0·114	2·34	0·539	1·84	0·330	2·37
0·290	2·11	0·225	2·26	0·808	1·74	0·428	2·16

TABLE III, 57 (Continued)

$\frac{1}{2}K_2SO_4$		$\frac{1}{2}SrCl_2$		$\frac{1}{2}BaCl_2$	
C	$\varDelta$	C	$\varDelta$	C	$\varDelta$
0·031	2·39	0·036	3·16	0·103	2·68
0·052	2·38	0·071	2·99	0·131	2·49
0·093	2·37	0·107	2·89	0·247	2·28
0·124	2·16	0·132	2·88	0·306	2·24
0·150	2·13	0·192	2·78	0·353	2·25
0·208	2·08	0·203	2·71		
0·217	2·11				

K. ARIYAMA, *Bull. Chem. Soc. Japan*, 1937, **12**, 36.

See also:

A. HEYDWEILLER, *Ann. Physik*, 1910, **33**, 145.

TABLE III, 58

SURFACE TENSION (γ) OF AQUEOUS SOLUTIONS OF INORGANIC COMPOUNDS

$\Delta\gamma$ = difference between the surface tension of the solution and that of the pure solvent at the same temperature.

γ is in dyne per cm.

Compound	Temp. °C.	$\Delta\gamma$ for 0·5 mol/1000 g.	Calculated $\Delta\gamma$ due to H-bond formation at interface
HCl	20	—0·16	—0·57 ± 0·1
NH_3	18	—1·4	—0·46 ± 0·3
HNO_3	20	—0·42	—0·61 ± 0·2
HBr	18	—3·8 ± 0·2	—0·56 ± 0·2
H_2SO_4 *	20	—0·18	—0·55 ± 0·3
Na_2HPO_4	30	—0·81 ± 0·2	—0·23 ± 0·3
KH_2PO_4 *	20	—0·53 ± 0·05	—0·81 ± 0·3
H_3PO_4 *	20	—0·00 ± 0·3	—0·33 ± 0·3

TABLE III, 58 (*Continued*)

Ionic contributions					
Uni-univalent ions		Uni-divalent ions		Uni-trivalent ions	
Na·	0·41	Na·	0·23	Na·	0·11
Cl′	0·41	SO_4''	0·91	K·	0·11
NO_3'	0·19			PO_4'''	0·99
OH′	0·50				
Br′	0·29				
NH_4·	0·50				

K. ARIYAMA, *Bull. Chem. Soc. Japan*, 1937, **12**, 109.

* J. L. R. MORGAN and G. A. BOLE, *J. Am. Chem. Soc.*, 1913, **35**, 1750.

TABLE III, 59

RELATIVE VISCOSITY (η) OF AQUEOUS MIXED SALT
AND NON-ELECTROLYTE SOLUTIONS AT 25 °C.

m = total molality of salt; N_2 = mol. fraction of component 2 in the *solute* mixture

	Urethane (1) — Urea (2)				
N_2	$m = 0{\cdot}5$ η	$m = 1{\cdot}0$ η			Ref.
0·00	1·089	1·755			
0·25	1·071	1·141			
0·50	1·053	1·107			(1)
0·75	1·036	1·073			
1·0	1·019	1·039			

	$ZnSO_4$ (1) — K_2SO_4 (2)				
N_2	$m = 0{\cdot}1$ η	$m = 0{\cdot}5$ η			Ref.
0·00	1·066	1·365			
0·25	1·054	1·293			
0·50	1·044	1·226			(1)
0·75	1·033	1·166			
1·0	1·023	1·111			

	HCl (1) — KCl (2)				
N_2	$m = 0{\cdot}5$ η	$m = 1{\cdot}0$ η	$m = 2{\cdot}0$ η	$m = 4{\cdot}0$ η	Ref.
0·00	1·031	1·061	1·121	1·237	
0·2	1·025	1·048	1·097	1·206	
0·4	1·018	1·035	1·073	1·171	(2)
0·6	1·011	1·022	1·050	1·134	
0·8	1·004	1·010	1·028	1·095	
1·0	0·998	0·998	1·007	1·057	

TABLE III, 59 (*Continued*)

KCl (1) —NaCl (2)

N_2	$m = 0.5$ η	$m = 1.0$ η	$m = 2.0$ η	$m = 4.0$ η	Ref.
0·00	0·998	0·998	1·007	1·057	
0·2	—	1·016	1·043	1·130	
0·4	1·016	1·035	1·081	1·211	(2)
0·6	1·026	1·053	1·120	1·302	
0·8	—	1·073	1·163	1·403	
1·0	1·045	1·093	1·206	1·513	

HCl (1) — NaCl (2)

0·00	1·031	1·093	1·206	1·513	
0·2	—	1·086	1·187	1·448	
0·4	1·036	1·079	1·168	1·387	(2)
0·6	1·039	1·073	1·150	1·332	
0·8	—	1·067	1·135	1·283	
1·0	1·045	1·061	1·121	1·237	

Accuracy of η about ± 0.003.

Values of η are given as viscosities relative to that of water at 25 °C.

References:

[1] A. BANCHETTI, *Gazz. Chim. Ital.*, 1934, **64**, 229; 1935, **65**, 159; 1936, **66**, 446.

[2] C. E. RUBY and J. KAWAI, *J. Am. Chem. Soc.*, 1926, **48**, 1120.

See also: T. ISHIKAWA, *Bull. Chem. Soc. Japan*, 1937, **12**, 16.

CHAPTER IV

TRANSPORT IN SOLUTIONS OF STRONG ELECTROLYTES. ELECTROLYTIC MIGRATION AND DIFFUSION

This chapter contains data on the conductance of salts in aqueous and organic solvents as well as conductances of salts in inorganic non-aqueous solvents. Considerable importance has been attached to the provision of data for non-aqueous solvents and aqueous non-aqueous solvent mixtures. Conductances of organic salts including a number of tetra-alkyl ammonium salts are listed. The conductance of some salts in methanol and acetone measured at high temperatures using a bomb cell are quoted from BLOKKER (*Rec. Trav. Chim.*, 1935, **54**, 975). Tables of single ion mobilities in aqueous and non-aqueous solvents are given. Calculated values of the theoretical limiting slopes in the ONSAGER equation $\Lambda_v = \Lambda_\infty - (A + B\Lambda_\infty)\sqrt{c}$ for conductance of salts in aqueous solution at various temperatures are given in Table IV, 1.

Some data for conductance of aggregate micellar colloidal electrolytes is given in this chapter but mobilities of macromolecular colloidal particles are given in Chapter VII.

Cation and anion transference numbers are given for aqueous and non-aqueous solvents in Tables IV, 26 to 34 and limiting slopes for the transference numbers of a number of salts in water are given in Table IV, 26.

Data on the diffusion constants of electrolytes, neutral molecules and some macromolecules are given in Tables IV, 35 to IV, 43. STOKES' (*Thesis*, Cambridge, 1949) recent values of the differential diffusion coefficients of KCl and sucrose determined by means of the NORTHROP (*J. Gen. Physiol.*, 1929, **12**, 543) sintered glass disc cell method are given in Table IV, 37, and also the very accurate data of HARNED and NUTTALL (*Ann. N.Y. Acad. Sci.*, 1949, **51**, 781), determined by a special conductance method, are given in Table IV, 38. Integral diffusion coefficients of KCl in aqueous solution at 25 °C. calculated by STOKES from the data of HARNED and NUTTALL and of GOSTING are given in Table IV, 39.

Some diffusion constants of materials of biological importance are given and in some of the cases for macromolecules frictional and axial ratios derived from diffusion and sedimentation measurements are given. In these cases derivation of axial ratios necessitates assumptions concerning the hydration of the macromolecule.

In polyelectrolyte systems, *e.g.*, the calf thymus deoxypentose nucleic acid, diffusion even in the most dilute solutions (0·02 - 0·05 wt.%) convenient for measurements by refractometric methods (the Schlieren or interferometric methods) is not free and particle interaction causes anomalous diffusion Schlieren diagrams from which diffusion coefficients can only be calculated by making certain rather unsatisfactory assumptions (see J. A. V. BUTLER and D. W. F. JAMES, *Nature*, 1951, **167**, 844). The considerable concentration dependence of diffusion coefficient (*e.g.*, see B. E. CONWAY, L. GILBERT and J. A. V. BUTLER, *J. Chem. Soc.*, 1950, 3421) of polyelectrolytes such as thymus deoxypentose nucleic acid renders any extrapolation to zero concentration, for the limiting diffusion coefficient at infinite dilution, highly uncertain. Recent studies by R. M. FUOSS *et al.* on the transport of synthetic polyelectrolytes are not included in these tables as the polymer and co-polymer salts are not sufficiently well defined or reproducible to give data comparable with that for simple electrolytes.

TABLE IV, 1

VALUES OF THE CONSTANTS APPEARING IN THE LIMITING SLOPE OF THE ONSAGER
EQUATION: $\Lambda_v = \Lambda_\infty - (A + B\Lambda_\infty)\sqrt{c}$, FOR CONDUCTANCE IN $1:1$ AQUEOUS
ELECTROLYTE SOLUTIONS

Temp. °C.	B	A
0	0·2198	29·47
5	·2205	34·87
10	·2220	40·56
15	·2237	46·35
18	·2249	50·31
20	·2257	52·95
25	·2277	59·86
30	·2299	67·15
35	·2322	74·81
40	·2348	82·79
45	·2374	90·99
50	·2401	99·28
55	·2431	107·93
60	·2461	116·98

Accuracy: In calculation of B, viscosities are accurate to $\pm 0 \cdot 1 \%$ from 0 to
40 °C. For higher temperatures viscosities are accurate to $\pm 0 \cdot 5 - 1 \%$.
The values of B are of the same accuracy. See International Critical Tables V, 10.
From H. S. HARNED and B. B. OWEN, *Physical Chemistry of Electrolytic Solutions*,
Reinhold, New York, 1943, p. 128.

TABEL IV, 2

EQUIVALENT CONDUCTANCES OF SALTS AT 25 °C. FOR VARIOUS DILUTIONS

(c in g.equiv./l.)

Salt $\diagdown$ c	0	0·0005	0·001	0·005	0·01	0·02	0·05	0·1	*Ref.*
HCl	426·16	422·74	421·36	415·80	412·00	407·24	399·09	391·32	1, 19
LiCl	115·03	113·15	112·40	109·40	107·32	104·65	100·11	95·86	1, 2, 3
NaCl	126·45	124·50	123·74	120·65	118·51	115·76	111·06	106·74	4, 20
KCl	149·86	147·81	146·95	143·55	141·27	138·34	133·37	128·96	1, 20

TABLE IV, 2 (*Continued*)

Salt \ c	0	0·0005	0·001	0·005	0·01	0·02	0·05	0·1	*Ref.*
NH_4Cl	149·7	—	—	—	141·28	138·33	133·29	128·75	5
KBr	151·9	—	—	146·09	143·43	140·48	135·68	131·39	6, 7
NaI	126·94	125·36	124·25	121·25	119·24	116·70	112·79	108·78	8
KI	150·38	—	—	144·37	142·18	139·45	134·97	131·11	7
KNO_3	144·96	142·77	141·84	138·48	132·82	132·41	126·31	120·40	1
$KHCO_3$	118·00	116·10	115·34	112·24	110·08	107·22	—	—	9
NaO_2CCH_3	91·0	89·2	88·5	85·72	83·76	81·24	76·92	72·80	10
$NaO_2C(CH_2)_2$ – CH_3	82·70	81·04	80·31	77·58	75·76	73·39	69·32	65·27	11
NaOH	247·8	245·6	244·7	240·8	238·0	—	—	—	18
$AgNO_3$	133·36	131·36	130·51	127·20	124·76	121·41	115·24	109·14	1
$MgCl_2$	129·40	125·61	124·11	118·31	114·55	110·04	103·08	97·10	12
$CaCl_2$	135·84	131·93	130·36	124·25	120·36	115·65	108·47	102·46	12
$SrCl_2$	135·80	131·90	130·33	124·24	120·29	115·54	108·25	102·19	12
$BaCl_2$	139·98	135·96	134·34	128·02	123·94	119·09	111·48	105·19	12
Na_2SO_4	129·9	125·74	124·15	117·15	112·44	106·78	97·75	89·98	7
$CuSO_4$	133·6	121·6	115·26	94·07	83·12	72·20	59·05	50·58	13
$ZnSO_4$	132·8	121·4	114·53	95·49	84·91	74·24	61·20	52·64	13
$LaCl_3$	145·8	139·6	137·0	127·5	121·8	115·3	106·2	99·1	6, 14
$K_3Fe(CN)_6$	174·5	166·4	163·1	150·7	—	—	—	—	15
$K_4Fe(CN)_6$	184·5	—	167·24	146·09	134·83	122·82	107·70	97·87	16, 17
KIO_4	127·92	125·80	124·94	121·24	118·51	114·14	106·72	98·12	23
$KReO_4$	128·20	126·03	125·12	121·31	118·49	114·49	106·40	97·40	23
$LiClO_4$	105·98	104·18	103·44	100·57	98·61	96·18	92·20	88·56	22
$NaClO_4$	117·48	115·64	114·87	111·75	109·59	106·96	102·40	98·43	22
$KClO_4$	140·04	138·76	137·87	134·16	131·46	127·92	121·62	115·20	22

Accuracy: $\pm$ 0·02%; for references, see below.

EQUIVALENT CONDUCTANCES OF BROMATES AND PERCHLORATES AT 25 °C. FOR
VARIOUS DILUTIONS
(*c* in g.mol/l. Λ_v = equivalent conductance)

KBrO₃		NaBrO₃		AgClO₄	
c	Λ_v	*c*	Λ_v	*c*	Λ_v
0·14774	103·62	0·48193	75·07	0·0010256	123·43
0·093616	107.53	0·10579	85·93	0·0029782	121·14
0·049083	112·26	0·057283	89·97	0·006093	118·57
0·011069	120·37	0·010836	97·97	0·011165	116·38

TABLE IV, 2 (*Continued*)

KBrO₃		NaBrO₃		AgClO₄	
c	Λ_v	c	Λ_v	c	Λ_v
0·0032819	124·88	0·0053638	100·12	0·061064	104·82
0·0010513	126·43	0·0010531	103·28	0·13630	96·50
0·0005443	127·27	0·0005078	104·12	0·28488	87·75
0	129·31	0	105·36	0	126·57

Accuracy: ±0·05%	Accuracy: ±0·05%.	Accuracy: ±0·1%.
Reference 21.	*Reference* 21.	*Reference* 24.

For the temperature dependence of conductance of some of the salts in the above tables see references 19 and 20.

References:

[1] T. SHEDLOVSKY, *J. Am. Chem. Soc.*, 1932, **54**, 1411.

[2] D. A. MacINNES, T. SHEDLOVSKY and L. G. LONGSWORTH, *ibid.*, 1932, **54**, 2758.

[3] K. A. KRIEGER and M. KILPATRICK, *ibid.*, 1937, **59**, 1878.

[4] T. SHEDLOVSKY, A. S. BROWN and D. A. MacINNES, *Trans. Electrochem. Soc.*, 1934, **66**, 165.

[5] L. G. LONGSWORTH, *J. Am. Chem. Soc.*, 1935, **57**, 1185.

[6] G. JONES and C. F. BICKFORD, *ibid.*, 1934, **56**, 602.

[7] Unpublished measurements of T. SHEDLOVSKY and L. G. LONGSWORTH quoted by MacINNES in *Principles of Electrochemistry*, Reinhold Publishing Corp., N.Y., 1939, 339.

[8] P. A. LASSELLE and J. G. ASTON, *J. Am. Chem. Soc.*, 1933, **55**, 3067.

[9] T. SHEDLOVSKY and D. A. MacINNES, *ibid.*, 1935, **57**, 1705.

[10] D. A. MacINNES and T. SHEDLOVSKY, *ibid.*, 1932, **54**, 1429.

[11] D. BELCHER, *ibid.*, 1938, **60**, 2744.

[12] T. SHEDLOVSKY and A. S. BROWN, *ibid.*, 1934, **56**, 1066.

[13] B. B. OWEN and R. W. GURRY, *ibid.*, 1938, **60**, 3074. These values have been corrected for presence of $M(OH)^{·}$ and $HSO_4{'}$ ions.

[14] L. G. LONGSWORTH and D. A. MacINNES, *ibid.*, 1938, **60**, 3070.

[15] G. S. HARTLEY and G. W. DONALDSON. *Trans. Faraday Soc.*, 1937, **33**, 457.

[16] G. JONES and F. C. JELEN, *J. Am. Chem. Soc.*, 1936, **58**, 2561.

[17] E. SWIFT Jr., *ibid.*, 1938, **60**, 728.

[18] V. SIVERTZ, R. E. REITMEIER and H. V. TARTAR, *ibid.*, 1940, **62**, 1379.

[19] Values up to c equal to 12 and at 10° intervals between 5° and 65° are given by B. B. OWEN and F. H. SWEETON, *ibid.*, 1941, **63**, 2811.

[20] Values from 15° to 45° are given by H. E. GUNNING and A. R. GORDON, *J. Chem. Phys.*, 1942, **10**, 126.

[21] J. H. JONES, *J. Am. Chem. Soc.*, 1944, **66**, 1115.

[22] J. H. JONES, *ibid.*, 1945, **67**, 855.

[23] J. H. JONES, *ibid.*, 1946, **68**, 240.

[24] J. H. JONES, *ibid.*, 1947, **69**, 2065.

TABLE IV, 3

TEMPERATURE DEPENDENCE OF THE CONDUCTANCE OF KCl, KBr AND NaCl IN AQUEOUS SOLUTION

KBr.	$10^4 c = 0$	5	10	20	50	100	Ref.
15 °C.	122·8 *	121·22	120·57	119·69	128·02	116·3	(1)
25 °C.	151·64 *	149·60	141·78	147·64	145·49	143·23	(1)
35 °C.	182·24 *	179·76	178·74	177·34	174·70	171·94	(1)
45 °C.	214·17 *	211·07	209·84	208·13	204·91	201·53	(1)
							* (2)

c in g.mol/l.

TEMPERATURE DEPENDENCE OF IONIC MOBILITIES l_∞ AT INFINITE DILUTION
(*cf.* Table IV, 4)

Ion	15 °C.	25 °C.	35 °C.	40 °C.	Ref.
Cl' (KCl)	61·41	76·35	92·21	108·92	(2)
Cl' (NaCl)	61·43	76·35	92·22	108·88	,,
Br' (KBr)	63·15	78·14	94·03	110·68	,,
K· (KCl)	59·66	73·50	88·21	103·49	,,
Na· (NaCl)	39·75	50·10	61·53	73·77	,,
H· (HCl)	300·6	349·82	397·0	441·4	,,
Li· (LiCl)	(18 °C.)				
	33·03	38·68			

And $\Lambda_{(LiCl)} = 60·559 \ (1 + 0·00314 \ t + 0·0001137 \ t^2)$ where t is in °C. (3)

TEMPERATURE DEPENDENCE OF CONDUCTANCE OF KCl, KBr AND NaCl

Values of $\dfrac{d(\ln l_\infty)}{dT}$.

Ion	15 °C.	25 °C.	35 °C.	45 °C.
Cl'	0·02340	0·02020	0·01765	0·01570
Br'	0·02285	0·01930	0·01730	0·01535
K·	0·02235	0·01950	0·01705	0·01500
Na·	0·02445	0·02180	0·01930	0·01695

[1] H. E. GUNNING and A. R. GORDON, *J. Chem. Phys.*, 1943, **11**, 18.
[2] G. C. BENSON and A. R. GORDON, *J. Chem. Phys.*, 1945, **13**, 473.
(See also *J. Chem. Phys.*, 1942, **10**, 126.)
[3] M. M. JACOPETTI, *Gazz. Chim. Ital.*, 1942, **72**, 251.
(See also F. GIORDANO and T. MARESCA, *ibid.*, 1929, **59**, 878, 892.)

TABLE IV, 4

LIMITING IONIC CONDUCTANCES (l_∞) IN WATER AT 25 °C.

Cation	l_∞	Ref.	Anion	l_∞	Ref.
H·	349·8	1, 13, 19	OH′	197·6	8, 22
Li·	38·69	1, 27	Cl′	76.34	1, 19, 21
Na·	50·11	1, 13, 21	Br′	78·3	9, 2
K·	73·52	1, 21	I′	76·8	10, 2
NH_4·	73·4	2	NO_3′	71·44	1
Ag·	61·92	1	HCO_3′	44·5	11
Tl·	74·7	3	HCO_2′	54·6	18
$^1/_2Mg$··	53·06	4	CH_3CO_2′	40·9	1, 13
$^1/_2Ca$··	59·50	4	$ClCH_2CO_2$′	39·8	12, 13
$^1/_2Sr$··	59·46	4	$CH_3CH_2CO_2$′	35·8	14
$^1/_2Ba$··	63·64	4	$CNCH_2CO_2$′	41·8	18
$^1/_2Cu$··	54	5	$CH_3(CH_2)_2CO_2$′	32·6	14, 18
$^1/_2Zn$·	53	5	$C_6H_5CO_2$′	32·3	15, 16
$^1/_3La$···	69·5	6, 2	HC_2O_4′	40·2	20
$^1/_3Co(NH_3)_6$···	102·3	7	$^1/_2C_2O_4$″	24·0	20
			$^1/_2SO_4$″	80	2, 7
			$^1/_3Fe(CN)_6$‴	101	7
			$^1/_4Fe(CN)_6$⁗	111	17
			IO_4′	54·38	23
			ReO_4′	54·68	23
			ClO_4′	67·32 ± 0·06	24 (cf. 26)
			BrO_3′	55·78 ± 0·05	25

References:

All values have been corrected to conform to the standard of G. JONES and B. C. BRADSHAW [28].

[1] D. A. McINNES, T. SHEDLOVSKY and L. G. LONGSWORTH, *J. Am. Chem. Soc.*, 1932, **54**, 2758.

[2] D. A. McINNES, *J. Franklin Inst.*, 1938, **225**, 661.

[3] R. A. ROBINSON and C. W. DAVIES, *J. Chem. Soc.*, 1937, **139**, 574.

[4] T. SHEDLOVSKY and A. S. BROWN, *J. Am. Chem. Soc.*, 1934, **56**, 1066.

[5] B. B. OWEN and B. W. GURRY, *ibid.*, 1938, **60**, 3074.

[6] G. JONES and C. F. BICKFORD, *ibid.*, 1934, **56**, 602.

[7] G. S. HARTLEY and G. W. DONALDSON, *Trans. Faraday Soc.*, 1937, **33**, 457.

[8] V. SIVERTZ, R. E. REITMEIER and H. V. TARTAR, *J. Am. Chem. Soc.*, 1940, **62**, 1379.

[9] G. JONES and C. F. BICKFORD, *ibid.*, 1934, **56**, 602.

[10] P. A. LASSELLE and J. G. ASTON, *ibid.*, 1933, **55**, 3067.

[11] T. SHEDLOVSKY and D. A. MacINNES, *ibid.*, 1935, **57**, 1705.

TABLE IV, 4 (*Continued*)

[12] T. SHEDLOVSKY, A. S. BROWN and D. A. McINNES, *Trans. Electrochem. Soc.*, 1935, **66**, 165.

[13] B. SAXTON and T. W. LANGER, *J. Am. Chem. Soc.*, 1933, **55**, 3638.

[14] D. BELCHER, *ibid.*, 1938, **60**, 2744.

[15] B. SAXTON and H. F. MEIER, *ibid.*, 1934, **56**, 1918. These authors also report 30·3 and 31·0 for the ortho and meta chlorobenzoate ions respectively.

[16] F. G. BROCKMAN and M. KILPATRICK, *ibid.*, 1934, **56**, 1483.

[17] G. JONES and F. C. JELEN, *ibid.*, 1936, **58**, 2581; C. W. DAVIES, *ibid.*, 1937, **59**, 1760.

[18] B. SAXTON and L. S. DARKEN, *J. Am. Chem. Soc.*, 1940, **62**, 846.

[19] Values at 10° intervals are given by B. B. OWEN and F. H. SWEETON, *ibid.*, 1941, **63**, 2811.

[20] L. S. DARKEN, *ibid.*, 1941, **63**, 1007.

[21] Values at 15, 25, 35 and 45° are given by H. E. GUNNING and A. R. GORDON, *J. Chem. Phys.*, 1942, **10**, 126.
See also N. C. LI and W. BRULL, *J. Am. Chem. Soc.*, 1942, **64**, 1635 and A. R. GORDON, *ibid.*, 1942, **64**, 2517.

[22] L. S. DARKEN and H. F. MEIER, *ibid.*, 1942, **64**, 621.

[23] J. H. JONES, *ibid.*, 1946, **68**, 240.

[24] J. H. JONES, *ibid.*, 1945, **67**, 855.

[25] J. H. JONES, *ibid.*, 1944, **66**, 1115.

[26] J. H. JONES, *ibid.*, 1947, **69**, 2065.

[27] M. M. JACOPETTI, *Gazz. Chim. Ital.*, 1942, **72**, 251.

[28] G. H. JONES and BRADSHAW, *J. Am. Chem. Soc.*, 1933, **55**, 1780.

See also Table IV, 3.

TABLE IV, 5

CONDUCTANCE OF SOME PERCHLORATES IN ORGANIC SOLVENTS AT 25 °C.

Values of the constants Λ_∞ and B in the equation

$$\Lambda_\nu = \Lambda_\infty - B\sqrt{c}$$

For $Mg(ClO_4)_2$ at 25 °C.			
Solvent	Λ_∞	B	
H_2O	128·5	244	
* $MeNO_2$	115·7	873	
* MeOH	83·2	190	
* Me_2CO	185·5	2350	
n-PrOH	25·8	412	
i-PrOH	13·5	189	
Perchlorates in acetone at 25 °C.			
Salt	Λ_∞	B	
$Mg(ClO_4)_2$	185·5	2350	Theoretical limiting slopes not
$Ca(ClO_4)_2$	198·9	2817	in agreement with observed
$Ba(ClO_4)_2$	201·3	1603	B values.

P. VAN RYSSELBERGHE and R. M. FRISTROM, *J. Am. Chem. Soc.*, 1945, **67**, 680.

TABLE IV, 6

CONDUCTANCE OF TETRAMETHYLAMMONIUM SALTS IN ETHANOL AT 25 °C.

Constants of the equation $\Lambda_\nu = \Lambda_\infty - B\sqrt{c}$.

Values valid up to $\sqrt{c} = 0.04$.

Salt	Λ_∞	B	
(Me_4N) Cl	52·68	307	
(Me_4N) Br	55·10	338	
(Me_4N) CNS	58·45	340	
(Me_4N) NO_3	56·85	325	
(Me_4N) Picrate	55·63	282	

T. H. MEAD, O. M. HUGHES and H. HARTLEY, *J. Chem. Soc.*, 1933, 1207. See also
P. WALDEN, *Z. physik. Chem.*, 1931, **153**, 1.

TABLE IV, 7

CONDUCTANCE OF HYDROGEN CHLORIDE IN DIOXAN-WATER MIXTURES

(c in mol/l.; Λ_v = equivalent conductance)

15 °C.		25 °C.		35 °C.		45 °C.	
$\sqrt{c}$	Λ_v	$\sqrt{c}$	Λ_v	$\sqrt{c}$	Λ_v	$\sqrt{c}$	Λ_v
20% Dioxan							
0·01175	249·28	0·03661	297·68	0·02407	349·65	0·01061	405·28
0·01638	248·94	0·05198	295·56	0·03731	347·48	0·02918	401·02
0·04760	245·45	0·12353	287·01	0·05280	344·86	0·06620	393·30
0·10710	239·63	0·14518	285·02	0·10467	337·03	0·09912	387·08
0·15451	235·84	0·15854	283·68	0·14141	332·46	0·13701	381·56
0·17866	234·11	0·17329	282·19	0·16717	329·50	0·15917	378·13
0	250·7	0	302·7	0	354·2	0	406·0
45% Dioxan							
0·01400	144·99	0·01289	178·05	0·02345	211·79	0·01144	249·62
0·02749	142·74	0·03190	174·92	0·03964	208·59	0·02406	247·41
0·04172	140·86	0·04259	173·17	0·05505	205·36	0·05625	239·25
0·09701	134·68	0·09685	165·26	0·10734	196·16	0·10050	229·52
0·14143	130·94	0·12540	161·84	0·14669	190·91	0·11804	226·23
0·16344	129·39	0·16230	158·29	0·17403	187·84	0·13752	222·94
0	146·7	0	180·2	0	216·5	0	253·6
70% Dioxan							
0·00819	72·54	0·01160	89·14	0·00835	108·88	0·00936	126·93
0·02602	67·20	0·02888	81·45	0·02401	99·97	0·03046	112·51
0·05320	59·71	0·05079	73·43	0·05080	87·16	0·05707	98·19
0·10288	51·61	0·10421	62·05	0·07881	78·35	0·11009	82·54
0·14058	48·17	0·13990	57·94	0·10725	72·45	0·15090	76·27
0	74·5	0	93·1	0	112·4	0	131·9
82% Dioxan							
0·00819	38·53	0·01212	40·89	0·00563	58·01	0·00751	65·88
0·02077	28·31	0·02842	28·04	0·01322	45·63	0·02323	39·55
0·04769	18·86	0·05099	20·69	0·03239	29·53	0·04462	27·25
0·09304	13·87	0·10966	14·63	0·06916	19·72	0·09640	18·36
0·12698	12·49	0·14723	13·42	0·11014	16·14	0·13223	16·43
0	47·2	0	57·5	0	69·6	0	88·3

B. B. OWEN and G. W. WATERS, *J. Am. Chem. Soc.*, 1938, **60**, 2371.

TABLE IV, 8

CONDUCTANCE OF SULPHURIC ACID IN METHANOL

Constants of the equation $\Lambda_V = \Lambda_\infty - B\sqrt{c}$

$$(\Lambda_V)_{20\,°C.} = 177\cdot2 - 491\cdot9\sqrt{c}$$
$$(\Lambda_V)_{30\,°C.} = 198\cdot8 - 592\cdot9\sqrt{c}$$
$$(\Lambda_V)_{35\,°C.} = 210\cdot9 - 677\cdot2\sqrt{c}$$

Equations valid up to $c = 2\cdot24 \cdot 10^{-3}$ molar.

Λ_V accurate to $\pm0\cdot2\%$ assuming no error in $\sqrt{c}$.

E. W. KANNING, J. B. BYRNE and E. G. ROBALEK, *J. Am. Chem. Soc.*, 1944, **66**, 1700.

TABLE IV, 9

CONDUCTANCE OF SULPHURIC ACID IN ETHER AT 0 °C. AND 25 °C.

$\varkappa_0$, $\varkappa_{25}$ = Specific conductance at 0 °C. or 25 °C.

H₂SO₄		at 0 °C.	at 25 °C.
vol. %	wt. %	$\varkappa_0 \cdot 10^4$ mho.cm.	$\varkappa_{25} \cdot 10^4$ mho.cm.
27·44	22·22	1·8	2·7
52·39	45·37	23	38
12·99	56·24	87	147
77·17	71·85	265	398
87·78	84·43	458	765
92·85	90·76	469	831
96·53	95·46	367	—
100	100	50	117

S. YCAHOBNY, *J. Gen. Chem. Russ.*, 1934, **14**, 215.

TABLE IV, 10

CONDUCTANCE OF SALTS IN GLYCEROL AT 25 °C.

$\Lambda_{V'}$ = molecular conductance at a dilution of V litre/mol.

Salt	V	$\Lambda_{V'}$	Salt	V	$\Lambda_{V'}$	Salt	V	$\Lambda_{V'}$
CaCl₂	1·951	1·297	BaCl₂	3·922	2·263	SrCl₂	2·472	1·474
	4·045	1·993		7·496	2·654		4·002	2·133
	8·653	2·51		15·45	3·028		7·930	2·528
	16·98	2·865		34·35	3·153		15·91	2·852

J. SZPER and Z. GAJEWSKI, *J. Chim. Phys.*, 1935, **32**, 705, and *Rocz. Chem.*, 1934, **24**, 570.

TABLE IV, 11

CONDUCTANCE OF SALTS IN BENZENE AND DIOXAN

c in mol/l., Λ_v = equivalent conductance

$AgClO_4$ at 25 °C. in Benzene			
$c \cdot 10^4$	$\Lambda_v \cdot 10^6$	$c \cdot 10^2$	$\Lambda_v \cdot 10^6$
0·23	2·20	0·473	0·72
0·10	1·12	3·49	2·41
12·6	0·63	9·05	11·70
33·0	0·66	14·10	26·3

$\Lambda_\infty = 150$

Tetra-iso-amylammonium iodide at 60 °C. in Benzene			
$c \cdot 10^6$	$\Lambda_v \cdot 10^4$	$c \cdot 10^4$	$\Lambda_v \cdot 10^4$
3·01	6·49	0·88	6·22
14·20	4·21	6·88	16·8
43·3	4·66	28·2	23·3

$\Lambda_\infty = 155$

Tetrabutylammonium acetate at 25 °C. in Benzene			
$c \cdot 10^4$	$\Lambda_v \cdot 10^5$	$c \cdot 10^4$	$\Lambda_v \cdot 10^5$
0·1136	2·13	3·136	0·622
1·132	0·804	5·505	0·764
2·095	0·596		

$\Lambda_\infty = 100$

Tetrabutylammonium perchlorate at 25 °C. in Benzene			
$c \cdot 10^4$	$\Lambda_v \cdot 10^4$	$c \cdot 10^4$	$\Lambda_v \cdot 10^4$
0·00766	2·34	54·9	5·65
0·1216	1·23	129·4	13·30
1·125	2·19		
12·89	3·14		

$\Lambda_\infty = 100$

Tetrabutylammonium acetate at 25 °C. in Dioxan			
$c \cdot 10^5$	$\Lambda_v \cdot 10^5$	$c \cdot 10^5$	$\Lambda_v \cdot 10^5$
1·120	1·230	17·67	0·494
3·98	0·712	32·1	0·484
		45·8	0·515

$\Lambda_\infty = 51$

Tetrabutylammonium perchlorate at 25 °C. in Dioxan			
$c \cdot 10^4$	$\Lambda_v \cdot 10^4$	$c \cdot 10^4$	$\Lambda_v \cdot 10^4$
0·0294	1·24	5·53	1·64
0·1251	0·687	19·20	2·68
1·001	0·836	104·5	7·32

$\Lambda_\infty = 51$

R. M. Fuoss, C. A. Kraus and W. F. Luder, *J. Am. Chem. Soc.*, 1936, **58**, 255.

TABLE IV, 12

CONDUCTANCE OF ELECTROLYTES IN ANHYDROUS LIQUID AMMONIA AT —40 °C.

$V =$ dilution in litre/g. equiv.

$\Lambda_V =$ equivalent conductance at dilution V.

V	Λ_V	V	Λ_V	V	Λ_V	V	Λ_V
	NH_4NO_3				NH_4Cl		
9·39	106·02	333·6	187·5	10·08	62·8	345·8	148·1
19·51	115·37	699·1	209·55	20·98	72·38	736·7	177·9
40·58	129·26	1458	229·3	43·81	86·42	1546	206·1
86·57	147·88	3017	244·75	94·05	106·87	3225	231·9
182·8	169·78	6341	254·56	194·2	130·58	6824	250·0
388·0	198·34	13360	260·53	411·2	158·13	14471	263·4
827·5	216·4	28620	266·1	877·0	188·0	30294	270·6
1758	235·63	60780	270·4			63060	273·5

V	Λ_V	V	Λ_V	V	Λ_V	V	Λ_V
	NaCl				NH_4Br		
74·31	124	49·35	112	2·93	86·03	49·63	126·8
166·2	149·9	111·5	135	6·23	91·67	108·5	148·2
379·7	179·5	255·2	163·4	13·34	100·1	236·9	173·3
860·5	210·4	579·3	194	28·07	112·6	517·1	199·2
1961·4	238·2	1322	222·9	59·99	130·05	1137	224
4430	260·1	3042	249·5	129·1	152·0	2464	243·6
10020	273·2	6906	268·5	272·5	177·0	5317	258·8
22740	282·6	15470	280	579·5	201·8	11410	270·0
50920	284	35090	285·2	1228	225·5	24920	279
		79070	287·7	2597	244·2	54150	278·8
				5559	259·2		
				11650	269·2		

V	Λ_V	V	Λ_V	V	Λ_V	V	Λ_V
	NH_4ClO_4				$KClO_4$		
22·49	142	18·69	139·2	46·52	159·3	35·98	152·6
51·37	156·4	41·68	152·7	106·4	185·2	79·67	173·8
116·7	175·7	94·98	171·5	246·6	210·5	185·1	200·6
262·2	197·3	214·8	192·8	557·9	238·3	421·4	227·2
600·9	218·1	485·6	213·7	1241	262·5	953·7	253·6
1323	236	1108	231·5	2809	283·7	2137	273·9
2971	248·9	2526	245	6372	297·1	4826	289·6
6663	258	5773	256·7	14180	302	11010	298·5
15240	266·2	13020	263·9	31290	306·3	24490	204·2
33310	269·1	29150	267·9	68330	207	55370	305·7

TABLE IV, 12 (*Continued*)

CH₃COOH				CH₃COONa			
V	Λ_V	V	Λ_V	V	Λ_V	V	Λ_V
4·12	11·25	29·51	16·55	101·3	28·9	107·8	30·48
9·32	12·45	67·52	22·3	225·8	40·1	240·9	41·45
21·59	15·17	154·5	30·9	522·3	56·3	547·7	57·78
48·91	19·85	354·1	43·4	1178	74·5	1259	81·8
111·5	27·17	803·1	60·7	2732	105·4	2844	107·8
257·9	38·18	1842	84·2	6121	136·0	6514	140·4
578·8	53·54	4185	113·1	13710	169·5	14920	173·4
1346	74·44	9596	148·7	30940	200·0	33370	202
3061	101·6	21840	183·9	71480	226·4	76340	229·7
6993	132·3	49890	216·5				
		112600	246·1				

CH₃COOK				HCOOH			
V	Λ_V	V	Λ_V	V	Λ_V	V	Λ_V
89·46	28·82	89·59	28·87	4·62	26·83	11·52	30·12
205·4	40·5	201·2	39·98	10·37	29·67	26·01	37·51
470·4	56·86	460·7	56·11	51·75	45·71	137·7	63·85
1072	79	1045	78·01	116·8	60·48	309·7	85·16
2432	108·2	2406	107·2	610·4	108·1	1598	144
5524	143·6	5513	180·6	1423	141·0	3699	180·7
12520	182·3	12470	180·6	3158	174·9	8431	213·6
28120	220·5	28040	218·5	7124	208·1	19060	237·9
64450	256·3	63020	253·1	16330	236·1	43480	255·2
				36940	252·3		
				84730	260·6		

HCOONa				C₆H₅COOH			
V	Λ_V	V	Λ_V	V	Λ_V	V	Λ_V
70·01	54·2	90·46	59·1	91·57	30·84	81·66	29·62
160·5	72·4	208·0	80·65	206·5	42·27	184·5	40·63
366·0	96·5	475·1	107·0	466·0	57·94	421·0	55·95
888·3	125·9	1087	139·3	1068	79·15	960·0	76·35
1889	160·5	2500	175·6	2453	105·15	2206	102
4239	193·9	5621	205·3	5634	135·1	5018	130·7
9648	224	13200	234·5	12860	160·5	11490	160·1
21560	245	29750	257·7	29500	191·7	26330	186·7
48800	262			66680	209·2	60440	206

TABLE IV, 12 (*Continued*)

C_6H_5COONa				H_2S			
V	Λ_v	V	Λ_v	V	Λ_v	V	Λ_v
394	60·54	211·6	47·54	17·3	67·97	38·85	82·54
898·6	82·09	479·2	64·48	38·85	82·33	87·81	103·05
2071	109·2	1091	86·71	89·53	103·0	197·8	129·5
4718	139·0	2497	114·0	194·6	128·2	452·0	160·7
10500	168·1	5654	142·7	441·7	158·9	1030	194·4
24340	192·0	13050	171·4	985·3	190·2	2333	225·5
54190	208·0	20920	194·6	2204	220·1	5223	250·1
		66030	208·2	4981	243·8	11760	266·9
				11250	263·2	26500	273·1
				24800	268·7	59600	273·2
				56700	271·1		

HCN				$Sr(NO_3)_2$			
V	Λ_v	V	Λ_v	V	Λ_v	V	Λ_v
5·82	73·25	6·05	73·32	4·05	83·53	7·92	96·75
12·78	81·42	10·22	80·62	9·29	101·3	17·87	118·6
28·65	94·88	22·88	92·67	20·8	124·0	40·39	145·45
63·49	116·7	51·08	110·6	47·83	152·9	93·93	177·4
141·8	138·6	115·2	134·4	109·7	184·9	215·1	211·7
319·0	167·6	261·3	163·7	249·3	219·8	493·4	253·1
721·0	199·2	585·8	193	569·3	255·7	1132	299·9
1639·5	228·1	1309	222·3	1319	308·3	2592	356·3
3719	251·8	2951	244·8	3064	368	5946	423·3
8416	269·9	6587	261·7	6930	434·5	13580	487·8
18890	274·2	15040	275·6	15794	498·4		
42690	276·2	33400	277·6				

$Ba(NO_3)_2$				$Ca(NO_3)_2$			
V	Λ_v	V	Λ_v	V	Λ_v	V	Λ_v
159·3	113·1	77·03	93·12	123·1	106·3	21·65	70·63
359·9	139·1	173·5	114·5	273·7	131·1	48·47	83·56
816·6	168·8	382·5	139·9	628·4	161·5	108·0	101·0
1819	199·9	867·8	169·9	1433	194·4	247·2	126·3
4096	234·4	1940	201·6	3234	229·9	565·1	155·6
9292	273·8	4383	235·9	7212	270	1296	188·5
21100	324·5	9753	275	16090	317·9	2950	224·1
47870	384·3	22070	383·6	36790	379·2	6713	265·1
110300	452·6	49150	384·3	83090	447·2	15610	316·5
						35220	376·4
						72370	443·8

V. A. PLESKOV, *Acta Physicochim. U.R.S.S.*, 1936, **5**, 509. For older work see also C. A. KRAUS and W. B. BRAY, *J. Am. Soc. Chem.*, 1913, **35**, 1335. FRANKLIN and C. A. KRAUS, *J. Am. Chem. Soc.*, 1900, **23**, 237; *ibid.*, 1905, **27**, 191; *Z. physik. Chem.*, 1909, **69**, 272.

TABLE IV, 13

CONDUCTANCE OF SALTS IN LIQUID SULPHUR DIOXIDE

Equivalent conductance at dilution V litre/g.equiv.

Compound	$V = 64$	$V = 128$	$V = 250$	t °C.
NaI	35·7	—	—	0
NH_4I	44·3	—	—	0
KI	48·3	57·7	—	0
RbI	53·0	63·0	—	0
KBr	—	48·8	—	—10
$KSbCl_6$	—	95·2	—	—12
NH_4SCN	10	—	—	0
$(CH_3)_3SI$	86·0	100·6	—	0
$(CH_3)_4NCl$	—	103·5	—	0
$(CH_3)_4NBr$	—	105·9	—	0
$(CH_3)_4NI$	—	111·5	—	—12
$[(CH_3)_4N]_2SO_4$	—	76·5	—	—12
$[(CH_3)_4N]ClO_4$	—	85	—	—12
$[(CH_3 . C_6H_4)_3C]ClO_4$	—	—	113	0
$[(CH_3 . C_6H_4)_3C]Cl$	—	—	128	0

G. JANDER and H. MESECH, Z. physik. Chem., 1939, **183** A, 255.

TABLE IV, 14

CONDUCTANCE OF SALTS IN HYDROGEN CYANIDE AT 18 °C.

The following equations express the dependence of Λ_V upon $\sqrt{c}$ for values of $\sqrt{c}$ up to 0·04 (where c is in mol/l.) to an accuracy of $\pm 0.03\%$.

Salts	Constants in the equation $\Lambda_V = \Lambda_\infty - B\sqrt{c}$		Salts	Constants in the equation $\Lambda_V = \Lambda_\infty - B\sqrt{c}$	
	Λ_∞	B		Λ_∞	B
LiCl	345	335	$NaClO_4$	323·5	235
LiBr	346·9	270	NaCNS	333·7	230
LiI	348·0	258	Sodium Picrate	266·9	195
$LiNO_3$	336·6	402	KCl	361·4	280
$LiClO_4$	336·9	230	KBr	363·2	248
LiCNS	340·6	400	KI	363·9	235
NaBr	343·8	243	KNO_3	353·9	253
NaI	344·9	238	RbCl	363·2	195
$NaNO_3$	333·8	250	CsCl	368·2	200
			NEt_4Cl	282·3	195

J. E. COATES and E. G. TAYLOR, J. Chem. Soc., 1936, 1245.

See also J. E. COATES and E. G. TAYLOR, Nature, 1934, **134**, 241.

TABLE IV, 15

EQUIVALENT CONDUCTANCE (Λ_v) OF SALTS IN METHANOL:
VALUES OF THE CONSTANTS V_∞ AND B OF THE EQUATION $\Lambda_v = \Lambda_\infty - B\sqrt{c}$ at 25 °C.

(Λ_∞ = equivalent conductance at infinite dilution, c = concentration in g.equiv./l.)

Salt	Λ_∞	B	Salt	Λ_∞	B
LiCNS	101·8	253	Mg(CNS)$_2$	120 ± 0·5	2000
NaCNS	107·0	255	Ca(CNS)$_2$	122 ± 0·5	1400
KCNS	114·5	268	Sr(CNS)$_2$	122 ± 0·5	980
RbCNS	118·2	271	Ba(CNS)$_2$	122·5 ± 0·5	850
CsCNS	123·2	304			
NH$_4$CNS	118·7	279			
LiCl	90·9	224	LiNO$_3$	100·2	250
NaCl	96·9	230	NaNO$_3$	106·4	288
KCl	105·0	261	KNO$_3$	114·5	345
RbCl	108·6	281	RbNO$_3$	118·1	355
CsCl	113·6	293	CsNO$_3$	122·9	379

Accuracy: Λ_∞, ±0·2.   Equation valid up to c. $2 \times 10^{-3} M$.

A. UNMACK, D. M. MURRAY-RUST and H. HARTLEY, *Proc. Roy. Soc.*, 1930, A **127**, 228.

TABLE IV, 16

CONDUCTANCE OF HCl IN METHANOL-DIOXAN MIXTURES AT 25 °C.

Mol % Dioxan	ε	(±7%) K_s	(±1%) a_s (c = 0·002)	(±3%) a	(±1%) Λ_v	Mean observed slope of $\Lambda_v/\sqrt{c}$
0	32·6	0·5	1·00	7·8	192·3	277·2
14·9	26·13	1·0 . 10^{-2}	0·910	3·1	163·7	614·0
27·75	20·85	1·8 . 10^{-3}	0·690	2·8	110·4	975·0

Notes:

1. For details see MeOH/H$_2$O/HCl system, Table IV, 17.
2. For Λ_v values at different 'c' 's, see Table IV, 17.
3. Slope of $\Lambda_v/\sqrt{c}$ is in this case not obtained statistically, but empirically.

H. ROSENBERG, *Thesis*, London, 1950.

TABLE IV, 17

CONDUCTANCE OF HCl IN METHANOL-WATER MIXTURES AT 25 °C.

Mol.% Me-thanol and dielectric constant (±0.4%)	$\Lambda_{0.002}$ (±0.4%)	$\Lambda_{0.004}$ (±0.4%)	$\Lambda_{0.006}$ (±0.4%)	$\Lambda_{0.008}$ (±0.4%)	$\Lambda_{0.01}$ (±0.4%)	Λ_{∞} (±1%)	Mean obsv. slope $\Lambda_v/\sqrt{c}$	C=0·002 to C=0·01 Δ C = 0·01 (±0.01)	C=0·002 to C=0·002 Δ' C = 0·01	K_s (±50%)	a_s C = 0·01 (±1%)	a C = 0·01 (±20%) Å
$\varepsilon = 69\cdot40$ 12·94	273·8	270·8	268·7	267·5	266·5	279·4	132·6	+12·6	+17·6	1·9	0·994	3·5
$\varepsilon = 58\cdot85$ 30·83	178·4	175·8	174·8	175·0	173·4	181·5	80·6	−22·4	−19·1	—	1·000	4·8
$\varepsilon = 47\cdot00$ 57·22	119·5	116·9	114·7	113·8	113·3	124·8	115·6	−3·1	+10·0	0·5	0·994	4·9
$\varepsilon = 39\cdot00$ 80·02	98·90	95·15	92·87	91·39	90·86	105·3	148·3	−7·2	+15·0	0·2	0·988	5·6
$\varepsilon = 32\cdot60$ 100	176·9	172·6	169·2	164·9	161·6	192·3	277·2	−14·7	+11·6	0·5	0·986	7·8

Notes:

1. Mean observed slope given is the statistical "most probable" value.

2. $\Delta = 100 \dfrac{\text{(Mean observed slope} - \text{ONSAGER limiting slope)}}{\text{mean observed slope}}$ = % deviation from ONSAGER slope.

3. $\Delta' = 100 \dfrac{\text{(Mean observed slope} - *\text{mean slope SHEDLOVSKY curve)}}{\text{mean observed slope}}$ = % deviation from SHEDLOVSKY slope.

4. Suffices on Λ indicate HCl concentration in mol/l.

5. K_s = dissociation constant of HCl.

6. a_s = degree of dissociation.

7. a = closest distance of approach of the ions.

* T. SHEDLOVSKY, *J. Franklin Inst.*, 1938, **225**, 739.

H. ROSENBERG, *Thesis*, London, 1950.

TABLE IV, 18

CONDUCTANCE OF 1 : 1 ELECTROLYTES IN ETHANOL

VALUES OF THE CONSTANTS Λ_ψ AND B IN THE EQUATION $\Lambda_\psi = \Lambda_\infty - B\sqrt{c}$ AT $25 \pm 0.005\,°C$.

Salt	Λ_∞	B	Salt	Λ_∞	B
LiCl	39·2	166	Li Picrate	41·6	163
NaCl	42·5	197	Na Picrate	45·8	298
LiBr	40·6	161	LiClO$_4$	48·6	164
NaBr	44·85	192	NaClO$_4$	52·45	232
KBr	48·0	237	AgClO$_4$	51·45	195
LiI	43·4	156	NH$_4$ClO$_4$	53·0	213
NaI	47·3	176	(NEt$_4$)Cl	51·9	248
KI	50·8	209	(NEt$_4$)Br	54·3	285
RbI	51·8	228	(NEt$_4$)I	57·3	325
LiCNS	44·5	171	(NEt$_4$) Picrate	54·95	277
NaCNS	47·75	183	(NEt$_4$)NO$_3$	56·2	288
KCNS	51·05	208	(NEt$_4$)ClO$_4$	62·6	438
RbCNS	52·8	237	NaNO$_2$	44·6	269
CsCNS	54·7	279	NaClO$_3$	48·0	299
NH$_4$CNS	48·4	182	NaOEt	42·0	182
LiNO$_3$	42·7	171	NaEtCO$_3$	40·05	338
AgNO$_3$	46·25	336			
NH$_4$NO$_3$	47·5	233			

Equation valid up to c. $2 \times 10^{-3}\,M$.

M. BARAK and H. HARTLEY, Z. *physik. Chem.*, 1933, **A 165**, 272.

TABLE IV, 19

EQUIVALENT CONDUCTANCE OF 0·1N HCl IN ORGANIC SOLVENT-WATER, AND IN MeOH-EtOH MIXTURES AT 25 °C.

Vol.% org. solvent	0	10	20	30	40	50	60	70	80	90	100
Methanol	389·4	337·5	280·6	235·1	198·3	163·7	136·7	111·7	90·20	73·50	122·5
Ethanol	389·4	320·3	259·8	205·7	160·2	127·2	100·2	75·52	53·80	34·74	35·43
Glycol	389·4	326·2	260·0	204·8	158·6	118·4	84·04	56·41	35·27	21·40	—
Glycerol	389·4	321·8	246·9	185·1	124·0	86·98	51·86	27·91	11·87	4·51	—
Acetone	389·4	431·7	287·7	241·0	199·2	161·0	126·9	92·57	54·65	21·48	—
Dioxan	389·4	329·1	273·3	221·9	173·4	128·7	88·50	50·30	15·90	10·80	—
Formic acid	389·4	370·3	327·6	282·1	233·6	188·0	149·8	115·8	87·29	64·22	—
(Formic acid without HCl)	—	89·02	112·7	113·7	102·9	87·29	—	49·51	—	14·10	—
Acetic acid	389·4	332·1	267·4	210·7	160·2	116·6	80·80	52·60	31·00	14·90	—
(Acetic acid without HCl)	—	17·31	18·60	16·29	12·46	8·73	5·23	2·67	0·95	0·14	—
n-Propanol	389·4	324·7	257·4	210·7	168·4	128·7	95·20	64·06	38·50	20·42	8·80
Ethanol in Methanol	122·5	—	101·1	—	82·05	—	63·78	—	48·02	—	35·43

Reproducibility of conductance values within ±0·4%.

H. ROSENBERG, *Thesis*, London, 1950.

TABLE IV, 20

CONDUCTANCE OF ALKYL AMMONIUM CHLORIDES IN LIQUID HYDROGEN SULPHIDE
AT $-78 \cdot 5\ °C$.

c = concentration in mol/l. Λ_ν = equivalent conductance.

Ethylammonium chloride		Diethylammonium chloride	
c	$\Lambda_\nu \cdot 10^4$	c	$\Lambda_\nu \cdot 10^3$
0·001073	1·56	0·0002032	19·3
0·004993	1·12	0·0003154	18·1
0·008965	0·740	0·0005182	8·89
		0·001465	6·94
		0·002023	6·04
		0·01127	3·91
		0·01996	3·86

Triethylammonium chloride		Tetrapropylammonium chloride	
c	$\Lambda_\nu \cdot 10^2$	c	Λ_ν
0·0001556	12·6	0·0003434	7·29
0·001115	8·05	0·001556	4·01
0·004863	5·87	0·01086	3·23
0·009710	5·55	0·02573	4·69
0·0222	6·49	0·07463	8·64
0·1211	26·8		

Tetraethylammonium chloride		Tetramethylammonium chloride	
c	Λ_ν	c	Λ_ν
0·0004173	4·72	0·000837	2·22
0·001437	2·50	0·002479	2·14
0·002145	2·56	0·02556	1·47
0·02375	2·66	0·05786	2·58
0·05606	4·91	0·07994	3·14

E. E. LINEKEN and J. A. WILKINSON, *J. Am. Chem. Soc.*, 1940, **62**, 251.

TABLE IV, 21

TEMPERATURE DEPENDENCE OF CONDUCTANCE OF SALTS IN METHANOL AND ACETONE

c in g.equiv./l.

Methanol
Equivalent conductance

Salt	Conc.	t °C.	25·0	70·0	110·0	140·0	185·0	218·0
LiCl	$c = 0·814$		22·90	40·0	58·2	70·3	81·3	78·7
	$c = 0·2131$		40·5	68·9	94·5	109·3	110·1	83·1
	$c = 0·02044$		63·5	108·0	152·4	179·1	177·9	107·2
	$c = 0·001980$		83·4	142·1	210	265	317	225
LiBr	$c = 0·882$		25·10	45·1	66·5	81·2	100·4	108·9
	$c = 0·2244$		43·6	74·0	102·4	118·1	123·7	98·6
	$c = 0·01853$		69·6	117·8	168·0	201·4	216·6	146·2
	$c = 0·001910$		85·4	147·1	220	278	349	275
LiI	$c = 0·786$		28·29	50·6	73·9	92·1	113·6	127·3
	$c = 0·1822$		44·5	74·2	106·0	125·1	140·8	132·0
	$c = 0·01997$		59·0	98·0	139·8	171·3	197·0	150·7
	$c = 0·002557$		71·4	123·2	179	230	297	264
NaI	$c = 0·775$		39·5	69·6	99·7	119·3	140·5	149·7
	$c = 0·1924$		56·9	95·6	133·9	155·1	164·9	131·0
	$c = 0·01824$		80·4	135·7	191·6	228·5	249·1	159·7
	$c = 0·001899$		97·6	167·8	250	311	390	316
KI	$c = 0·494$		51·9	85·2	115·1	134·5	151·4	140·6
	$c = 0·2077$		62·2	100·1	134·5	151·4	157·0	127·6
	$c = 0·01969$		87·1	142·8	198·9	230·8	242·2	160·3
	$c = 0·001970$		105·2	178·1	260	329	395	314
CaI$_2$	$c = 0·996$		24·87	42·8	58·7	65·6	68·5	62·8
	$c = 0·1054$		41·4	63·4	77·6	77·1	62·2	37·1
	$c = 0·01110$		61·7	94·9	116·9	119·8	109·6	66·5
	$c = 0·001161$		82·4	135	178	192	185	137
i-(C$_5$H$_{11}$)$_4$NI	$c = 0·1832$		37·59	67·3	98·0	121·5	144·3	146·4
	$c = 0·02096$		67·3	113·4	163·0	195·0	227·8	194·5
	$c = 0·001866$		94·2	158·9	233	292	375	296

P. C. BLOKKER, *Rec. Trav. Chim.*, 1935, **54**, 975.

TABLE IV, 21 (*Continued*)

Acetone
Equivalent conductance

Salt	Conc. t °C.	25·0	70·0	110·0	140·0	185·0	218·0
LiCl	$c = 0.0600$	4·90	5·14	3·94	2·34	—	—
	$c = 0.00999$	12·06	12·36	11·2	9·3	6·2	2·7
LiBr	$c = 0.802$	6·17	8·92	10·17	10·45	10·45	10·09
	$c = 0.1752$	12·86	15·23	15·10	13·67	10·35	7·23
	$c = 0.01717$	30·7	35·7	33·0	27·37	17·93	30·6
	$c = 0.002007$	70·4	84·3	79·8	67·0	43·2	21·9
LiI	$c = 0.802$	17·04	26·20	33·6	37·7	40·3	42·8
	$c = 0.2004$	31·1	42·6	49·0	49·4	42·2	33·1
	$c = 0.01978$	64·3	85·1	93·2	90·0	68·4	45·0
	$c = 0.001972$	106·2	146·4	167·4	172·8	125·8	74·0
NaI	$c = 0.448$	42·1	44·4	41·4	35·8	—	—
	$c = 0.1594$	59·1	61·3	54·3	44·2	—	—
	$c = 0.01439$	104·7	120·2	127·9	106·2	61·2	32·7
	$c = 0.002016$	144·0	184·3	190·9	180·8	127·8	68·5
KI	$c = 0.01478$	105·2	120·8	116·1	99·0	—	—
	$c = 0.000339$	176·9	237	279	299	240	150
CaI$_2$	$c = 0.983$	77·5	106·6	125·6	129·3	—	—
	$c = 0.2544$	121·9	145·0	148·6	135·5	117·3	93·8
	$c = 0.02526$	271·6	310	308	263·7	193·8	146·1
	$c = 0.002494$	527	656	693	663	506	376
i-(C$_5$H$_{11}$)$_4$NI	$c = 0.1762$	30·8	40·3	47·3	51·3	—	—
	$c = 0.01913$	64·1	81·6	91·8	93·9	—	—
	$c = 0.001907$	98·1	131·3	155·2	168·1	—	—

P. C. BLOKKER, *Rec. Trav. Chim.*, 1935, 54, 975.

TABLE IV, 22

IONIC MOBILITIES (l_∞) AT INFINITE DILUTION FOR METHANOL AND ETHANOL

Ion	Methanol		Ethanol	
	(25 °C.)	(4 °C.)	(25 °C.)	(4 °C.)
H˙	141·8	113·2	57·40	37·24
Li˙	—	—	15·00	9·62
K˙	53·6	39·35	—	—
Hg₂˙˙	49·7	36·6	20·85	13·53
Me₄N˙	70·10 *	—	28·3 *	—
Et₄N˙	61·5	46·65	27·85	18·75
Cl′	51·27	37·12	24·30	16·01
Br′	56·4	41·85	—	—
I′	—	—	28·80	19·30
ClO₄′	70·1	52·85	33·55	22·40
NO₃′	60·5	45·2	—	—
OMe′	53·02	36·76	—	—
OEt′	—	—	25·35	16·01
MeCO₃′	44·7	32·65	—	—
EtCO₃′	—	—	21·15	14·27
Picrate′	46·5	34·1	26·30	17·55

l_∞ values accurate to 0·5 - 1%

A. G. OGSTON, *Trans. Faraday Soc.*, 1936, **32**, 1679.

* T. H. MEAD, O. M. HUGHES and H. HARTLEY, *J. Chem. Soc.*, 1933, 1207.

TABLE IV, 23

IONIC MOBILITIES (l_∞) AT INFINITE DILUTION IN ETHANOL-WATER MIXTURES AT 25 °C.*

Mol % EtOH	Picrate′	Li˙	Mol % EtOH	Cl′
5	21·7	26·7	2·17	60·2
10	16·5	19·9	10·83	34·2
15	14·1	16·7	17·19	28·2
20	13·4	15·2	46·87	23·2
30	13·6	14·0	93·55	22·4
40	14·4	13·8		
60	17·6	14·7		
80	21·8	15·8		

TABLE IV, 23 (*Continued*)

Mol % EtOH	Sr"	Br′	Mol % EtOH	H'
2·02	53·6	—	40	75·9 †
8·90	35·1	—	72·9	29·2
20·68	24·1	27·8	87·3	23·6
36·97	20·5	25·00	92·2	23·1
61·00	18·8	—	96·0	22·8
			99·0	31·4
			99·8	48·4
l_∞ values accurate to 0·5 - 1%.			100	61·3

* A. WELLER, *Dissertation*, Tübingen, 1950.
† J. J. HERMANS, *Rec. Trav. Chim.*, 1937, 56, 658.

TABLE IV, 24

EQUIVALENT CONDUCTANCE OF COLLOIDAL ELECTROLYTE DYES AT 25 °C.
c in g.equiv./l.

Methyl Orange		Meta-Benzopurpurine		Congo Red	
$\sqrt{c} . 10^2$	Λ_v	$\sqrt{c} . 10^2$	Λ_v	$\sqrt{c} . 10^2$	Λ_v
9·24	69·3	8·96	77·8	6·22	82·4
6·52	69·8	5·45	85·4	2·65	99·7
4·98	70·3	4·01	88·6	1·90	101·6
4·12	68·4	6·39	84·2	1·40	103·7
3·36	70·8	2·71	91·7	0·928	104·5
1·80	71·5	1·52	91·2	0·658	103·9
0·726	71·7	0·70	88·1	0·465	103·4
		0·37	84·1	0·332	98·2
				0·287	96·3

Benzopurpurine 4B		MC . 1 *		MC . 3 *	
6·30	86·1	6·34	67·9	3·00	70·5
5·21	89·3	1·93	70·3	1·35	100·6
3·68	94·0	1·45	70·3	1·04	110·7
2·33	98·2	0·84	70·5	0·77	122·0
1·64	99·3	0·56	71·9	0·57	130·9
1·693	99·6	0·37	72·6	0·40	134·8
0·414	99·3	0·26	73·9	0·26	141·0
0·295	98.5				

Accuracy of Λ values: ±0·3%
C. ROBINSON and H. E. GARRETT, *Trans. Faraday Soc.*, 1939, 35, 775.
* See C. ROBINSON and H. E. GARRETT, *loc. cit.*

TABLE IV, 25

EQUIVALENT CONDUCTANCE OF COLLOIDAL ELECTROLYTE DETERGENTS AT 25 °C.

Na Dodecyl Sulphate (1)		Cetyl Pyridinium Sulphate (1)	
Conc. mol/l.	Λ_v	Conc. mol/l.	Λ_v
0·002	80	0·0005	98
0·005	77	0·0008	98
0·008	76	0·001	93
0·010	63	0·002	79
0·015	49	0·003	72
0·020	43		

(1) H. G. Schmid and E. C. Larson, Z. *Elektrochem.*, 1938, 44, 651.

Cetyl Pyridinium Bromide (2)		Na Oleate (2)	
0·00040	118	0·005	50
0·00087	107·1	0·0075	44
0·00121	86·9	0·01	39
0·00247	60·3	0·02	34
0·00499	46·5	0·03	30
0·0138	35·8		
0·1099	29·1		

Accuracy: ±0·5%

Cetyl-trimethylammonium Bromide (2)		Potassium Oleate (2)	
Conc. g./l.	Λ_v (35 °C.)	Normality	Λ_v
0·00038	120·2	0·25	34·0
0·00080	118	0·5	37·0
0·00236	67·8		
0·00868	40·5	Potassium Laurate (2)	
0·0534	29·5		
0·123	28·3	0·20	41·8
0·421	27·7	1·0	47·1

Cetane Sulphonic Acid (2)		Sodium Oleate (2)	
Normality	Λ_p		
0·013 N	146	0·2	19·8
0·046	135	0·4	20·8
0·073	143	0·5	21·2
0·102	159	0·6	21·7

Accuracy: Λ values ±0·5%
(2) G. S. Hartley, B. Collie and C. S. Samis, *Trans. Faraday Soc.*, 1936, 32, 799.

Selected further References on Conductance of Salts in Non-Aqueous
and Aqueous non-Aqueous solutions.

Aromatic solvents:

A. R. MARTIN, *J. Chem. Soc.*, 1930, 530.

D. M. MURRAY-RUST, H. J. HADOW and
H. HARTLEY, *J. Chem. Soc.*, 1931, 215.

P. WALDEN and E. J. BIRR, *Z. physik.
Chem.*, 1933, **A. 163**, 263.

M. M. DAVIES, *Trans. Faraday Soc.*, 1935,
31, 1561.

R. L. MCINTOSH, D. J. MEAD and R. M.
FUOSS, *J. Am. Chem. Soc.*, 1940, **62**,
506.

W. F. LUDER and C. A. KRAUS, *J. Am.
Chem. Soc.*, 1947, **69**, 2481.

E. G. TAYLOR and C. A. KRAUS, *J. Am.
Chem. Soc.*, 1947, **69**, 1731.

C. R. WITSCHONKE and C. A. KRAUS,
J. Am. Chem. Soc., 1947, **69**, 2472.

D. S. BURGESS and C. A. KRAUS, *J. Am.
Chem. Soc.*, 1948, **70**, 706.

L. E. STRONG and C. A. KRAUS, *J. Am.
Chem. Soc.*, 1950, **72**, 166.

Aliphatic solvents:

E. C. EVERS and A. G. KNOX, *J. Am.
Chem. Soc.*, 1951, **73**, 1739.

J. P. BUTLER *et al.*, *J. Chem. Phys.*,
1951, **19**, 752.

C. P. WRIGHT, D. M. MURRAY-RUST and
H. HARTLEY, *J. Chem. Soc.*, 1931, 199.

M. BARAK and H. HARTLEY, *Z. physik.
Chem.*, 1933, **A. 163**, 272.

N. L. COX, C. A. KRAUS and R. M. FUOSS,
Trans. Faraday Soc., 1935, **31**, 749.

P. VAN RYSSELBERGHE and R. M.
FRISTROM, *J. Am. Chem. Soc.*, 1945,

67, 680.

E. W. KANNING, E. G. BABOLEK and
J. B. BYRNE, *J. Am. Chem. Soc.*,
1943, **65**, 1111.

E. R. KLINE and C. A. KRAUS, *J. Am.
Chem. Soc.*, 1947, **69**, 814.

L. F. GLEYSTEEN and C. A. KRAUS,
J. Am. Chem. Soc., 1947, **69**, 451.

L. M. TUCKER and C. A. KRAUS, *J. Am.
Chem. Soc.*, 1947, **69**, 454.

W. E. THOMPSON and C. A. KRAUS,
J. Am. Chem Soc., 1947, **69**, 1016.

Inorganic solvents:

K. FRENDENHAGEN and G. CADENBACH,
Z. physik. Chem., 1930, **A. 146**, 245.

A. M. MONOSSOHN and W. A. PLESKOV,
Z. physik. Chem., 1931, **A. 156**, 176.

C. A. KRAUS and W. W. HAWES, *J. Am.
Chem. Soc.*, 1933, 55, 4422, 2776.

P. WALDEN and H. HILGERT, *Z. physik.*

Chem., 1933, **A. 165**, 241.

J. G. DAUNT, M. DÉSIRANT, K. MEN-
DELSOHN and A. J. BIRCH, *Physical
Rev.*, 1946, (ii), **70**, 219.

I. S. BIGICH, *J. Gen. Chem. Russ.*, 1946,
16, 1783.

TABLE IV, 26

CATION TRANSFERENCE NUMBER IN AQUEOUS SOLUTIONS AT 25 °C.

The values of (n_+) calculated by equation (1) below, require that the concentration be expressed in mol/l. If the data are plotted against the square root of the equivalent concentration, the limiting slopes become -0.18508, $+0.0447$, $+0.1048$ and -0.3170 for $CaCl_2$, Na_2SO_4, K_2SO_4 and $LaCl_3$ respectively.

n_+ may be expressed as $f(c)$ by the equation:

$$n_+ = n_{+\infty} + S_{(n_+)} \sqrt{c} \qquad (1)$$

for high dilutions, or in general by the equation:

$$n_+ = n_{+\infty} + S_{(n_+)} \sqrt{c} \, \frac{\Lambda_\infty}{\Lambda_\nu} \, ,$$

where Λ_ν is a calculated value.

TABLE IV, 26 (*Continued*)

Electrolyte	Ref.	Λ_∞	$S_{(n+)}$ see eqn. (1)	$n_{+\infty}$	Concn. (g. equiv./litre)				
					0·01	0·02	0·05	0·10	0·20
HCl	(1)	426·17	+0·04507	0·8209	0·8251	0·8266	0·8292	0·8314	0·8337
Na Acetate	(2)	90·99	+ ·03336	·5507	·5537	·5550	·5573	·5594	·5610
K Acetate	(6)	114·40	+ ·07467	·6427	·6498	·6523	·6569	·6609	—
KNO$_3$	(2)	144·96	+ ·00297	·5072	·5084	·5087	·5093	·5103	·5120
NH$_4$Cl	(2)	149·94	− ·00363	·4909	·4907	·4906	·4905	·4907	·4911
KCl	(1)	149·86	− ·00376	·4906	·4902	·4901	·4899	·4898	·4894
KI	(2)	150·29	− ·00430	·4892	·4884	·4883	·4882	·4883	·4887
KBr	(2)	151·63	− ·00596	·4849	·4833	·4832	·4831	·4833	·4841
AgNO$_3$	(3)	133·36	− ·01604	·4643	·4648	·4652	·4664	·4682	—
NaCl	(1)	126·43	− ·04910	·3963	·3918	·3902	·3876	·3854	·3821
LiCl	(1)	115·03	− ·08514	·3364	·3289	·3261	·3211	·3168	·3112
CaCl$_2$	(2)	135·84	− ·26174	·4380	·4264	·4220	·4140	·4060	·3953
Na$_2$SO$_4$	(2)	129·9	+ ·0632	·386	·3848	·3836	·3829	·3828	·3828
K$_2$SO$_4$	(4)	153·3	+ ·1482	·479	·4829	·4848	·4870	·4890	·4910
LaCl$_3$	(5)	145·9	− ·5491	·477	·4625	·4576	·4482	·4375	·4233
K$_4$Fe(CN)$_6$	(7)	—	—	—	·515	·555	·604	·647	—
K$_3$Fe(CN)$_6$	(7)	—	—	—	—	—	·475	·491	—

Accuracy: ±0·02%

References:

[1] L. G. LONGSWORTH, *J. Am. Chem. Soc.*, 1932, **54**, 2741.
[2] L. G. LONGSWORTH, *ibid.*, 1935, **57**, 1185.
[3] D. A. MacINNES and I. A. COWPERTHWAITE quoted by D. A. MacINNES and L. G. LONGSWORTH, *Chem. Rev.*, 1932, **11**, 171.
[4] G. S. HARTLEY and G. W. DONALDSON, *Trans. Faraday Soc.*, 1937, **33**, 457.
[5] L. G. LONGSWORTH and D. A. MacINNES, *J. Am. Chem. Soc.*, 1938, **60**, 3070.
[6] D. J. LE ROY and A. R. GORDON, *J. Chem. Phys.*, 1938, **6**, 398.
[7] G. PRIDEAUX, *J. Chem. Soc.*, 1944, 606.

TABLE IV, 27

TRANSFERENCE NUMBERS (n_+) OF THE ZINC ION IN AQUEOUS ZINC SULPHATE SOLUTIONS AT 25 °C.

m	0·0	0·005	0·01	0·05	0·1	0·15
n_+	0·398	0·389	0·389	0·389	0·384	0·359

m	0·25	0·5	1·0	1·5	2·0	
n_+	0·331	0·294	0·255	0·226	0·197	

Data obtained from activity coefficients and e.m.f.'s of cells with transport.
E. P. PURSER and R. H. STOKES (to be published in 1952).

TABLE IV, 28

CATION TRANSFERENCE NUMBERS FOR HIGHER CONCENTRATIONS OF ELECTROLYTES
IN AQUEOUS SOLUTIONS AT 25 °C.

(c in g.mol/l.)

1. ZnI_2 [1]		2. $Zn(ClO_4)_2$ [2]		3. $ZnCl_2$ [3]	
c	n_+	c	n_+	c	n_+
0·05	0·382	0·1	0·409	0·3271	0·333
0·1	0·363	0·2	0·397	0·1344	0·342
0·3	0·332	0·3	0·389	0·0500	0·365
0·6	0·317	0·4	0·377	0·0210	0·379
1·0	0·291	0·5	0·368	0·0097	0·390
2·5	0·115	0·7	0·349		
3·0	0·056	1·0	0·335	4. $ZnBr_2$ [3]	
4·0	—0·050 *	1·5	0·317		
5·0	—0·190 *	2·0	0·303	c	n_+
8·0	—0·444 *	3·0	0·281		
10·0	—0·550 *	4·0	0·271	0·3291	0·341
				0·1011	0·368
				0·0499	0·384
Accuracy: ±0·002		Accuracy: ±0·002		0·0201	0·398
* Complex formation				0·0119	0·402

5. NaCl and KCl in 50 mol. % methanol [4]

c	n_+ (NaCl)	n_+ (KCl)	c	n_+ (NaCl)	n_+ (KCl)
0	0·4437	0·5068	0·007	0·4413	0·5075
0·0005	0·4428	0·5069	0·01	0·4412	0·5077
0·001	0·4425	0·5070	0·02	0·4412	0·5085
0·002	0·4421	0·5071	0·03	0·4408	0·5092
0·003	0·4418	0·5072	0·05	0·4398	0·5105
0·005	0·4415	0·5074	0·08	0·4388	0·5114

Accuracy: ±0·0005

References:
[1] R. H. STOKES and B. J. LEVIEN, J. Am. Chem. Soc., 1946, 68, 1852.
[2] R. H. STOKES and B. J. LEVIEN, J. Am. Chem. Soc., 1946, 68, 333.
[3] D. M. EGAN and J. R. PARTINGTON, J. Chem. Soc., 1945, 191.
[4] L. W. SHEMILT, J. A. DAVIES and A. R. GORDON, J. Chem. Phys., 1948, 16, 342.

TABLE IV, 28 (*Continued*)

6. $CaCl_2$ [5]				7. $MgCl_2$ [6]	
c	n_{+} (15°C.)	n_{+} (25°C.)	n_{+} (35°C.)	c	n_{+}
0	0·4334	0·4380	0·4427	0	0·395
0·005	0·4261	0·4307	0·4354	0·0032	0·396
0·01	0·4231	0·4277	0·4424	0·0038	0·404
0·02	0·4188	0·4234	0·4281	0·0073	0·391
0·03	0·4156	0·4204	0·4249	0·017	0·380
0·05	0·4105	0·4151	0·4198	0·028	0·380
0·07	0·4067	0·4113	0·4160	0·036	0·376
0·10	0·4024	0·4070	0·4117	0·052	0·375
0·15	0·3964	0·4010	0·4057		

Accuracy: $\pm 0·0002$

References:
[5] A. G. KEENAN, H. G. MCLEOD and A. R. GORDON, *J. Chem. Phys.*, 1945, **13**, 466.
[6] C. DRUCKER, *Rec. Trav. Chim.*, 1932, **51**, 574.

TABLE IV, 29

CATION TRANSFERENCE NUMBERS OF ELECTROLYTES IN NON-AQUEOUS SOLUTIONS

NaOAc and NH_4OAc in Anhydrous Acetic Acid at 25 °C. [1]

NH_4OAc		NaOAc	
Molality	n_{+}	Molality	n_{+}
0·1923	0·520	0·3439	0·48
0·3003	0·500	0·5578	0·45
0·5214	0·486	0·7093	0·43
0·9750	0·478	0·8869	0·39
1·4455	0·469		
2·4298	0·449		

Accuracy: $\pm 0·02$
Values are obtained by the HITTORF method and agree with those obtained by the moving boundary method.

TABLE IV, 29 (Continued)

MgCl₂ in Methanol and Ethanol at 25 °C. [2]

	wt.% $MgCl_2$	n_+	wt.% $MgCl_2 . 6H_2O$	n_+
MeOH	1·93	0·405	6·2	0·387
	10·6	0·399	8·0	0·385
EtOH	0·57	0·371	2·1	0·480
			6·93	0·469

Values obtained by HITTORF method.

NaI, LiBr, LiCl in Acetone. [3]

	wt.%	n_+	Temperature °C.
NaI	2·812	0·386	18·8
LiBr	2·136	0·167	19·5
LiCl	1·0737	—0·210	14·5
	0·7513	—0·100	14·5

N.B.   No concentration dependence of t_+ is given in this work.

AgNO₃, KI, NaI in Ethanol at 25 °C. [4]

AgNO₃	$n_{+\infty} = 0.39$
KI	$n_{+\infty} = 0.56$
NaI	$n_{+\infty} = 0.605$

Accuracy: ±0·01

References:
[1] W. C. LANNING and A. W. DAVIDSON, *J. Am. Chem. Soc.*, 1938, **61**, 147.
[2] F. OLMER, *Bull. Soc. Chim.*, 1938, (v) **5**, 1685.
[3] W. BIRKENSTOCK, *Z. physik. Chem.*, 1928, **128**, 432.
[4] J. W. WOOLCOCK, H. HARTLEY and O. L. HUGHES, *Phil. Mag.*, 1931, (vii) **11**, 222.

TABLE IV, 30

TRANSFERENCE NUMBER $(n_{+\infty})$ OF Li picrate AT INFINITE DILUTION
IN ETHANOL-WATER MIXTURES AT 25 °C.

Mol% EtOH	$n_{+\infty}$		Mol% EtOH	$n_{+\infty}$	
0	0·555		30	0·507	
5	0·550		40	0·489	
10	0·546	±0·5 - 1%	60	0·455	±0·5 - 1%
15	0·542		80	0·422	
20	0·530		100	0·390	

A. WELLER, *Dissertation*, Tübingen, 1950.

TABLE IV, 31

TRANSFERENCE NUMBERS OF THE HYDROGEN ION IN NON-AQUEOUS SOLVENTS AT 25 °C.

HCl in aqueous-non-aqueous solvent mixtures. $(0.01/0.1N$ HCl concentration-cell-e.m.f. determination [1])

EtOH – H_2O mixtures		Me.CO.Me – H_2O mixtures		Glycerol – H_2O mixtures	
wt.% EtOH	n_+	wt.% Me_2CO	n_+	wt.% Glycerol	n_+
16·18	0·835	15·80	0·836	23·50	0·840
32·35	0·849	33·32	0·815	47·96	0·850
52·35	0·813	49·07	0·712	31·32	0·876
63·67	0·741	66·54	0·491	94·60	0·902
100	0·540	100	0·220	100	0·760

Mannitol – H_2O.		Chloral hydrate – H_2O		Glucose – H_2O	
wt.% Mannitol	n_+	wt.% $CCl_3.CHO.2H_2O$	n_+	wt.% Sugar	n_+
7·06	0·851	14·99	0·835	15·02	0·807
14·06	0·841	30·98	0·846	31·04	0·718

H_2SO_4 in anhydrous methanol at 25 °C. [2]

Molality	n_+	Molality	n_+
0·54434	0·742	0·07151	0·727
0·27714	0·734	0·02522	0·725
0·14118	0·729	0·01375	0·726

Accuracy probably: ± 0.001
Values obtained by e.m.f. method (cf. 1).

References:
[1] T. ERDEY-GRUZ, Z. physik. Chem., 1927, 131, 87.
[2] E. W. KANNING and J. E. WALTZ, J. Am. Chem. Soc., 1941, 63, 2676.

See also data in Table IV, 7 and 34 for HCl in dioxan-H_2O mixtures.

TABLE IV, 32

CATION TRANSFERENCE NUMBERS AT 25 °C. IN 50 MOL. % METHANOL-WATER MIXTURES

c mol/l.	$n_{+\,(25\,°C.)}$	
	NaCl	KCl
0	0·4437	0·5068
0·0005	0·4428	0·5069
0·001	0·4425	0·5070
0·002	0·4421	0·5071
0·003	0·4418	0·5072
0·005	0·4415	0·5074
0·007	0·4413	0·5075
0·01	0·4412	0·5077
0·02	0·4412	0·5085
0·03	0·4408	0·5092
0·05	0·4398	0·5105
0·08	0·4388	0·5114

Accuracy c. $\pm 0·0003$.

L. N. SHEMILT, A. R. GORDON and J. A. DAVIES, *J. Chem. Phys.*, 1948, **16**, 340.

TABLE IV, 33

CATION TRANSFERENCE NUMBERS OF QUATERNARY AMMONIUM IODIDES

	n_+
Tetra-methylammonium iodide	$0·322 \pm 0·002$
Tetra-ethylammonium iodide	$0·236 \pm 0·001$
Tetra-n-propylammonium iodide	$0·175 \pm 0·005$
Tetra-n-butylammonium iodide	$0·104 \pm 0·002$

C. H. HALE and T. DE VRIES, *J. Am. Chem. Soc.*, 1948, **70**, 2473.

TABLE IV, 34

CATION TRANSFERENCE NUMBERS OF HYDROGEN CHLORIDE IN WATER AND
DIOXAN–WATER MIXTURES

$X = $ wt.% Dioxan.

m	0°	5°	10°	15°	20°	25°	30°	35°	40°	45°	50°
					$X = 0$						
0·0	—	0·842	0·837	0·831	0·826	0·821	0·816	0·811	0·806	0·801	0·796
0·005	—	·844	·840	·834	·829	·824	·819	·814	·809	·804	·799
·01	—	·845	·841	·835	·830	·825	·821	·816	·811	·806	·801
·02	—	·846	·842	·836	·832	·827	·822	·818	·813	·808	·803
·05	—	·848	·844	·838	·834	·830	·825	·821	·816	·811	·806
·1	—	·850	·846	·840	·837	·832	·828	·823	·819	·814	·810
·2	—	·851	·847	·843	·839	·835	·830	·827	·823	·818	·814
·5	—	·854	·850	·846	·842	·838	·834	·831	·827	·822	·819
1·0	—	·855	·852	·848	·844	·841	·837	·833	·829	·824	·821
1·5	—	·857	·853	·849	·845	·842	·839	·835	·830	·825	·822
2·0	—	·857	·853	·849	·846	·843	·839	·835	·831	·826	·822
3·0	—	·858	·854	·850	·846	·843	·840	·836	·832	·827	·823
					$X = 20$						
0·0	0·856	0·851	0·846	0·841	0·836	0·831	0·825	0·821	0·816	0·810	0·805
·005	·861	·855	·850	·845	·840	·835	·829	·825	·820	·814	·809
·01	·862	·857	·851	·846	·841	·836	·831	·827	·821	·816	·811
·02	·865	·859	·853	·848	·843	·838	·833	·829	·824	·818	·813
·05	·867	·861	·856	·851	·846	·841	·837	·832	·827	·822	·816
·1	·868	·862	·857	·852	·848	·843	·839	·834	·829	·823	·818
·2	·869	·863	·858	·853	·849	·844	·840	·835	·830	·825	·820
·5	·867	·862	·857	·852	·847	·843	·838	·833	·829	·823	·818
1·0	·864	·860	·854	·849	·844	·840	·836	·831	·826	·821	·816
1·5	·862	·857	·852	·847	·842	·838	·834	·829	·824	·819	·814
2·0	·860	·855	·850	·845	·841	·836	·832	·828	·823	·818	·813
3·0	·856	·852	·847	·842	·838	·833	·829	·825	·820	·816	·811
					$X = 45$						
0·0	0·828	0·824	0·820	0·816	0·811	0·806	0·801	0·796	0·791	0·787	0·793
0·005	·833	·829	·825	·821	·816	·811	·807	·801	·797	·793	·788
·01	·835	·830	·827	·823	·818	·813	·809	·804	·799	·795	·790
·02	·838	·833	·829	·825	·820	·816	·811	·807	·802	·798	·793
·05	·842	·837	·833	·829	·824	·820	·816	·812	·807	·803	·798
·1	·845	·840	·836	·831	·827	·823	·819	·816	·811	·807	·803
·2	·849	·844	·840	·834	·830	·826	·823	·820	·816	·812	·807
·5	·851	·846	·842	·836	·833	·829	·826	·822	·819	·815	·811
1·0	·851	·846	·841	·836	·832	·828	·825	·822	·819	·815	·811
1·5	·850	·845	·840	·835	·832	·828	·824	·821	·818	·814	·810
2·0	·849	·844	·839	·835	·831	·827	·824	·820	·817	·813	·809
3·0	·847	·843	·838	·833	·830	·825	·822	·817	·814	·810	·807

TABLE IV, 34 (Continued)

$X = 70$

m	$0°$	$5°$	$10°$	$15°$	$20°$	$25°$	$30°$	$35°$	$40°$	$45°$	$50°$
0·0	—	0·772	0·768	0·764	0·760	0·755	0·750	0·746	0·742	0·738	0·734
·005	—	·781	·778	·774	·770	·766	·761	·757	·753	·750	·747
·01	—	·783	·780	·777	·773	·769	·764	·760	·756	·753	·751
·02	—	·786	·783	·779	·776	·772	·767	·763	·760	·757	·755
·05	—	·788	·785	·782	·778	·774	·770	·766	·763	·760	·758
·1	—	·789	·786	·783	·780	·775	·771	·768	·765	·762	·759
·2	—	·789	·786	·784	·780	·776	·771	·768	·765	·762	·759
·5	—	·789	·786	·783	·779	·774	·770	·766	·764	·760	·757
1·0	—	·788	·785	·782	·777	·772	·768	·764	·762	·758	·754
1·5	—	·788	·784	·781	·776	·771	·766	·763	·760	·757	·752

$X = 82$

m	$0°$	$5°$	$10°$	$15°$	$20°$	$25°$	$30°$	$35°$	$40°$	$45°$	$50°$
0·0	—	0·677	0·675	0·673	0·672	0·670	0·668	0·667	0·665	0·663	
·05	—	·742	·735	·730	·726	·722	·717	·712	·708	·702	
·1	—	·767	·764	·762	·759	·756	·754	·752	·750	·747	
·2	—	·755	·751	·747	·744	·740	·738	·735	·732	·729	
·3	—	·718	·715	·711	·708	·705	·702	·699	·696	·693	
·5	—	·660	·657	·654	·651	·648	·645	·642	·639	·637	

Accuracy: Uncertainties in the third decimal place for H_2O, 20%, 45% and 70% dioxan in H_2O, are respectively ±3, ±7, ±4 and ±8.

See also Table IV, 7.

H. S. HARNED and E. C. DREBY, J. Am. Chem. Soc., 1939, 61, 3113.

TABLE IV, 35

VALUES OF THE FUNCTION $\varphi(y)$ IN THE IDEAL GENERAL DIFFUSION EQUATION:

$$c = \frac{c_0}{2} \left(1 - \frac{2}{\sqrt{\pi}} \int_0^y e^{-v^2} \cdot dy \right)$$

where

$$\varphi(y) = \frac{2}{\sqrt{\pi}} \int_0^y e^{-v^2} \cdot dy = 1 - \frac{2c}{c_0}$$

and

$$y = x/2\sqrt{Dt},$$

where x is measured from the median line of the concentration gradient and c is the concentration at a point x after time t seconds of diffusion of a substance of diffusion constant D cm.²/sec. c_0 is the initial concentration of diffusing substance.

TABLE IV, 35 (*Continued*)

c/c_0		$\varphi(y)$	y	c/c_0		$\varphi(y)$	y
0·0005 or	0·9995	0·999	2·3268	0·030 or	0·970	0·940	1·3301
0·001	0·999	0·998	2·1852	0·040	0·960	0·920	1·2379
0·002	0·998	0·996	2·0352	0·050	0·950	0·900	1·1632
0·004	0·996	0·992	1·8753	0·060	0·940	0·880	1·0994
0·005	0·995	0·990	1·8214	0·080	0·920	0·840	0·9936
0·006	0·994	0·988	1·7764	0·100	0·900	0·800	0·9061
0·008	0·992	0·984	1·7034	0·150	0·850	0·700	0·7329
0·010	0·990	0·980	1·6450	0·200	0·800	0·600	0·5951
0·012	0·988	0·976	1·5961	0·250	0·750	0·500	0·4769
0·014	0·986	0·972	1·5538	0·300	0·700	0·400	0·3708
0·016	0·984	0·968	1·5164	0·400	0·600	0·200	0·1791
0·020	0·980	0·960	1·4522	0·500	0·500	0	0

$\varphi(y)$ is positive for $c/c_0 < 0.5$ and negative for $c/c_0 > 0.05$.

TABLE IV, 36

DIFFUSION COEFFICIENTS OF SOLUTES IN AQUEOUS SOLUTION AT 18 °C.

Compound	M	$D . 10^5$
H_2	2	4·87
* D_2O	20	2·07
O_2	32	1·98
CH_3OH	32	1·40
NH_4OH	35	1·90
CH_3CN	41	1·38
CO_2	44	1·71
N_2O	44	1·61
C_2H_5OH	46	1·27
CH_3COOH	60	1.09
$CO(NH_2)_2$	60	1.12
$C_3H_5(OH)_3$	92	0.91
C_6H_5OH	94	0.93
$m\text{-}C_6H_4(OH)_2$	110	0.87
Arabinose	150	0.64

TABLE IV, 36 (*Continued*)

Compound	M	$D \cdot 10^5$
Glucose	180	0·56
Maltose	342	0·41
Lactose	342	0·41
Sucrose	342	0·42
Raffinose	504	0·35

M = Rounded molecular weight
D = Diffusion coefficient in cm.^{2}/sec.

Note: These values are not corrected to zero solute concentration.

L. J. OHOLM, *Z. physik. Chem.*, 1910, **70**, 370.
* J. A. V. BUTLER and W. J. C. ORR, *J. Chem. Soc.*, 1935, 1273.

TABLE IV, 37

DIFFERENTIAL DIFFUSION COEFFICIENTS AT 25 °C. FOR AQUEOUS SOLUTIONS

D in cm.^{2}/sec.. 10^5; c in mol/l.

For $c = 0$ the values are the NERNST limiting values.

c	Electrolyte $D \cdot 10^5$ cm.^{2}/sec.							
	HCl	HBr	LiCl	LiBr	NaCl	NaBr	KCl	KBr
0	3·34	3·403	1·368	1·379	1·612	1·627	1·995	2·078
0·05	3·07	3·156	1·280	1·300	1·506	1·533	1·863	1·892
0·1	3·05	3·146	1·269	1·239	1·484	1·517	1·848	1·874
0·2	3·06	3·190	1·267	1·285	1·478	1·507	1·835	1·870
0·3	3·09	3·249	1·269	1·296	1·477	1·515	1·826	1·872
0·5	3·18	3·388	1·278	1·328	1·474	1·542	1·835	1·880
0·7	3·28	3·552	1·288	1·360	1·475	1·569	1·846	1·917
1·0	3·43	3·869	1·302	1·404	1·483	1·596	1·876	1·975
1·5	3·74	—	1·331	1·473	1·495	1·629	1·951	2·062
2·0	4·04	—	1·363	1·542	1·514	1·668	2·011	2·132
2·5	4·33	—	1·397	1·597	1·529	1·702	2·064	2·199
3·0	4·66	—	1·430	1·650	1·544	—	2·110	2.280
3·5	4·92	—	1·464	1·693	1·559	—	2·152	2·354
4·0	5·17	—	—	—	1·584	—	—	2·434
4·5	—	—	—	—	1·607	—	—	—

Accuracy: ±0·002

TABLE IV, 37 (*Continued*)

SUCROSE IN AQUEOUS SOLUTION AT 25 °C. (REFERENCE SUBSTANCE)

c	$D \cdot 10^5$ cm.^{2}/sec.
0·146	0·510
0·708	0·499
0·463	0·479
0·962	0·416

Accurate to ±0·01

R. H. STOKES, *Thesis*, Cambridge, 1949.

TABLE IV, 38

DIFFUSION CONSTANT OF POTASSIUM CHLORIDE IN WATER AT 25 °C.

Concentration in mol./l.	$D \cdot 10^5$ cm.^{2}/sec.
(0)	(1·9958 theoretical)
0·00125	1·961
0·00194	1·954
0·00325	1·943
0·00585	1·931
0·00704	1·924
0·00980	1·918
0·01261	1·908
0·02654	1·879
0·0462	1·872
0·0545	1·860
0·1298	1·838
0·3323	1·842
0·5276	1·852

Measurements are made in a special cell by conductance determinations (H. S. HARNED and R. L. NUTTALL, *J. Am. Chem. Soc.*, 1947, **69**, 736).

Values are accurate to ±0·05 to ±0·2%.

H. S. HARNED and R. L. NUTTALL, *Ann. N.Y. Acad. Sci.*, 1949, **51**, 781.

TABLE IV, 39

INTEGRAL DIFFUSION COEFFICIENTS $(\overline{D}{}^\circ)$ OF AQUEOUS POTASSIUM CHLORIDE SOLUTIONS AT 25 °C.

$$\overline{D}{}^\circ = \frac{1}{c} \int_0^c D\, dc$$

c in mol/l., $\overline{D}{}^\circ$ in cm.^{2}sec.$^{-1}$. 10^{-5}

c	$\overline{D}{}^\circ$	c	$\overline{D}{}^\circ$	c	$\overline{D}{}^\circ$
0·000	1·996	0·05	1·893	1·4	1·874
0·001	1·979	0·07	1·883	1·6	1·882
0·002	1·969	0·1	1·873	1·8	1·892
0·003	1·962	0·2	1·857	2·0	1·901
0·005	1·953	0·3	1·850	2·5	1·927
0·007	1·946	0·5	1·848	3·0	1·952
0·01	1·938	0·7	1·851	3·5	1·979
0·02	1·920	1·0	1·859	3·9	2·000
0·03	1·908	1·2	1·866		

(Calculated from the data of HARNED and NUTTALL, *J. Am. Chem. Soc.*, 1947, **69**, 736 and of GOSTING, *ibid.*, 1930, **72**, 4418.)

R. H. STOKES, private communication, in course of publication.

TABLE IV, 40

DIFFUSION CONSTANTS (D°) OF AMINO ACIDS AT INFINITE DILUTION

Amino Acid	Ref.	Temperature °C. of experimental measurement	D_{20}° . 10^6 cm.^{2}/sec. (reduced to 20 °C. where necessary)
Glycine	3	20	9·5
	3	20	9·1
	1	20	8·6
	5	25	9·6 *
			11·1
DL-Alanine	2	20	8·3
	1	20	7·3
			8·2 *
DL-Valine	2	20	7·35
	1	20	6·3
			7·1 *
DL-Leucine	2	20	6·3

TABLE IV, 40 (*Continued*)

Amino Acid	Ref.	Temperature °C. of experimental measurement	$D_{20}^{\circ} \cdot 10^6$ cm.^{2}/sec. (reduced to 20 °C. where necessary)
DL-Proline	2	20	8·0
	1	20	7·2
			8·1 *
L-Asparagine	1	20	6·8
			7·8 *
Arginine	2	20	5·8
Tryptophan	2	20	6·1
	3	20	5·7
Leucylglycylglycine	3	20	4·6

Notes:
The measurements of MEHL and SCHMIDT were made by the porous disc method.
* Diffusion cells calibrated with KCl using COHEN and BRUINS value for the diffusion constant of KCl.
(E. COHEN and H. R. BRUINS, *Z. physik. Chem.*, 1923, **103**, 349. Better values are now available — see Table IV, 37, 38 and 39.)

References:
[1] J. W. MEHL and C. L. A. SCHMIDT, *Univ. Col. Pub. Physiol.*, 1937, **8**, No. 13.
[2] A. POLSON, *Biochem. J.*, 1937, **31**, 1903.
[3] M. ANNETTS, *Biochem. J.*, 1936, **30**, 1807.
[4] J. W. McBAIN and C. R. DAWSON, *J. Am. Chem. Soc.*, 1934, **56**, 52.

TABLE IV, 41

DIFFUSION CONSTANTS OF OVALBUMIN AT HIGH CONCENTRATION AT 20 °C.

Mean albumin concentration in g./100 ml.	$D \cdot 10^7$ cm.^{2}/sec.
2·5	7·43
2·5	6·86
8·5	6·11
1·4	7·64
0·91	7·71
0·88	7·76
0·83	7·73
0·70	7·71

Values accurate to about $\pm 0 \cdot 01$ cm.^{2}/sec.
A. POLSON, *Kolloid Z.*, 1939, **87**, 149.

TABLE IV, 42

DIFFUSION AND OTHER CONSTANTS OF SOME MATERIALS OF BIOLOGICAL IMPORTANCE

Compound	$D_{20} \cdot 10^7$	f/f_0	axial ratio	S_{20}	Mol. weight M	Ref.
Tubercle bacilli *polysaccharide*						
A. human	11·0	1·5		1·8	9,000	2
human	12·4	1·40	7·4	1·39	7,200	2
human [1]	7·0	1·71	13	2·0	23,000	3
[2]	7·6	1·71	13	1·7	18,000	3
B. Avian	13·6			1·54	7,300	2
leprosy-bacilli	24·9	0·99	1·0	0·97	2,500	2
Glycogen	1·1	1·90	18	65	4·1 . 10⁶	4
	1·1	1·94		61	3·9 . 10⁶	
	1·1	1·96		82	5·2 . 10⁶	
	1·1	1·83		73	4·6 . 10⁶	
Pectins						
Apple [1]	0·83	8·3		2·8	117,000	5
[2]	1·4	5·1		2·3	99,000	
Currant	2·85	3·7		2·0	33,000	
Citrus (albedo)	0·65	8·0		4·0	271,000	

Notes:

D_{20} is the diffusion coefficient in cm.²/sec. at 20 °C.

S_{20} is the sedimentation constant in SVEDBERGS at 20 °C.

f/f_0 the frictional ratio and M the molecular weight computed from sedimentation and diffusion measurements.

[1] F. B. SEIBERT, K. O. PEDERSEN and A. TISELIUS, *J. Exptl. Med.*, 1938, **68**, 413.

[2] D. M. TENNENT and D. W. WATSON, *J. Immunol*, 1942, **45**, 179.

[3] E. B. BEVILCAQUA, *Dissert.*, Univ. of Wisconsin, 1944.

[4] R. SIGNER and H. GROSS, *Helv. Chim. Acta*, 1934, **17**, 726.

[5] S. SAVERBORN, *Koll. Z.*, 1940, **90**, 41.

TABLE IV, 43

MOLECULAR CONSTANTS OF SOME OTHER MACROMOLECULES OF BIOLOGICAL INTEREST

Substance	$D_{20} \cdot 10^7$ cm.^{2}/sec.	Frictional ratio f/f_0 and mol. wt. M	Ref.
Calf thymus nucleohistone, 0·51 g./100 ml. aq.phosphate buffer at pH 6·4, in 0·86M NaCl	1·39 ⎫		1
0·20 g./100 ml. *ditto*	1·12 ⎬ $f/f_0 = 2·5$ $M = 2·3 \cdot 10^6$		1
0·46 g./100 ml. phosphate buffer pH 7·0	1·07 ⎭		1
Rabbit papilloma virus	0·59	$\begin{cases} f/f_0 = 1·49 \\ M = 47 \cdot 10^6 \end{cases}$	1
Tobacco mosaic virus	0·41 ± 0·1	$\begin{cases} f/f_0 = 2·5 \\ M = 45 ± 15 \cdot 10^6 \end{cases}$	1
Calf thymus deoxypentosenucleic acid	0·2 — 0·7	$M = 1 \text{ - } 1·5 \cdot 10^6$	2

[1] E. B. BEVILACQUA *et al.*, *Ann. N.Y. Acad. Sci.*, 1945, **46**, 309.
[2] B. E. CONWAY, J. A. V. BUTLER and L. GILBERT, *J. Chem. Soc.*, 1950, 3421.

CHAPTER V

DISSOCIATION CONSTANTS, SOLUBILITIES AND BUFFER SOLUTIONS

This chapter contains data on the thermodynamic dissociation constants of a number of acids and bases in aqueous and organic solvents and aqueous non-aqueous mixtures at 25 °C. and also for some materials over a range of temperature. Considerable importance has been attached to the provision of dissociation constant data for amino acids and peptides and for the constituent dissociable groups in more complicated peptides of biological interest. These values are of use in considerations of protein reactivity with various agents at different pH's. The dissociation constants of peptides and most of those for the amino acids given in Table V, 8 have been obtained using hydrogen electrodes to measure H˙ activity in cells with liquid junctions, usually of the type

$$
\text{H}_2 \left| \begin{array}{c} \text{amino acid solution} \\ + \\ \text{acid or base} \end{array} \right\| \; \text{Satd. KCl} \; \left\| \; \text{Satd. or } N/10 \text{ KCl} \; \right| \text{Hg}_2\text{Cl}_2 \; \left| \; \text{Hg} \; \right. .
$$

The potentials of the cells are primarily determined by the H˙ activity in the amino acid or peptide solution but a liquid junction potential between the amino acid solution and the KCl is unavoidable; this potential is usually small but nevertheless significant and its exact evaluation is difficult.

The majority of the dissociation constants given are apparent dissociation constants pK', since in most cases measurements have been made at a fixed ionic strength and no extrapolation to infinite dilution has been made. The few cases where this has been carried out are indicated appropriately. More accurate values have been obtained for some amino acids (see Table V, 7), using cells without liquid junction and full extrapolation to infinite dilution has also been carried out in these cases. As a natural sequence to the pK data, information is given on solubilities of a number of materials and the composition of buffer solutions of various pH values. Attention is particularly directed to the recently published composition data in Table V, 15 for buffers of ionic strength 0·1 and 0·2 from pH 2 to 12 for electrophoretic studies in the TISELIUS apparatus. Graphical data for a range of pH values and ionic strengths for acetate and phosphate buffers in the pH range 3·5 to 8·0 have been published by A. A. GREEN (*J. Am. Chem. Soc.*, 1933, **55**, 2331). True degrees of dissociation of some inorganic acids and salts are given in Table V, 12. These values have been determined by RAMAN spectra and by the conductance method of DAVIES.

TABLE V, 1

THERMODYNAMIC DISSOCIATION CONSTANTS OF ACIDS IN AQUEOUS SOLUTION AT 25 °C.

Acid	$K_A \cdot 10^5$	Ref.	Acid	$K_A \cdot 10^5$	Ref.
Acetic	1·753	[1]	p-Fluorobenzoic	7·22	[7]
Monochloracetic	139·6	[2]	Phenylacetic	4·88	[9]
Propionic	1·343	[3]	o-Chlorophenylacetic	8·60	[6]
n-Butyric	1·506	[3]	m-Chlorophenylacetic	7·24	[6]
Benzoic	6·30	[4,6]	p-Chlorophenylacetic	6·45	[8]
o-Chlorobenzoic	119·7	[5]	o-Bromophenylacetic	8·84	[6]
m-Chlorobenzoic	15·06	[5]	p-Bromophenylacetic	6·49	[8]
p-Chlorobenzoic	10·4	[5]	p-Methoxyphenylacetic	4·36	[6]
o-Bromobenzoic	140	[7]	p-Iodophenylacetic	6·64	[8]
p-Bromobenzoic	10·7	[7]	Acrylic	5·50	[9]
Lactic	13·87	[10]	Diethylmalonic	70·8	[13]
Carbonic	0·0431	[11]	Ethyl-n-propylmalonic	78·4	[13]
Malonic	139·7	[12]	Di-n-propylmalonic	92·0	[13]
Succinic	6·63	[12]	Phenylmalonic	277	[14]
Glutaric	4·54	[12]	Cyclopropane-1,1-di-		
Adipic	3·72	[12]	carboxylic	150	[15]
Pimelic	3·10	[12]	Cyclobutane-1,1-di-		
Suberic	2·99	[12]	carboxylic	7·55	[15]
Methylmalonic	8·47	[13]	Cyclopentane-1,1-di-		
Ethylmalonic	10·9	[13]	carboxylic	5·96	[15]
n-Propylmalonic	10·3	[13]	Cyclohexane-1,1-di-		
Dimethylmalonic	7·06	[13]	carboxylic	3·54	[15]
Methylethylmalonic	15·4	[13]			

Reproducibility between various workers is about $\pm(0·01 - 0·02)10^{-5}$ for K_A.

References:

[1] D. A. MacInnes and T. Shedlovsky, *J. Am. Chem. Soc.*, 1932, **54**, 1429.
[2] B. Saxton and T. W. Langer, *ibid.*, 1933, **55**, 3638; T. Shedlovsky, A. S. Brown, and D. A. MacInnes, *Trans. Electrochem. Soc.*, 1934, **66**, 165.
[3] D. Belcher, *J. Am. Chem. Soc.*, 1938, **60**, 2744.
[4] F. G. Brockman and M. Kilpatrick, *ibid.*, 1934, **56**, 1483.
[5] B. Saxton and H. F. Meier, *ibid.*, 1934, **56**, 1918; see also J. F. C. Dippy, F. R. Williams and R. H. Lewis, *J. Chem. Soc.*, 1935, 343.
[6] J. F. C. Dippy and F. R. Williams, *ibid.*, 1934, 1888.
[7] J. F. C. Dippy, F. R. Williams and R. H. Lewis, *ibid.*, 1935, 343.
[8] J. F. C. Dippy and F. R. Williams, *ibid.*, 1934, 161.
[9] W. I. German, G. H. Jeffery and A. I. Vogel, *ibid.*, 1937, 1604.
[10] A. W. Martin and H. V. Tartar, *J. Am. Chem. Soc.*, 1937, **59**, 2672.
[11] T. Shedlovsky and D. A. MacInnes, *ibid.*, 1935, **57**, 1705.
[12] G. H. Jeffery and A. I. Vogel, *J. Chem. Soc.*, 1936, 1756.
[13] G. H. Jeffery and A. I. Vogel, *ibid.*, 1936, 1756.
[14] S. Basterfield and J. W. Tomecko, *Can. J. Research*, 1933, **8**, 447.
[15] W. L. German, G. H. Jeffery and A. I. Vogel, *J. Chem. Soc.*, 1935, 1624.

T.

IONIZATION CONSTANTS (

Acids		0°	5°	10°	15°	
Formic	$K_A . 10^4$	1·638	1·691	1·728	1·749	1
Acetic	$K_A . 10^5$	1·657	1·700	1·729	1·745	1
Propionic	$K_A . 10^5$	1·274	1·305	1·326	1·336	1
n-Butyric	$K_A . 10^5$	1·563	1·574	1·576	1·569	1
Chloracetic	$K_A . 10^3$	1·528	—	1·488	1·440 **	
Lactic	$K_A . 10^4$	1·287	—	1·361 *	—	
Glycollic	$K_A . 10^4$	1·334	—	1·427 *	—	
Oxalic	$K_{2A} . 10^5$	5·91	5·82	5·70	5·55	5
Malonic	$K_{2A} . 10^6$	2·140	2·165	2·152	2·124	2
Phosphoric	$K_A . 10^3$	8·968	—	8·394 *	—	
Boric	$K_A . 10^{10}$	—	3·63	4·17	4·72	5

		Solvent	0°	5°	
Carbonic	$K_{1A} . 10^7$	water	2·64	3·04	3
	$K_{1A} . 10^7$	0·1M NaCl	4·48	5·16	5
	$K_{1A} . 10^7$	0·2M NaCl	5·15	5·93	6
	$K_{1A} . 10^7$	0·5M NaCl	6·23	7·14	8
	$K_{1A} . 10^7$	0·7M NaCl	6·62	7·56	8
	$K_{1A} . 10^7$	1·0M NaCl	7·02	7·98	8
Phosphoric	$K_{2A} . 10^8$	water	4·85	5·24	5
Phenol-sulphonic	$K_{2A} . 10^{10}$	water	4·45	5·20	6
Glycine	$K_{1A} . 10^7$	water	—	3·82	3
Citric	$K_{1A} . 10^4$	water	6·03	6·31	6
	$K_{2A} . 10^5$	water	1·45	1·54	1
	$K_{3A} . 10^7$	water	4·05	4·11	4

Reproducibility between various workers is about   * at 12·5°;   **
±(0·01 - 0·02) . 10⁻⁵ compare Table V, 1.

[1] H. S. HARNED and N. D. EMBREE, *J. Am. Chem. Soc.*, 1934, 56, 1042.

[2] H. S. HARNED and R. W. EHLERS, *ibid.*, 1933, 55, 652.

[3] H. S. HARNED and R. W. EHLERS, *ibid.*, 1933, 55, 2379.

[4] H. S. HARNED and R. O. SUTHERLAND, *ibid.*, 1943, 56, 2039.

[5] D. D. WRIGHT, *ibid.*, 1934, 56, 314.

[6] L. F. NIMS and P. K. SMITH, *J. Biol. Chem.*, 1936, 113, 145.

[7] L. F. NIMS, *J. Am. Chem. Soc.*, 1936, 58, 987.

[8] H. S. HARNED and L. D. FALLON, *ibid.*, 1939, 61, 3111.

[8a] W. J. HAMER, J. O. BURTON and S. F. ACREE, *J. Res. Nat. Bur. Stand.*, 1940, 24, 292.

AT VARIOUS TEMPERATURES

30°	35°	40°	45°	50°	55°	60°	Ref.
1·768	1·747	1·716	1·685	1·650	1·607	1·551	1
1·750	1·728	1·703	1·670	1·633	1·589	1·542	2
1·326	1·310	1·280	1·257	1·229	1·195	1·160	3
1·484	1·439	1·395	1·347	1·302	1·252	1·199	4
1·308 †	—	1·230	—	—	—	—	5
—	1·336 ††	—	—	1·270	—	—	6
—	1·471 ††	—	—	1·415	—	—	7
4·92	4·67	4·41	4·09	3·83	—	—	8
1·948	1·863	1·768	1·670	1·575	1·469	1·362	8a
—	6·531 ††	—	—	5·495	—	—	9
6·34	6·86	7·38	—	8·32	—	—	10

20°	25°	30°	35°	40°	45°	50 °C.	Ref.
4·16	4·45	4·71	4·90	5·04	5·13	5·19	11
7·11	7·66	8·14	8·54	8·85	9·06	9·16	12
8·14	8·78	9·33	9·79	10·15	10·39	10·51	12
9·70	10·41	11·03	11·53	11·92	12·19	12·32	12
10·15	10·81	11·51	12·03	12·45	12·75	12·93	12
10·63	11·37	12·02	12·58	13·03	13·37	13·58	12
6·12	6·34	6·46	6·53	6·58	6·59	6·55	13
7·85	8·85	9·89	10·94	12·00	13·09	14·16	14
4·32	4·46	4·57	4·66	4·73	4·77	4·79	15
7·21	7·45	7·66	7·78	7·96	7·99	8·04	16
1·70	1·73	1·76	1·77	1·78	1·76	1·75	16
4·09	4·02	3·99	3·78	3·69	3·45	3·28	16

† at 32°;   †† at 37·5°.   All values are on the m-scale.

[9] L. F. NIMS, *J.Am. Chem. Soc.*, 1934, 56, 1110.
[10] B. B. OWEN, *ibid.*, 1934, 56, 1695, 2785.
[11] H. S. HARNED and R. DAVIS, Jr., *ibid.*, 1943, 65, 2030.
[12] H. S. HARNED and F. T. BONNER, *ibid.*, 1945, 67, 1026.
[13] R. G. BATES and S. F. ACREE, *J. Res. Nat. Bur. Stand.*, 1943, 30, 129.
[14] R. G. BATES, G. L. SIEGEL and S. F. ACREE, *ibid.*, 1943, 31, 205.
[15] E. J. KING, *J. Am. Chem. Soc.*, 1945, 67, 2178.
[16] R. G. BATES and G. D. PINCHING, *J. Am. Chem. Soc.*, 1949, 71, 1274.

TABLE V, 3

THERMODYNAMIC DISSOCIATION CONSTANTS OF BASES IN AQUEOUS AND ALCOHOLIC SOLUTION

Substance	pK_A	t °C.	Ref.	Substance	pK_A	t °C.	Ref.
Methylamine	10·64	25	(²)	o-Anisidine	4·49	25	(²)
Ethylamine	10·67	25	(²)	m-Anisidine	4·20	25	(²)
Propylamine	10·58	25	(²)	p-Anisidine	5·29	25	(²)
n-Butylamine	10·61	25	(²)	N-Ethylaniline	5·11	25	(²)
iso-Propylamine	10·63	25	(²)	N-Methylaniline	4·85	25	(²)
iso-Butylamine	10·42	25	(¹)	Pyrrolidine	2·90	25	(⁶)
iso-Amylamine	10·60	25	(¹)	N-Methylpyrrolidine	3·83	25	(⁶)
Dimethylamine	10·70	25	(²)	Quinoline	5·06	25	(⁷)
Trimethylamine	9·80	25	(²)	Quinine　pK_1	5·70	20	(⁸)
Diethylamine	11·00	25	(²)	pK_2	9·87	20	(⁸)
Triethylamine	10·72	25	(²)	Atebrin　pK_1	3·88	20	(⁸)
α ω-Diaminopentane	10·78	25	(²)	pK_2	6·47	20	(⁸)
Ethanolamine	9·44	25	(²)	Acridine	4·11*	20	(⁹)
Diethanolamine	8·88	25	(²)	Crystal violet	9·36	25	(¹⁰)
Triethanolamine	7·77	25	(²)	Pyrrole	0·4	20	(¹¹)
Cyclohexylamine	10·64	25	(²)	Diphenylamine	0·85	20	(¹¹)
Piperidine	11·12	25	(³)	Pyridine	5·19	25	(²)
1:2 Dimethylpiperidine	10·26	25	(³)	2-Amino-pyridine	7·14	25	(²)
1-Ethylpiperidine	10·41	25	(²)	Aniline	4·58	25	(²)
1-Propylpiperidine	10·23	25	(³)	o-Toluidine	4·39	25	(²)
1-Butylpiperidine	10·48	25	(²)	m-Toluidine	4·69	25	(²)
1 : 2 Dimethyl-tetra-				p-Toluidine	5·07	25	(²)
hydro-pyridine	11·42	25	(³)	N-Dimethylaniline	5·21	25	(⁴)
N-Methyl-m-toluidine	4·94	25	(²)	N-Methyl-o-toluidine	4·59	25	(²)
N-Methyl-p-toluidine	5·33	25	(²)				
N-Dimethyl-o-toluidine	5·86	25	(²)				
p-Chloraniline	4·07	25	(⁵)				
α-Naphthylamine	3·92	25	(²)	* In 50% aq. alcoholic solution			
β-Naphthylamine	4·11	25	(²)				

1 C. W. HOERR, M. R. McCORKLE and A. W. RALSTON, J. Am. Chem. Soc., 1943, 65, 328.
2 N. F. HALL and M. R. SPRINKLE, ibid., 1932, 54, 3469 (quoted or experimentally determined). See also J. Am. Chem. Soc., 1930, 52, 5079.
3 R. ADAMS and J. E. MAHAN, ibid., 1942, 64, 2588.
4 R. BEALE and A. LIBERMAN, private communication.
5 A. V. FEW and J. W. SMITH, J. Chem. Soc., 1949, 2663.
6 L. C. CRAIG and R. M. HIXON, J. Am. Chem. Soc., 1931, 53, 4370.
7 F. ARNALL, J. Chem. Soc., 1920, 835.
8 R. CHRISTOPHER, Ann. Trop. Med., 1937, 31, 43.
9 A. ALBERT and R. J. GOLDACRE, J. Chem. Soc., 1946, 706.
10 R. J. GOLDACRE and J. N. PHILLIPS, J. Chem. Soc., 1949, 1724.
11 N. F. HALL, J. Am. Chem. Soc., 1930, 52, 5123.

For dissociation constants of acids see Table V, 1.

TABLE V, 4

IONIC PRODUCT OF WATER (K_w)

$-\log_{10} K_w$	Temp. °C.	$-\log_{10} K_w$	Temp. °C.
14·9435	0	13·6801	35
14·7338	5	13·5348	40
14·5346	10	13·3960	45
14·3463	15	13·2617	50
14·1669	20	13·1369	55
13·9965	25	13·0171	60
13·8330	30		

Accurate to $\pm 0\cdot 0007$

H. S. HARNED and R. A. ROBINSON, *Trans. Faraday Soc.*, 1940, **36**, 977.

For earlier work see also:

[1] A. HEYDWEILLER, *Ann. Physik*, 1909, **28**, 503.

[2] F. KOHLRAUSCH and A. HEYDWEILLER, *Ann. Physik*, 1894, **53**, 209.

[3] C. W. KANOLT, *J. Am. Chem. Soc.*, 1907, **29**, 1402.

[4] A. A. NOYES *et al.*, *J. Am. Chem. Soc.*, 1910, **32**, 159.

[5] H. LUNDEN, *J. Chim. Phys.*, 1907, **5**, 574.

See also Table V, 9.

TABLE V, 5

ACID DISSOCIATION CONSTANTS OF SOME WEAK ACIDS IN DEUTERIUM OXIDE AT 25 °C.

System	Value in H_2O K_{H_2O}	Value in D_2O K_{D_2O}	K_{H_2O}/K_{D_2O}	Ref.
$H_3O^{\cdot} \rightleftharpoons H_2O + H^{\cdot}$	55·5	55·4	~ 1 Calculated	
Chlordeutacetic acid	$1\cdot 7 \, . \, 10^{-3}$	$0\cdot 6 \, . \, 10^{-3}$	3	1
Salicylic acid	$0\cdot 97 . \, 10^{-3}$	$0\cdot 25 . \, 10^{-3}$	3·8	2
Acetic acid	$1\cdot 84 . \, 10^{-5}$	$0\cdot 58 . \, 10^{-5}$	3·2	3
$NH^{\cdot}_4 \rightleftharpoons NH_3 + H^{\cdot}$	5·5	2·0	2·3	1
Hydroquinone	$2\cdot 6 \, . \, 10^{-11}$	$0\cdot 68 . \, 10^{-11}$	3·8	2
$[H^{\cdot}] [OH']$	$1\cdot 00 . \, 10^{-14}$	$0\cdot 16 . \, 10^{-14}$	6·2	4

[1] G. N. LEWIS and P. W. SCHUTZ, *J. Am. Chem. Soc.*, 1934, **56**, 1913.

[2] S. KORMAN and V. K. LAMER, *J. Am. Chem. Soc.*, 1936, **58**, 1396.

[3] V. K. LAMER and J. P. CHITTUM, *J. Am. Chem. Soc.*, 1936, **58**, 1642.

[4] E. ABEL, E. BRATU and O. REDLICH, *Z. physik. Chem.*, 1935, **173** A, 353.

Compare Table V, 1.

TABLE V, 6

THERMODYNAMIC BASIC DISSOCIATION CONSTANTS (K_b) OF AQUEOUS AMMONIA
FROM 0 TO 50 °C.

Temp. °C.	pK_b	$K_b . 10^4$
0	4·862	1·374
5	4·830	1·479
10	4·804	1·570
15	4·782	1·652
20	4·767	1·710
25	4·751	1·774
30	4·740	1·820
35	4·733	1·849
40	4·730	1·862
45	4·726	1·879
50	4·723	1·892

Values of K_b accurate to ± 0.005; determined by e.m.f. method by:
R. G. BATES and G. D. PINCHING, *J. Am. Chem. Soc.*, 1950, **72**, 1393.

TABLE V, 7

FIRST IONIZATION CONSTANTS OF AMINO ACIDS IN WATER

Amino acid		Values of K at the given temp.				
		1	12·5	25	37·5	50 °C.
DL-Alanine	$K_A . 10^3$	3·75	4·14	4·49	4·68	4·66
	$K_B . 10^5$	4·83	6·10	7·40	8·73	9·86
DL-α-Amino-n-butyric acid	$K_A . 10^3$	4·63	4·90	5·18	5·15	5·05
	$K_B . 10^5$	4·25	5·50	6·81	8·22	9·38
DL-α-Amino-n-valeric acid	$K_A . 10^3$	4·21	4·57	4·81	4·91	4·86
	$K_B . 10^5$	4·04	5·18	6·47	7·64	8·63
DL-Norleucine	$K_A . 10^3$	4·04	4·41	4·62	4·74	4·70
	$K_B . 10^4$	4·41	5·62	6·87	8·05	9·16
α-Amino-iso-butyric acid	$K_A . 10^3$	3·81	4·17	4·40	4·46	4·41
	$K_B . 10^4$	1·14	1·38	1·61	1·84	1·99
DL-Valine	$K_A . 10^3$	4·79	5·05	5·18	5·11	4·90
	$K_B . 10^5$	3·24	4·21	5·27	6·28	7·28
DL-Leucine	$K_A . 10^3$	4·14	4·49	4·70	4·71	4·65
	$K_B . 10^5$	3·57	4·52	5·60	6·71	7·59
DL-iso-Leucine	$K_A . 10^3$	4·32	4·59	4·81	4·82	4·66
	$K_B . 10^5$	3·61	4·57	5·77	6·79	7·85

Accurate to $\pm 0·01$ pK.

All values are on the m-scale.

P. K. SMITH, A. C. TAYLOR and E. R. B. SMITH, *J. Biol. Chem.*, 1937, **122**, 109.

See also *Trans. Faraday Soc.*, 1940, **36**, 973.

TABLE V, 8

DISSOCIATION CONSTANTS * OF AMINO ACIDS, PEPTIDES AND AMINO ACID AMIDES
AT 25 °C.

Charge Type 1.
One Amino, one Carboxyl Group

	pK_1' (COOH)	pK_2' (NH$_3^\cdot$)	Reference
Glycine	2·34	9·60	5
Alanine	2·34	9·69	5
α-Amino-n-butyric acid .	2·55	9·60	5
Valine	2·32	9·62	14
α-Amino-n-valeric acid .	2·36	9·72	5
Leucine	2·36	9·60	14
iso-Leucine	2·36	9·68	14
Norleucine	2·39	9·76	14
Serine	2·21	9·15	14
Proline	1·99	10·60	24
Phenylalanine . . .	1·83	9·13	24
Tryptophan . . .	2·38	9·39	22
Methionine	2·28	9·21	6
iso-Serine	2·78	9·27	6
Hydroxy-valine . . .	2·61	9·71	4
Taurine	1·5 (SO$_3$H)	8·74	1
β-Alanine	3·60	10·19	22
γ-Amino-n-valeric acid .	4·02	10·40	22
δ-Amino-n-valeric acid .	4·270 **	10·766 **	16
ε-Amino-n-caproic acid .	4·43	10·75	5

Amides of Amino Acids

Glycine amide . . .	—	7·93	18
Glutamine (γ-amide) .	2·17	9·13	13
Asparagine (β-amide) .	2·02	8·80	3
γ-Hydroxy-asparagine .	2·12	8·26	3
iso-Glutamine (α-amide) .	3·81	7·88	13
iso-Asparagine (α-amide) .	2·97	8·02	13
α-Hydroxy-asparagine .	2·31	7·17	3

TABLE V, 8 (*Continued*)

	pK_1' (COOH)	pK_2' (NH$_3$')	Reference
Peptides			
Glycylglycine . . .	3·06	8·13	24
Glycylglycine . . .	3·12	8·17	10
Glycylglycine . . .	3·083 **	8·265 **	16
Glycylalanine . . .	3·15	8·25	24
Glycylleucine . . .	3·18	8·29	24
Glycylvaline . . .	3·17	8·25	24
Alanylalanine . . .	3·17	8·42	24
Alanylglycine . . .	3·11	8·18	24
Glycylproline . . .	2·84	8·53	13
Alanylproline . . .	3·04	8·38	13
Alanyldiglycine . . .	3·21	8·15	21 (at 20 °C.)
Glycylalanylalanylglycine	3·30	7·93	24
Leucyl-octaglycyl-glycine	2·2	7·84	21 (at 20 °C.)
Phenylalanylglycine .	3·10	7·71	10
Triglycine	3·26	7·91	24
Tetraglycine . . .	3·05	7·75	24
Pentaglycine . . .	3·05	7·70	24
Hexaglycine . . .	3·05	7·60	24

N-Methylated Amino Acids and Peptides

	pK_1' (COOH)	pK_2' (Amino)	Reference
Sarcosine	2·23	10·01	12
Sarcosylglycine . . .	3·10	8·51	12
Glycylsarcosine . . .	2·83	8·54	12
Sarcosylsarcosine . .	2·86	9·10	12
N-Dimethylglycine . .	1·94	9·86	11
Betaine	1·84	—	20

TAB

C

Amino acids and Peptides with one ⸺

	pK_1' (COOH
L-Tyrosine	2·20
Diiodo-L-tyrosine	2·12
3, 4,-dihydroxyphenyl-alanine	2·36
Glycyltyrosine	2·98
Tyrosyltyrosine	3·52
Cysteine	1·96 1·71 **
Cysteinylcysteine	2·65

C

Two or More Carboxyl

	pK_1' (COOH
Aspartic acid	1·88
Glutamic acid	2·19
	2·155 **
β-Hydroxylglutamic acid	2·23
Glycylaspartic acid	2·81
Aspartylglycine	2·10
Aspartylaspartic acid	2·70
Glutaminylglycine	3·15
Glutaminylglutamic acid	3·14
Aspartyltyrosine	3·13
α-Aminotricarballylic acid	2·10
Glycyl-α-aminotricarballylic acid	2·70

inued)

boxyl, and Phenolic or Sulphydryl Groups

pK_2'	pK_3'	Reference
9·11 (NH$_3^{\cdot}$)	10·07 (OH)	19
6·48 (OH)	7·82 (NH$_3^{\cdot}$)	19
8·68 (NH$_3^{\cdot}$)	$\left\{ \begin{array}{l} 9·88 \\ 11·68 \end{array} \right.$ (OH)	14
8·40 (NH$_3^{\cdot}$)	10·40 (OH)	8
7·68 (NH$_3^{\cdot}$)	$\left\{ \begin{array}{l} 9·80 \\ 10·26 \end{array} \right.$ (OH)	8
8·18 (NH$_3^{\cdot}$) 8·33 ** (NH$_3^{\cdot}$)	$\left\{ \begin{array}{l} 10·28 \\ 10·78 \end{array} \right.$ (SH)	20 (at 30 °C.) 2
7·27 (NH$_3^{\cdot}$)	$\left\{ \begin{array}{l} 9·35 \\ 10·85 \end{array} \right.$ (SH)	

e Basic Group

K_2' (COOH)	pK_3'	pK_4'	References
3·65	9·60 (NH$_3^{\cdot}$)	—	14
4·25	9·67 (NH$_3^{\cdot}$)	—	14
4·324 **	9·960 ** (NH$_3^{\cdot}$)	—	15
4·24	9·56 (NH$_3^{\cdot}$)	—	14
4·45	8·60 (NH$_3^{\cdot}$)	—	24
4·53	9·07 (NH$_3^{\cdot}$)	—	24
3·40	4·70 (COOH)	8·26 (NH$_3^{\cdot}$)	7
—	7·52 (NH$_3^{\cdot}$)	—	13
4·38	7·62 (NH$_3^{\cdot}$)	—	13
3·57	8·92 (NH$_3^{\cdot}$)	10·23 (OH)	10
3·60	4·60 (COOH)	9·82 (NH$_3^{\cdot}$)	11
4·10	5·35 (COOH)	8·32 (NH$_3^{\cdot}$)	11

TAB

C

One Carboxyl, Mo

	pK_1' (COOH)
Histidine	1·82
	1·78
Arginine	2·17
	2·18
Ornithine	1·94
Lysine	2·18
α-β-Diaminopropionic acid	1·33
Histidylhistidine	2·25
Histidylglycine	2·40
L-Methylhistidine	1·69
Carnosine	2·64
Lysyllysine	1·95
Phenylalanylarginine	2·66
Tyrosylarginine	2·65
	2·63

C

Two Carboxyl (

	pK_1' (COOH)
Cystine	1·65
	1·00
	1·04 **
Lysylglutamic acid	2·93
Diglycylcystine	2·71
Cystinyldiglycine	3·12
Cystinyldidiglycine	3·21
α-Aspartylhistidine	2·45
β-Aspartylhistidine	1·93

* *Note:* pK' values given in this table are not the thermodynamic —log dissociation co
since no extrapolations to zero ionic strength have been made except in thos
indicated by the asterisks **.

inued)

.

sic Group

pK_2'	pK_3'	pK_4'	References
6·00 (Im)	9·17 ($NH_3^{\cdot}$)	—	22
5·97 (Im)	8·97 ($NH_3^{\cdot}$)	—	25
9·04 ($NH_3^{\cdot}$)	12·48 (Guan.)	—	24
9·09 ($NH_3^{\cdot}$)	13·2 (Guan.)	—	25 (at 23 °C.)
8·65 ($NH_3^{\cdot}$)	10·76 ($NH_3^{\cdot}$)	—	23
8·95 (α-$NH_3^{\cdot}$)	10·53 (ε-$NH_3^{\cdot}$)	—	24
6·80 (α-$NH_3^{\cdot}$)	9·60 (β-$NH_3^{\cdot}$)	—	9
5·60 (Im)	6·80 ($NH_3^{\cdot}$)	7·80 ($NH_3^{\cdot}$)	7
5·80 (Im)	7·82 ($NH_3^{\cdot}$)	—	10
6·48 (Im)	8·85 ($NH_3^{\cdot}$)	—	17
6·83 (Im)	9·51 ($NH_3^{\cdot}$)	—	17
8·17 ($NH_3^{\cdot}$)	9·45 ($NH_3^{\cdot}$)	10·63 ($NH_3^{\cdot}$)	10
7·57 ($NH_3^{\cdot}$)	12·40 (Guan.)	—	10
7·39 ($NH_3^{\cdot}$)	9·36 (OH)	11·62 (Guan.)	10
7·55 ($NH_3^{\cdot}$)	9·80 (OH)	12·3 (Guan.)	13

.

mino Groups

K_2' (COOH)	pK_3' ($NH_3^{\cdot}$)	pK_4' ($NH_3^{\cdot}$)	References
2·26	7·85	9·85	16
1·7	7·48	9·02	2 (at 30 °C.)
2·05 **	8·00 **	10·25 **	2
4·47	7·75	10·50	10
2·71	7·94	7·94	11 (at 35 °C.)
3·12	6·36	6·95	11 (35 °C.)
3·21	6·01	6·87	11 (35 °C.)
3·02	6·82 (Im)	7·98	11 (38 °C.)
2·95	6·93 (Im)	8·72	11 (38 °C.)

TABLE V, 8 (*Continued*)

References:
[1] S. ANDREWS and C. L. A. SCHMIDT, *J. Biol. Chem.*, 1927, **73**, 651.
[2] H. BORSOOK, E. L. ELLIS and H. M. HUFFMAN, *J. Biol. Chem.*, 1937, **117**, 281.
　　R. K. CANNAN and B. C. J. C. KNIGHT, *Biochem. J.*, 1927, **21**, 1384.
[3] A. C. CHIBNALL and R. K. CANNAN, *Biochem. J.*, 1930, **24**, 945.
[4] E. J. CZARNETSKY and C. L. A. SCHMIDT, *J. Biol. Chem.*, 1931, **92**, 453.
[5] E. J. CZARNETSKY and C. L. A. SCHMIDT, *Z. Physiol. Chem.*, 1931, **204**, 129.
　　J. T. EDSALL and M. H. BLANCHARD, *J. Am. Chem. Soc.*, 1933, **55**, 2337.
[6] O. H. EMERSON, P. L. KIRK and C. L. R. SCHMIDT, *J. Biol. Chem.*, 1931, **92**, 449.
[7] J. P. GREENSTEIN, *J. Biol. Chem.*, 1931, **93**, 479.
[8] J. P. GREENSTEIN, *ibid.*, 1932, **95**, 465.
[9] J. P. GREENSTEIN, *ibid.*, 1932, **96**, 499.
[10] J. P. GREENSTEIN, *ibid.*, 1933, **101**, 603.
[11] J. P. GREENSTEIN and N. R. JOSEPH, *ibid.*, 1935, **110**, 619.
　　J. P. GREENSTEIN and F. W. KLEMPERER, *ibid.*, 1939, **128**, 245.
　　J. P. GREENSTEIN, F. W. KLEMPERER and J. WYMAN, *ibid.*, 1939, **129**, 681.
　　S. JOHNSON, *Proc. Roy. Soc.*, *London*, 1906-7, A **78**, 101.

T

IONIZATION CONSTANTS IN DIOXAN-

				1. Water in D
W		$0°$	$5°$	$10°$	1
0	$K_w . 10^{14}$	0·1139	0·1846	0·2920	0·
20	$K_w . 10^{15}$	0·2702	0·4375	0·6918	1·
45	$K_w . 10^{16}$	0·2114	0·3409	0·5349	0·
70	$K_w . 10^{18}$	0·1789	0·2819	0·4348	0·

				2. Formic Acid in I
0	$K_A . 10^4$	1·638	1·691	1·728	1·
20	$K_A . 10^5$	6·412	6·548	6·625	6·
45	$K_A . 10^6$	8·702	8·702	8·614	8·
70	$K_A . 10^8$	11·077	10·876	10·641	10·
82	$K_A . 10^9$	—	1·883	1·836	1·

				3. Acetic Acid in I
0	$K_A . 10^5$	1·657	1·700	1·729	1·
20	$K_A . 10^6$	4·75	4·87	4·98	5·
45	$K_A . 10^7$	4·78	4·89	4·96	4·
70	$K_A . 10^9$	4·75	4·83	4·89	4·
82	$K_A . 10^{11}$	—	7·41	7·50	7·

W = Weight percent of organic solvent

TABLE V, 8 (*Continued*)

[12] P. A. Levene, H. S. Simms and M. H. Pfaltz, *J. Biol. Chem.*, 1924, **61**, 445.
[13] J. Melville and G. M. Richardson, *Biochem. J.*, 1935, **29**, 187.
[14] S. Miyamoto and C. L. A. Schmidt, *J. Biol. Chem.*, 1931, **90**, 165.
[15] A. Neuberger, *Biochem. J.*, 1936, **30**, 2085.
[16] A. Neuberger, *Proc. Roy. Soc.*, London, 1937, A **158**, 68.
    K. Sano, *Biochem. Z.*, 1926, **168**, 14.
[17] A. Deutsch and P. Eggleton, *Biochem. J.*, 1938, **32**, 209.
[18] M. Zief and J. T. Edsall, *J. Am. Chem. Soc.*, 1937, **59**, 2245.
[19] P. S. Winnek and C. L. A. Schmidt, *J. Gen. Physiol.*, 1935, **18**, 889.
[20] O. Weider, *Ber.*, 1935, **68**, 263.
[21] J. Tillmans, P. Hirsch and H. Strache, *Biochem. Z.*, 1928, **199**, 399.
[22] C. L. A. Schmidt, W. K. Appleman and P. L. Kirk, *J. Biol. Chem.*, 1929, **81**, 723; **85**, 137.
[23] C. L. A. Schmidt, P. L. Kirk and W. Schmidt, *ibid*, 1929, **81**, 249.
[24] E. J. Cohn, *Ergeb. d. Physiol.*, 1931, **33**, 781.
[25] T. W. Birch and L. J. Harris, *Biochem. J.*, 1930, **24**, 564.

ETHANOL-WATER MIXTURES

Mixtures ([1])

)°	25°	30°	35°	40°	45°	50 °C.
·809	1·008	1·469	2·089	2·919	4·018	5·474
·22	2·399	3·477	4·922	6·947	9·531	12·87
·34	1·809	2·594	3·655	5·077	6·914	9·277
·654	1·395	1·974	2·743	3·779	5·064	6·719

Mixtures ([2])

	25°	30°	35°	40°	45°	50 °C.
·65	1·772	1·768	1·747	1·716	1·685	1·650
·51	6·605	6·519	6·394	6·243	6·077	5·876
·18	8·099	7·834	7·537	7·212	6·867	6·510
·05	9·634	9·213	8·778	8·310	7·842	7·359
·90	1·588	1·472	1·339	1·208	1·079	—

Mixtures ([3])

	25°	30°	35°	40°	45°	50 °C.
·53	1·754	1·750	1·728	1·703	1·670	1·633
·9	5·11	5·08	5·03	4·95	4·86	4·73
·6	4·93	4·86	4·75	4·61	4·44	4·28
·3	4·78	4·69	4·56	4·42	4·22	4·05
·5	7·24	6·92	6·61	6·09	5·49	—

All values are on the m-scale.

TAB

4. Propionic Acid in D

W		$0°$	$5°$	$10°$	1
0	$K_A . 10^5$	1·274	1·305	1·326	1·3
20	$K_A . 10^6$	3·175	3·267	3·337	3·3
45	$K_A . 10^7$	2·641	2·713	2·764	2·7
70	$K_A . 10^9$	2·299	2·364	2·410	2·4
82	$K_A . 10^{11}$	—	3·797	3·917	3·9

5. Acetic Acid in

| 10 | $K_A . 10^5$ | 1·138 | — | 1·200 | – |
| 20 | $K_A . 10^6$ | 7·38 | — | 7·94 | – |

6. Glycine in D

20	$K_A . 10^3$	1·832	1·953	2·067	2·1
45	$K_A . 10^4$	6·339	6·707	7·034	7·3
70	$K_A . 10^5$	8·933	9·350	9·759	10
20	$K_B . 10^5$	1·179	1·317	1·473	1·6
45	$K_B . 10^6$	1·789	2·024	2·272	2·5
70	$K_B . 10^7$	1·47	1·68	1·91	2·1

7. Propionic Acid in

0	$K_A . 10^5$	1·274	1·305	1·326	1·3
10	$K_A . 10^5$	0·881	—	0·885	–
20	$K_A . 10^5$	0·603	—	0·608	–

8. Propionic Acid in

| 10 | $K_A . 10^5$ | 0·870 | — | 0·900 | – |
| 20 | $K_A . 10^5$ | 0·673 | — | 0·755 | – |

9. Propionic Acid in *iso-*

5	$K_A . 10^5$	1·015	1·038	1·052	1·0
10	$K_A . 10^5$	0·780	0·803	0·815	0·8
20	$K_A . 10^5$	0·431	0·448	0·459	0·4

10. *n*-Butyric Acid in *iso-*

5	$K_A . 10^5$	1·190	1·197	1·189	1·1
10	$K_A . 10^5$	0·922	0·929	0·925	0·9
20	$K_A . 10^5$	0·466	0·475	0·476	0·4

11. Acetic Acid in Gl

		$0°$	$5°$	$10°$	$15°$	$20°$	$25°$	
50	$K_A . 10^6$	4·78	4·96	5·10	5·22	5·32	5·35	

tinued)

Mixtures ([4])

°	25°	30°	35°	40°	45°	50 °C.
38	1·336	1·326	1·310	1·280	1·257	1·229
12	3·417	3·403	3·370	3·319	3·252	3·172
08	2·801	2·776	2·734	2·677	2·607	2·526
50	2·444	2·422	2·386	2·336	2·274	2·202
46	3·860	3·716	3·524	3·293	3·035	—

l-Water Mixtures ([5])

42	1·247	1·237	—	1·214	—	—
4	8·34	8·30	—	8·19	—	—

Mixtures ([6])

57	2·352	2·428	2·481	2·533	2·573	2·591
28	7·847	8·091	8·232	8·350	8·457	8·484
43	10·84	10·98	11·15	11·26	11·36	11·39
81	1·937	2·088	2·241	2·407	2·548	2·690
40	3·120	3·408	3·707	4·015	4·342	4·680
9	2·66	2·94	3·24	3·60	3·96	4·34

l-Water Mixtures ([7])

38	1·336	1·326	1·310	1·280	1·257	1·229
17	0·947	0·909	—	0·838	—	—
86	0·578	0·553	—	0·525	—	—

l-Water Mixtures ([8])

00	0·900	0·906	—	0·902	—	—
71	0·781	0·788	—	0·780	—	—

l-Water Mixtures ([9])

60	1·053	1·044	1·032	1·012	—	—
24	0·820	0·812	0·800	0·785	—	—
66	0·466	0·462	0·454	0·444	—	—

l-Water Mixtures ([10])

57	1·133	1·104	1·077	1·040	—	—
07	0·888	0·864	0·839	0·813	—	—
65	0·456	0·446	0·432	0·417	—	—

Mixtures (0 - 90°) ([11])

40°	45°	50°	55°	60°	65°	70°	75°	80°	85°	90 °C.
5·33	5·27	5·18	5·07	4·95	4·81	4·65	4·47	4·31	4·14	3·93

TABLE V, 9 (*Continued*)

[1] H. S. HARNED and L. D. FALLON, *J. Am. Chem. Soc.*, 1939, **61**, 2371.

[2] H. S. HARNED and R. S. DONE, *ibid.*, 1941, **63**, 2579.

[3] H. S. HARNED and G. L. KAZANJIAN, *ibid.*, 1936, **58**, 1912; H. S. HARNED and L. D. FALLON, *ibid.*, 1939, **61**, 2377. Revised by H. S. HARNED, *J. Phys. Chem.*, 1938, **43**, 275.

[4] H. S. HARNED and T. R. DEDELL, *ibid.*, 1941, **63**, 3308.

[5] H. S. HARNED and N. D. EMBREE, *ibid.*, 1935, **57**, 1669.

[6] H. S. HARNED and C. M. BIRDSALL, *ibid.*, 1943, **65**, 45, for values of K_A; *ibid.*, 1943, **65**, 1117; for values of K_B.

[7] H. S. HARNED and R. W. EHLERS, *ibid.*, 1933, **55**, 2379.

[8] A. PATTERSON and W. A. FELSING, *ibid.*, 1942, **54**, 1480.

[9] R. L. MOORE and W. A. FELSING, *ibid.*, 1947, **69**, 2420.

[10] W. A. FELSING and M. MAY, *ibid.*, 1948, **70**, 2904.

[11] H. S. HARNED and F. H. M. NESTLER, *ibid.*, 1946, **68**, 966.

TABLE V, 10

IONIZATION CONSTANT (K_A) OF BENZOIC ACID IN METHANOL-WATER MIXTURES

$t\,°C.$	10% Methanol		20% Methanol	
	log K_A	$K_A . 10^5$	log K_A	$K_A . 10^5$
15	$\bar{5}\cdot602$	4·00	$\bar{5}\cdot270$	1·86
20	$\bar{5}\cdot610$	4·07	$\bar{5}\cdot277$	1·89
25	$\bar{5}\cdot613$	4·10	$\bar{5}\cdot279$	1·90
30	$\bar{5}\cdot613$	4·10	$\bar{5}\cdot278$	1·90
35	$\bar{5}\cdot610$	4·07	$\bar{5}\cdot275$	1·88
40	$\bar{5}\cdot605$	4·03	$\bar{5}\cdot269$	1·86
45	$\bar{5}\cdot598$	3·96	$\bar{5}\cdot262$	1·83

K accurate to $\pm0\cdot01 . 10^{-5}$.

H. N. PARTON and J. ROGERS, *Trans. Faraday Soc.*, 1942, **38**, 239.

TABLE V, 11

THERMODYNAMIC DISSOCIATION CONSTANTS IN DIOXAN-WATER MIXTURES AT 25 °C.

% Dioxan (w/w)	*p*-Toluidine pK_A	Aniline pK_A	*p*-Chloroaniline pK_A
0	5·11	4·62	4·00
20	4·92	4·44	3·65
45	4·54	4·01	3·08
70	4·16	3·58	2·68
82	4·06	3·42	2·56

TABLE V, 11 (*Continued*)

% Dioxan (w/w)	m-Nitroaniline pK$_A$	% Dioxan (w/w)	m-Nitroaniline pK$_A$
0	(2·60*)	50	1·38
20	2·08	60	1·13
30	1·83	70	1·03
40	1·60	82	1·03
45	1·44	—	—

J. C. JAMES and J. G. KNOX, *Trans. Faraday Soc.*, 1950, **46**, 254.

* A. BRYSON, *Trans. Faraday Soc.*, 1949, **45**, 257.

TABLE V, 12

TRUE DEGREES OF DISSOCIATION OF ACIDS

(RAMAN spectra)

Nitric Acid at 25 °C.					
c(N) †	4·51	6·60	8·90	10·30	11·89	14·23
α	0·823	0·673	0·49	0·39	0·32	0·14

c(N)	0·1	1	2	3	4	
α	0·997	0·978	0·95	0·90	0·85	

T. F. YOUNG and L. A. BLATZ, *Chem. Rev.*, 1949, **44**, 97.   Accuracy: ± 2·5%

† Concentration expressed as normality.

Values of α for Nitric Acid at higher temperatures			
c(N)	10·5	12·58	14·50
20° C.	0·352	0·212	0·114
60°	0·300	0·135	0·095
90°	0·226	0·105	0·022

O. REDLICH and J. BIGELEISEN, *J. Am. Chem. Soc.*, 1943, **65**, 1883.

TABLE V, 12 (*Continued*)

Perchloric Acid at 20 °C.			
wt.%	c	a c	a
60	9·1	8·9	0·98
70	10·9	10·1	0·93
	12·0	10·3	0·86
84·8	14·7	8·1	0·45
	16·0	5·6	0·35

O. REDLICH *et al.*, *J. Am. Chem. Soc.*, 1944, **66**, 13.

Iodic Acid	
c(N)	a
0·4	0·56
0·8	0·40

N. R. RAO, *Ind. J. Phys.*, 1942, **16**, 71.

Trichloracetic Acid	
c(N) = 1·5	a = 0·60

N. R. RAO, *Ind. J. Phys.*, 1943, **17**, 332.

TRUE DEGREES OF DISSOCIATION (a) OF SALTS
(Conductance method)

		c = 0·01	0·02	0·05	0·1	0·5
NaNO$_3$	(1)			0·991	0·985	
KNO$_3$	(1)	0·994	0·989	0·975	0·961	
AgNO$_3$	(1)	0·993	0·989	0·973	0·957	0·883
TlNO$_3$	(1)	0·984		0·946	0·917	
NaClO$_3$	(2)			0·992	0·986	
NaIO$_3$	(1)		0·996	0·988	0·984	
KIO$_3$	(1)	0·997	0·994	0·984	0·976	
KClO$_3$	(1)	0·994	0·989	0·977	0·968	
KBrO$_3$	(1)		0·993	0·984	0·977	
TlCl	(1)	0·972				
RbCl	(1)				0·990	
CsCl	(1)				0·981	

Accuracy not specified. As method involves one of successive approximation an evaluation of the accuracy is difficult.
c in mol/l.

TABLE V, 12 (*Continued*)

TRUE DEGREES OF DISSOCIATION (α) OF SALTS (*Continued*)

(Conductance method)

$CdCl_2$ (18 °C.) (²)				
c (mol/l.)	0·002	0·005	0·007	0·01
α	0·798	0·655	0·598	0·538

$Ca(IO_3)_2$ (25 °C.) (³)				
$c . 10^4$ (mol/l.)	2·000	11·693	38·77	52·94	81·85
α	1	1	0·981	0·972	0·961

$La[Fe(CN)_6]$ (25 °C.) (⁵)				
c (mol/l.)	0·0016	0·0064	0·0144	0·0256	0·0400
α	0·63	0·50	0·49	0·52	0·57

Ca mandelate (25 °C.) (⁴)				
$c . 10^4$ (mol/l.)	7·224	24·51	49·80	81·11	121·98
α	0·979	0·951	0·912	0·872	0·834

Ba succinate (25 °C.) (⁶)			
$c . 10^3$ (mol/l.)	1·764	2·031	4·778
α	0·983	0·976	0·952

Ba tartrate (25 °C.) (⁶)			
$c . 10^3$ (mol/l.)	1·451	2·474	4·622
α	0·868	0·840	0·767

Ba o-phthalate (25 °C.) (⁶)			
$c . 10^3$ (mol/l.)	1·608	2·002	4·031
α	0·907	0·903	0·858

Ca o-phthalate (25° C.) (⁶)			
$c . 10^3$ (mol/l.)	1·743	4·773	5·511
α	0·871	0·876	0·813

Ca tartrate (25 °C.) (⁶)			
$c . 10^3$ (mol/l.)	1·758	2·372	3·050
α	0·805	0·725	0·714

[1] C. W. DAVIES, *Trans. Faraday Soc.*, 1927, **23**, 335.
[2] C. W. DAVIES, *J. Chem. Soc.*, 1938, 2093.
[3] W. C. A. WISE and C. W. DAVIES, *J. Chem. Soc.*, 1938, 273.
[4] C. W. DAVIES, *J. Chem. Soc.*, 1938, 271.
[5] C. W. DAVIES and J. C. JAMES, *Proc. Roy. Soc.*, 1948, A.**195**, 116.
[6] C. W. DAVIES, *J. Chem. Soc.*, 1940, 87.

TABLE V, 13

SOLUBILITIES AND SOLUBILITY PRODUCTS OF SPARINGLY SOLUBLE SALTS IN WATER

Substance	Solubility (s) in g.mol/l. or Solubility product (sp) in terms of g.ions/l.		Temp.°C.	Ref.
$Al(OH)_3$	$0 \cdot 96 \ . \ 10^{-5}$	s	29	[1]
$BaCO_3$	$2 \cdot 80 \ . \ 10^{-4}$	s	18	[2]
$BaCrO_4$	$3 \cdot 07 \ . \ 10^{-5}$	s	18	[3]
$BaSO_4$	$0 \cdot 957 . \ 10^{-5}$	s	25	[4]
CdS	$1 \cdot 14 \ . \ 10^{-28}$	sp	25	[6]
$CaCO_3$	$13 \cdot 4 \ \ . \ 10^{-5}$	s	25	[7]
$Ca(COO)_2$	$1 \cdot 78 \ . \ 10^{-9}$	sp	25	[5]
$CaSO_4$	$2 \cdot 01 \ . \ 10^{-2}$	s	25	[8]
CoS	$3 \ \ \ . \ 10^{-26}$	sp	20	[9]
$Cu(IO_3)_2$	$3 \cdot 69 \ . \ 10^{-3}$	s	25	[10]
CuS	$3 \cdot 48 \ . \ 10^{-38}$	sp	25	[6]
Cu_2S	$8 \cdot 5 \ \ . \ 10^{-45}$	sp	25	[5]
Cu_2Cl_2	$7 \cdot 64 \ . \ 10^{-2}$	s	25	[11]
Cu_2I_2	$5 \cdot 0 \ \ . \ 10^{-12}$	sp	18	[5]
$Fe(OH)_3$	$1 \cdot 412 . \ 10^{-6}$	s	18	[12]
$Fe(OH)_2$	$8 \cdot 14 \ . \ 10^{-6}$	s	18	[13]
$Fe(COO)_2$	$3 \cdot 90 \ . \ 10^{-4}$	s	18	[14]
FeS	$5 \cdot 01 \ . \ 10^{-5}$	s	18	[15]
$PbCO_3$	$5 \cdot 25 \ . \ 10^{-6}$	s	20	[16]
$PbCrO_4$	$5 \cdot 27 \ . \ 10^{-7}$	s	20	[17]
PbI_2	$1 \cdot 64 \ . \ 10^{-2}$	s	20	[18]
PbS	$3 \cdot 62 \ . \ 10^{-11}$	s	25	[5]
$PbSO_4$	$1 \cdot 49 \ . \ 10^{-4}$	s	25	[19]
$Mg(NH_4)_2(SO_4)_2$	$2 \cdot 5 \ \ . \ 10^{-13}$	sp	25	[20]
$Mg(OH)_2$	$4 \cdot 6 \ \ . \ 10^{-24}$	sp	25	[21]
$MgCO_3$	$7 \cdot 46 \ . \ 10^{-4}$	s	100	[22, 23]
Hg_2Cl_2	$5 \cdot 42 \ . \ 10^{-19}$	sp	19·2	[24]
Hg_2Br_2	$3 \cdot 88 \ . \ 10^{-23}$	sp	19·2	[29]
Hg_2I_2	$10 \cdot 5 \ \ . \ 10^{-20}$	sp	19·2	[24]
Hg_2CrO_4	$2 \cdot 0 \ \ . \ 10^{-9}$	sp	25	[24]
NiS	$4 \ \ \ . \ 10^{-10}$	s	20	[9]
$AgCl$	$1 \cdot 60 - 1 \cdot 65 . \ 10^{-5}$	s	20	[25]
$AgBr$	$1 \cdot 86 \ . \ 10^{-6}$	s	20	[26]
AgI	$1 \cdot 0 \ \ . \ 10^{-16}$	sp	25	[5]
$AgCrO_4$	$1 \cdot 03 \ . \ 10^{-6}$	s	27	[27]
Ag_2S	$3 \cdot 28 \ . \ 10^{-52}$	sp	25	[6]

TABLE V, 13 (*Continued*)

Substance	Solubility (s) in g.mol/l. or Solubility product (sp) in terms of g.ions/l.		Temp.°C.	Ref.
AgSCN	1·03 . 10^{-6}	s	18	(^{26})
AgCN	2·10 . 10^{-7}	s	18	(^{26})
SrCO₃	1·4 . 10^{-4}	s	18	(^{2})
Sr(COO)₂	2·8 . 10^{-4}	s	18	(^{2})
SrSO₄	7·5 . 10^{-4}	s	18	(^{2})
ZnS	1·4 . 10^{-9}	s	25	(^{6})
TlI	6·47 . 10^{-8}	sp	25	(^{28})

References:

1 W. Busch, *Z. anorg. Chem.*, 1927, **161**, 161.
2 J. Heyrovsky, *Coll. Czech. Chem. Comm.*, 1929, **1**, 19.
3 J. Waddell, *Analyst*, 1918, **43**, 287.
4 E. W. Neumann, *J. Am. Chem. Soc.*, 1933, **55**, 879.
5 O. Ruff, *Z. anorg. Chem.*, 1929, **185**, 387.
6 S. F. Revitz, *J. Phys. Chem.*, 1936, **40**, 61.
7 H. O. Askew, *Trans. New Zealand Inst.*, 1923, 54, 791.
8 A. E. Hill, *J. Am. Chem. Soc.*, 1937, 59, 2242.
9 L. Moser and M. Behr, *Z. anorg. Chem.*, 1924, **134**, 49.
10 B. H. Peterson and E. L. Meyers, *J. Am. Chem. Soc.*, 1930, **52**, 4853.
11 R. Kremann and F. Noss, *Monatsch.*, *Chem.*, 1912, **33**, 1205.
12 G. Almquist, *Z. anorg. Chem.*, 1918, **103**, 240.
13 F. Murata, *J. Soc. Chem. Ind.*, *Jap.*, 1932, **35**, 5238.
14 R. Scholder, E. Gadenne and H. Niemann, *Ber.*, 1927, **60**, 1510.
15 A. Michwitz, *Z. anorg. Chem.*, 1928, **171**, 285, 306; **176**, 277.
16 W. Böttger, *Z. physik. Chem.*, 1903, **46**, 521.
17 M. Huybrechts and C. Degard, *Bull. Soc. Chim. Belg.*, 1933, **42**, 331.
18 L. J. Burrage, *J. Chem. Soc.*, 1926, 1703, 1896.
19 H. D. Crockford and D. J. Brawley, *J. Am. Chem. Soc.*, 1934, **56**, 2600.
20 See P. Wenger, *Tables annuelles*, 1911, **2**, 411.
21 L. Whitby, *Trans. Faraday Soc.*, 1933, **29**, 415, 523, 853, 1327.
22 J. Leick, *Z. anal. Chem.*, 1932, **87**, 415; *Z. anorg. Chem.*, 1933, **210**, 203.
23 J. Leick, *Z. anorg. Chem.*, 1933, **210**, 203.
24 A. E. Brodsky, *Z. Elektrochem.*, 1929, **35**, 833.
25 A. Pinkus and P. Hanrez, *Bull. Soc. Chim. Belg.*, 1938, **47**, 532.
26 C. Bedel, *Comptes Rendus*, 1938, **207**, 632.
27 G. S. Whitby, *Z. anorg. Chem.*, 1910, **67**, 107.
28 C. W. Davies and R. A. Robinson, *Trans. Faraday Soc.*, 1937, **33**, 633.
29 A. Seidell, *Solubilities of Inorganic Compounds*, Van Nostrand, New York, 1940.

TABLE V, 14

SOLUBILITY PRODUCTS (sp) OF SOME SPARINGLY SOLUBLE SALTS IN METHANOL AND ETHANOL (FROM E.M.F. MEASUREMENTS)

Salt	sp MeOH	sp EtOH	sp H_2O
AgCl	$8 \cdot 9 \cdot 10^{-14}$	$1 \cdot 2 \cdot 10^{-14}$	$1 \cdot 8 \cdot 10^{-10}$
AgBr	$5 \cdot 8 \cdot 10^{-16}$	$1 \cdot 0 \cdot 10^{-16}$	$6 \cdot 5 \cdot 10^{-13}$
AgI	$6 \cdot 0 \cdot 10^{-19}$	$1 \cdot 4 \cdot 10^{-19}$	$1 \cdot 0 \cdot 10^{-16}$
AgCNS	$1 \cdot 8 \cdot 10^{-14}$	$4 \cdot 7 \cdot 10^{-15}$	$1 \cdot 44 \cdot 10^{-12}$
TlCl	$4 \cdot 4 \cdot 10^{-5}$	$1 \cdot 3 \cdot 10^{-5}$	$2 \cdot 25 \cdot 10^{-4}$

Accurate to c. $\pm 0 \cdot 05 \times$ relevant exponential term.

A. MacFarlane and H. Hartley, *Phil. Mag.*, 1932, **13**, 425.

See also:

Neustadt and Abegg, *Z. Phys. Chem.*, 1909, **69**, 486.

Igartschew, *Z. Elektrochem.*, 1912, **18**, 568 and 1913, **19**, 491.

Neustadt, *Z. Elektrochem.*, 1910, **16**, 866.

Carrara and Agostini, *Gazz. Chim. Ital.*, 1905, **35**, 132.

P. S. Buckley and H. Hartley, *Phil. Mag.*, 1928, **8**, 320.

TABLE V, 15

BUFFER SOLUTIONS OF KNOWN pH

Phthalate-HCl mixtures 20 °C.		
50 ml. of $M/5$ KHPhthalate	ml. of $M/5$ HCl to be added	Dilute to
2·2 pH	46·60 ml.	200 ml.
2·4	39·60	200
2·6	33·00	200
2·8	26·50	200
3·0	20·40	200
3·2	14·80	200
3·4	9·95	200
3·6	6·00	200
3·8	2·65	200

TABLE V, 15 (*Continued*)

Phthalate-NaOH mixtures 20 °C.

50 ml. of $M/5$ KHPhthalate	ml. of $M/5$ NaOH to be added	Dilute to
4·0 pH	0·40 ml.	200 ml.
4·2	3·65	200
4·4	7·35	200
4·6	12·00	200
4·8	17·50	200
5·0	23·65	200
5·2	29·75	200
5·4	35·25	200
5·6	39·70	200
5·8	43·10	200
6·0	45·40	200
6·2	47·00	200

KH_2PO_4-NaOH mixtures 20 °C.

50 ml. of $M/5$ KH_2PO_4	ml. of $M/5$ NaOH to be added	Dilute to
5·8 pH	3·66 ml.	200 ml.
6·0	5·64	200
6·2	8·55	200
6·4	12·60	200
6·6	17·74	200
6·8	23·60	200
7·0	29·54	200
7·2	34·90	200
7·4	39·34	200
7·6	42·74	200
7·8	45·17	200
8·0	46·85	200

Boric Acid, KCl-NaOH mixtures 20 °C.

50 ml. of $M/5$ H_3BO_3, $M/5$ KCl	ml. of $M/5$ NaOH to be added	Dilute to
7·8 pH	2·65 ml.	200 ml.
8·0	4·00	200
8·2	5·90	200
8·4	8·55	200
8·6	12·00	200
8·8	16·40	200

TABLE V, 15 (*Continued*)

50 ml. of $M/5$ H$_3$BO$_3$, $M/5$ KCl	ml. of $M/5$ NaOH to be added	Dilute to
9·0 pH	21·40 ml.	200 ml.
9·2	26·70	200
9·4	32·00	200
9·6	36·85	200
9·8	40·80	200
10·0	43·90	200

HCl-KCl mixtures of constant ionic strength $I_{(m)} = 0\cdot1$.
Calculated on assumption that $f_{H_3O^·} = 0\cdot84$

KCl molar	HCl molar	pH	Stock * KCl soln. ml.	Stock HCl soln. ml.	Dilute to	pH
0·00	0·10	1·076	0·00 +	59·5	100 ml.	(1·0) ($I_{(m)} = 0\cdot119$) †
0·01	0·09	1·122	2·72 +	47·28	100	1·1
0·02	0·08	1·173	12·45 +	37·55	100	1·2
0·03	0·07	1·231	20·16 +	29·84	100	1·3
0·04	0·06	1·298	26·30 +	23·70	100	1·4
0·05	0·05	1·377	31·18 +	18·82	100	1·5
0·06	0·04	1·474	35·03 +	14·95	100	1·6
0·07	0·03	1·599	38·12 +	11·88	100	1·7
0·08	0·02	1·774	40·57 +	9·43	100	1·8
0·09	0·01	2·076	42·51 +	7·49	100	1·9
0·095	0·005	2·377	44·05 +	5·95	100	2·0
0·098	0·002	2·775	45·27 +	4·73	100	2·1
0·099	0·001	3·076	46·24 +	3·76	100	2·2

* stock KCl: 0·2 molar.   † For the pure HCl solution, the ionic strength is
   stock HCl: 0·2 molar.   adjusted from 0·1 to 0·119 to give unit pH.

Sørensen's phosphate mixtures
11·876 g. Na$_2$HPO$_4$. 2H$_2$O per l.   9·078 g. KH$_2$PO$_4$ per l.
Temperature 18 °C.

Na$_2$HPO$_4$ solution	KH$_2$PO$_4$ solution	pH
0·25 ml.	9·75 ml.	5·288
0·5	9·5	5·589
1·0	9·0	5·906
2·0	8·0	6·239
3·0	7·0	6·468
4·0	6·0	6·643

TABLE V, 15 (*Continued*)

Secondary	Primary	pH
5·0 ml.	5·0 ml.	6·813
6·0	4·0	6·979
7·0	3·0	7·168
8·0	2·0	7·381
9·0	1·0	7·731
9·5	0·5	8·043

SØRENSEN'S citrate - NaOH mixtures
Citrate 21·008 g. cryst. Citric acid + 200 cc. *N* NaOH per l.
NaOH: 0·1*N*.

Temperature	10°	20°	30°	40°	50°	60°	70°
10·0 Citrate	4·93	4·96	5·00	5·04	5·07	5·10	5·14
9·5 ml. Citrate + 0·5 ml. NaOH	4·99	5·02	5·06	5·10	5·13	5·16	5·20
9·0 ,, + 1·0 ,,	5·08	5·11	5·15	5·19	5·22	5·25	5·29
8·0 ,, + 2·0 ,,	5·27	5·31	5·35	5·39	5·42	5·45	5·49
7·0 ,, + 3·0 ,,	5·53	5·57	5·60	5·64	5·67	5·71	5·75
6·0 ,, + 4·0 ,,	5·94	5·98	6·01	6·04	6·08	6·12	6·15
5·5 ,, + 4·5 ,,	6·30	6·34	6·37	6·41	6·44	6·47	6·51
5·25 ,, + 4·75 ,,	6·65	6·69	6·72	6·76	6·79	6·83	6·86

L. E. WALBUM, *Ergeb. Physiol.*, 1912, **12**, 393 and *Biochem. Z.*, 1920, **107**, 219.
L. E. WALBUM (1920) has determined the pH values for Sørensen mixtures at temp. of 10°, 18°, 28°, 37°, 46°, 62° and 70° C. and has interpolated data for intervening temperatures. He finds that the alteration of pH with temp. is for the most part negligible for the phosphate mixtures, the glycocoll-HCl mixtures and the citrate-HCl mixtures.

TAI

Sørensen's Gly

NaOH: 0·1N. Glycocoll so

Volume Parts		pH at indic					
Glycocoll	NaOH	10°	12°	14°	16°	18°	
9·5	0·5	8·75	8·70	8·66	8·62	8·58	
9·0	1·0	9·10	9·06	9·02	8·97	8·93	
8·0	2·0	9·54	9·50	9·45	9·40	9·36	
7·0	3·0	9·90	9·85	9·80	9·75	9·71	
6·0	4·0	10·34	10·29	10·24	10·18	10·14	1
5·5	4·5	10·68	10·63	10·58	10·53	10·48	1
5·1	4·9	11·29	11·24	11·18	11·12	11·07	1
5·0	5·0	11·53	11·48	11·42	11·36	11·31	1
4·9	5·1	11·80	11·74	11·68	11·62	11·57	1
4·5	5·5	12·34	12·28	12·22	12·16	12·10	1
4·0	6·0	12·65	12·59	12·52	12·46	12·40	1
3·0	7·0	12·92	12·86	12·80	12·73	12·67	1
2·0	8·0	13·12	13·06	12·99	12·92	12·86	1
1·0	9·0	13·23	13·16	13·09	13·03	12·97	1
		42°	44°	46°	48°	50°	
9·5	0·5	8·07	8·03	7·99	7·95	7·91	
9·0	1·0	8·41	8·37	8·32	8·28	8·24	
8·0	2·0	8·81	8·76	8·72	8·67	8·63	
7·0	3·0	9·13	9·08	9·03	8·99	8·94	
6·0	4·0	9·53	9·48	9·43	9·38	9·33	
5·5	4·5	9·86	9·81	9·76	9·71	9·66	
5·1	4·9	10·40	10·35	10·29	10·24	10·18	1
5·0	5·0	10·64	10·59	10·54	10·48	10·43	1
4·9	5·1	10·87	10·81	10·75	10·69	10·64	1
4·5	5·5	11·38	11·32	11·26	11·20	11·14	1
4·0	6·0	11·65	11·59	11·53	11·47	11·41	1
3·0	7·0	11·91	11·85	11·79	11·73	11·66	1
2·0	8·0	12·08	12·02	11·96	11·89	11·83	1
1·0	9·0	12·19	12·13	12·06	12·00	11·94	1

ntinued)

aOH mixtures

g. Glycocoll + 5·85 g. NaCl per l.

perature °C.

	24°	26°	28°	30°	32°	34°	36°	40°
9	8·45	8·40	8·37	8·32	8·28	8·24	8·18	8·12
4	8·79	8·75	8·71	8·67	8·62	8·58	8·52	8·45
6	9·22	9·17	9·13	9·08	9·04	9·00	8·92	8·85
1	9·56	9·51	9·46	9·42	9·37	9·32	9·25	9·18
8	9·98	9·93	9·88	9·83	9·78	9·73	9·66	9·58
7	10·32	10·27	10·22	10·17	10·12	10·07	9·99	9·91
6	10·90	10·85	10·79	10·74	10·68	10·62	10·54	10·46
0	11·14	11·09	11·03	10·97	10·92	10·86	10·78	10·70
5	11·39	11·33	11·27	11·22	11·16	11·10	11·02	10·93
8	11·92	11·86	11·80	11·74	11·68	11·62	11·53	11·44
7	12·21	12·15	12·09	12·03	11·96	11·90	11·81	11·72
4	12·48	12·42	12·35	12·29	12·23	12·17	12·07	11·98
3	12·66	12·60	12·53	12·47	12·41	12·34	12·25	12·15
3	12·77	12·70	12·64	12·57	12·51	12·45	12·35	12·25

	56°	58°	60°	62°	64°	66°	68°	70°
2	7·78	7·74	7·69	7·65	7·61	7·56	7·52	7·48
4	8·10	8·06	8·02	7·97	7·93	7·88	7·84	7·79
3	8·49	8·44	8·40	8·35	8·30	8·26	8·21	8·16
4	8·79	8·74	8·70	8·65	8·60	8·55	8·50	8·45
3	9·18	9·13	9·08	9·03	8·98	8·93	8·88	8·82
6	9·51	9·46	9·41	9·35	9·30	9·25	9·20	9·15
7	10·02	9·96	9·90	9·85	9·79	9·74	9·68	9·62
2	10·26	10·20	10·14	10·09	10·04	9·98	9·93	9·87
2	10·46	10·40	10·35	10·29	10·23	10·17	10·11	10·05
2	10·96	10·90	10·84	10·78	10·72	10·66	10·60	10·54
8	11·22	11·16	11·10	11·03	10·97	10·91	10·84	10·78
4	11·47	11·41	11·35	11·28	11·22	11·16	11·09	11·03
0	11·64	11·57	11·51	11·44	11·38	11·31	11·25	11·18
0	11·74	11·67	11·61	11·54	11·48	11·41	11·35	11·28

TABLE V, 15 (Continued)

SØRENSEN's borate - HCl mixtures
Borate Solution: 12·404 g. H_3BO_3 + 100 ml. N NaOH per l.
HCl: 0·1N.

Temperature				10°	20°	30°	40°	50°	60°	70°
10·0 ml. Borate				9·30	9·23	9·15	9·08	9·00	8·93	8·86
9·5 ,,	,,	+ 0·5	ml. HCl	9·22	9·15	9·08	9·01	8·94	8·87	8·80
9·0 ,,	,,	+ 1·0 ,,	,,	9·14	9·07	9·01	8·94	8·87	8·80	8·74
8·5 ,,	,,	+ 1·5 ,,	,,	9·06	8·99	8·92	8·86	8·80	8·73	8·67
8·0 ,,	,,	+ 2·0 ,,	,,	8·96	8·89	8·83	8·77	8·71	8·65	8·59
7·5 ,,	,,	+ 2·5 ,,	,,	8·84	8·79	8·72	8·67	8·61	8·55	8·50
7·0 ,,	,,	+ 3·0 ,,	,,	8·72	8·67	8·61	8·56	8·50	8·45	8·40
6·5 ,,	,,	+ 3·5 ,,	,,	8·54	8·49	8·44	8·40	8·35	8·30	8·26
6·0 ,,	,,	+ 4·0 ,,	,,	8·32	8·27	8·23	8·19	8·15	8·11	8·08
5·75 ,,	,,	+ 4·25 ,,	,,	8·17	8·13	8·09	8·06	8·02	7·98	7·95
5·5 ,,	,,	+ 4·5 ,,	,,	7·96	7·93	7·89	7·86	7·82	7·79	7·76
5·25 ,,	,,	+ 4·75 ,,	,,	7·64	7·61	7·58	7·55	7·52	7·49	7·47

SØRENSEN's citrate - HCl mixtures
Citrate: 21·008 g. cryst. citric acid + 200 cc. N NaOH per l.
HCl: 0·1N.
Temperature 18 °C.

Citrate	HCl	pH
0·0 ml.	10·0 ml.	1·038
1·0	9·0	1·173
2·0	8·0	1·418
3·0	7·0	1·925
3·33	6·67	2·274
4·0	6·0	2·972
4·5	5·5	3·364
4·75	5·25	3·529
5·0	5·0	3·692
5·5	4·5	3·948
6·0	4·0	4·158
7·0	3·0	4·447
8·0	2·0	4·652
9·0	1·0	4·830
9·5	0·5	4·887
10·0	0·0	4·958

L. E. WALBUM, Biochem. Z., 1920, **107**, 219.

TABLE V, 15 (*Continued*)

$M/15$ Phosphate mixtures at 20° and 38 °C.

0·1N HCl of pH 1·08 used as standard of reference.

$M/15$ Na$_2$HPO$_4$	$M/15$ KH$_2$PO$_4$	pH det. at 20°	pH det. at 38°
49·6 ml.	50·4 ml.	6·809	6·781
52·5	47·5	6·862	6·829
55·4	44·6	6·909	6·885
58·2	41·8	6·958	6·924
61·1	38·9	7·005	6·979
63·9	36·1	7·057	7·028
66·6	33·4	7·103	7·076
69·2	30·8	7·154	7·128
72·0	28·0	7·212	7·181
74·4	25·6	7·261	7·230
76·8	23·2	7·313	7·288
78·9	21·1	7·364	7·338
80·8	19·2	7·412	7·384
82·5	17·5	7·462	7·439
84·1	15·9	7·504	7·481
85·7	14·3	7·561	7·530
87·0	13·0	7·610	7·576
88·2	11·8	7·655	7·626
89·4	10·6	7·705	7·672
90·5	9·5	7·754	7·726
91·5	8·5	7·806	7·776
92·3	7·7	7·848	7·825
93·2	6·8	7·909	7·877
93·8	6·2	7·948	7·919
94·7	5·3	8·018	7·977

A. B. Hastings and J. Sendroy, *J. Biol. Chem.*, 1924, **61**, 695.

TABLE V, 15 (*Continued*)

COMPOSITION OF 0·1 AND 0·2 IONIC STRENGTH BUFFERS OF pH 2·0 TO 12·0 AT 2 °C.
MILLILITRES OF STOCK SOLUTION MADE UP TO 2 l. TO GIVE THE INDICATED pH

pH ([a])	5·0M NaCl ([a])	1·0M Glycine- 1·0M NaCl ([b])	2·0N HCl	2·0N NaOH	2·0M Sodium acetate	3·5M Acetic acid	0·5M Na₂- HPO₄	4·0M Na- H₂PO₄	0·5M Sodium veronal ([c])
2·00	72·0	10·6	14·7	—	—	—	—	—	—
2·50	72·0	22·8	8·6	—	—	—	—	—	—
3·00	72·0	31·6	4·2	—	—	—	—	—	—
3·50	72·0	36·6	1·7	—	—	—	—	—	—
4·00	72·0	—	—	—	20·0	33·7	—	—	—
4·50	72·0	—	—	—	20·0	11·5	—	—	—
5·00	72·0	—	—	—	20·0	3·7	—	—	—
5·50	72·0	—	—	—	20·0	1·2	—	—	—
6·00	72·0	—	—	—	—	—	9·2	6·6	—
6·50	72·0	—	—	—	—	—	16·6	3·7	—
7·00	72·0	—	—	—	—	—	22·7	1·6	—
7·50	72·0	—	—	—	—	—	24·3	0·5	—
8·00	72·0	—	10·4	—	—	—	—	—	80·0
8·50	72·0	—	5·3	—	—	—	—	—	80·0
9·00	72·0	—	2·0	—	—	—	—	—	80·0
9·50	72·0	34·5	—	2·7	—	—	—	—	—
10·00	72·0	28·8	—	5·6	—	—	—	—	—
10·50	72·0	23·2	—	8·4	—	—	—	—	—
11·00	72·0	19·6	—	10·2	—	—	—	—	—
11·50	72·0	17·6	—	11·2	—	—	—	—	—
12·00	72·0	15·2	—	12·4	—	—	—	—	—

[a] The BECKMAN pH meter used for the measurements was checked against known standards of pH 1·08, 2·27, 4·00, 7·00, 8·48 and 10·00.

[b] For 0·1 ionic strength buffers, 32 mls. of 5·0M NaCl should be used. The final pH is not affected appreciably.

[c] The stocks of glycine-NaCl and sodium veronal should be stored in the refrigerator.

G. L. MILLER and R. H. GOLDER, *Arch. of Biochem.*, 1950, **29**, 420.

CHAPTER VI

PROPERTIES OF THE ELECTRIC DOUBLE LAYER AT INTERFACES

A number of electrokinetic potentials for inorganic solid phase boundaries including those for quartz, pyrex and soft glasses are given. These experimental values are determined by direct streaming potential measurements. Some data for quartz and inorganic oxides determined by electroendosmotic measurements through diaphragms of the compressed oxide powders in a number of media of varying pH are given in Table VI, 3 which also includes figures for determinations in acetone, methanol and ethanol solutions. Electrokinetic properties of mammalian haemocytes have been derived theoretically from electrophoretic mobilities determined experimentally and are tabulated in VI, 4. In these figures the calculated net charge densities are corrected for the finite size of ions in the ionic atmosphere taking a mean ionic radius of 2·5 Å. Values of electrokinetic potentials for silver in aqueous HCl at 25 °C. are given in the Table VI, 7 from the STERN theory using VESELOVSKY's (*Acta Physicochim.*, 1939, **11**, 931) value for the cathodic double layer electrode capacity of silver. These values assume no specific adsorption of any solution components.

The recent accurate and carefully determined data of GRAHAME on the electrocapillary maximum potentials of the mercury electrode in a large number of 1 : 1, 2 : 1, 3 : 1 and 1 : 2 electrolytes in aqueous solution are quoted in the Table VI, 9. These values have been derived by six methods in some cases. For completeness and in order to give some idea of the reproducibility of the data, all the values obtained by the various methods have been given. Brief details of the six types of determination are given with the numerical data. Derived values of the surface charge densities of the electrical double layer of the polarised mercury electrode are given for various $0·1N$ aqueous solutions of metal chlorides at

25 °C. over a range of electrode potentials on the positive and negative sides of the electrocapillary maximum potential. Differential
capacities and frequency effects upon the latter for the mercury
electrode in aqueous electrolytes are given and the effect of a
typical "surface-active" non-electrolyte, octyl alcohol, is tabulated. The thermodynamic functions, derived from electrochemical
measurements, for mercurous salt transfer at the mercury electrode
interface at the electrocapillary maximum potential have been
computed by GRAHAME and are quoted in the Tables VI, 16 and 17.

Potentials for zero charge determined by several different
methods, for a number of solid metals are given in Table VI, 8.
These cannot be equated to null point potentials owing to unknown effects due to $p.ds$ of adsorbed dipoles and electron overlap
even at the potential of the electrocapillary maximum.

TABLE VI, 1

ELECTROKINETIC DATA FOR CAPILLARIES OF QUARTZ,
GLASS AND PLATINUM DETERMINED BY THE STREAMING METHOD

Capillary	Electrolyte and Concentration (normality)		$E_m \cdot 10^3$ volts	$\zeta \cdot 10^3$ volts
Quartz		$1 \cdot 10^{-3}$	24·0	61·4
$r = $ 0·23 mm.	KCl	$1 \cdot 10^{-4}$	219·9	73·5
$l = $ 10·6 cm.		$1 \cdot 10^{-5}$	1591·0	86·0
Pyrex		$1 \cdot 10^{-3}$	24·0	69·0
$r = $ 0·28 mm.	KCl	$1 \cdot 10^{-4}$	135·8	122·2
$l = $ 10·7 cm.		$1 \cdot 10^{-5}$	1501·0	151·0
Soft glass		$1 \cdot 10^{-3}$	28·5	56·7
$r = $ 0·32 mm.	KCl	$1 \cdot 10^{-5}$	1453·6	87·3
$l = $ 10·6 cm.				
Platinum	$CH_3 \cdot COOK$	$1 \cdot 10^{-5}$	129·6	58·3
$r = $ 0·26 mm.				
$l = $ 10·0 cm.				

$E_m = $ Streaming potential
$\zeta = $ Electrokinetic potential
$r = $ radius of capillary of length l.

W. G. EVERSOLE and W. W. BOARDMAN, *J. Phys. Chem.*, 1942, **46**, 914.

TABLE VI, 2

ELECTROKINETIC POTENTIALS OBTAINED BY THE STREAMING POTENTIAL METHOD
USING CAPILLARIES

Capillary	KCl Concentration	Electrokinetic potentials in mv.			
		Reference			
		(1)	(2)	(3)	(4)
Jena glass	$1\cdot0 \cdot 10^{-5}$	151 *	198	204	
	$2\cdot5 \cdot 10^{-5}$			186	104
	$1\cdot0 \cdot 10^{-4}$	122 *	164	166	105
	$1\cdot0 \cdot 10^{-3}$	69 *			72
Quartz	$1\cdot0 \cdot 10^{-5}$	86			
	$2\cdot5 \cdot 10^{-5}$				91
	$1\cdot0 \cdot 10^{-4}$	74			92
	$1\cdot0 \cdot 10^{-3}$	61			75

* Using Pyrex glass.
[1] W. G. EVERSOLE and W. W. BOARDMAN, *J. Phys. Chem.*, 1942, **46**, 914.
[2] A. J. RUTGERS, *Trans. Faraday Soc.*, 1940, **36**, 69.
[3] E. VERLENDE, *Proc. Acad. Sci. Amsterdam*, 1939, **42**, 764.
[4] H. R. KRUYT, *Kolloid Z.*, 1928, **45**, 307.

TABLE VI, 3

ELECTROKINETIC POTENTIALS (ζ) FOR VARIOUS SOLIDS IN DIFFERENT MEDIA

1. ζ for Solid Powders in $10^{-4}N$ HCl in Different Media (in mv.)

Medium	Conductance of the liquid mho/cm.	SiO_2	TiO_2 fine	TiO_2 coarse	ZrO_2
Water	$45 \cdot 10^{-6}$	—56	—21	—	16
Methanol	$14 \cdot 10^{-6}$	19	59	30	160
Ethanol	$2 \cdot 5 \cdot 10^{-6}$	3	26	16	190
Acetone	$0 \cdot 1 \cdot 10^{-6}$	—17	18	—	71

2. ζ of Quartz in various aq. Solutions (in mv.)

$3 \cdot 10^{-5}N$ KOH$+$ $5 \cdot 10^{-4}N$ KNO$_3$	$10^{-5}N$ HCl$+$ $5 \cdot 10^{-4}N$ KNO$_3$	$10^{-4}N$ HCl$+$ $5 \cdot 10^{-4}N$ KNO$_3$
—67	—63	—56

T

ELECTROKINETIC PROPERT

Animal	Phosphate pH 7·4 Mobility (cm.sec.$^{-1}$/volt cm.$^{-1}$)	ζ v.	$\sigma'_{uncorrected}$	σ_{corre}
Rabbit	0·55	0·0070	1890	141
Sloth	0·97	0·0124	3330	248
Pig	0·98	0·0125	3360	250
Opossum	1·07	0·0137	3680	274
Guinea Pig	1·11	0·0142	3780	282
Man	1·31	0·0168	4500	335
Rhesus Monkey	1·33	0·0170	4570	340
Cat	1·39	0·0178	4780	356
Mouse	1·40	0·0179	4800	358
Rat	1·45	0·0186	4980	371
Dog	1·65	0·0211	5660	422

σ = charge density corrected for size of ions in ionic atmosphere taking a mean ion radius of $2 \cdot 5$ Å. σ' = corresponding uncorrected value.

TABLE VI, 3 (*Continued*)

$10^{-3}N$ HCl	$10^{-2}N$ HCl	$10^{-1}N$ HCl
—37	—20	v. weakly positive.

3. ζ of TiO_2 and ZrO_2 in aq. Solutions

TiO_2 (coarse) in			ZrO_2 in		
$10^{-3}N$ HCl	$10^{-2}N$ HCl	$3 . 10^{-5}N$ KOH	H_2O ($pH = 6$)	$10^{-4}N$HCl	
—32	—8	—16	1·6	16	

Determined by measurements of electroendosmosis through diaphragms of the powders.

E. J. W. Verwey, *Rec. Trav. Chim.*, 1941, **60**, 625.

...LIAN RED BLOOD CELLS

f cell cm.^{2} . 10^6	Net charge e.s.u. $\times 10^3$	No. of electrons $\times 10^6$ per cell.	% area occupied by charges
1·10	1·48	3·10	0·28
0·95	2·36	4·76	0·50
1·56	4·07	8·53	0·56
1·15	3·09	6·49	0·56
1·63	5·21	10·9	0·67
1·37	4·45	9·38	0·68
0·80	2·72	5·70	0·71
0·96	3·28	6·90	0·72
1·02	3·61	7·60	0·74
1·22	4·90	10·3	0·84

H. A. Abramson and L. S. Moyer, *J. Gen. Physiol*, 1936, **19**, 601; H. A. Abramson, *J. Gen. Physiol.*, 1927, **12**, 711 - mobility data.

Values of surface area: E. Ponder, *The mammalian red cell and the properties of haemolytic systems.* Protoplasma Monographien (Berlin 1934).

TABLE VI, 5

ELECTROKINETIC POTENTIALS ζ AT THE GLASS-WATER INTERFACE

KCl conc. in μ mol/l.	ζ in mv.
10	73
25	72
50	70
100	67
250	62
500	58
1000	52
10^6	0

W. G. EVERSOLE and C. R. ESTEE, *J. Chem. Phys.*, 1943, **11**, 63.

TABLE VI, 6

ELECTROKINETIC POTENTIALS ζ AT THE $BaSO_4$-WATER INTERFACE IN VARIOUS ELECTROLYTE SOLUTIONS

Electrolyte solution	ζ in mv.
Sat. aq. $BaSO_4$	26·6
$N/50,000$ K_2SO_4 + sat. aq. $BaSO_4$	24·3
$N/20,000$ K_2SO_4 + sat. aq. $BaSO_4$	19·8
$N/10,000$ K_2SO_4 + sat. aq. $BaSO_4$	14·7
$3N/10,000$ K_2SO_4 + sat. aq. $BaSO_4$	7·6
$6N/10,000$ K_2SO_4 + sat. aq. $BaSO_4$	3·6
$N/50,000$ $BaCl_2$ + sat. aq. $BaSO_4$	32·6
$N/20,000$ $BaCl_2$ + sat. aq. $BaSO_4$	39·8
$N/10,000$ $BaCl_2$ + sat. aq. $BaSO_4$	47·6
$6N/10,000$ $BaCl_2$ + sat. aq. $BaSO_4$	60·8
$N/1,000$ $BaCl_2$ + sat. aq. $BaSO_4$	60·6

A. S. BUCHANAN and E. HEYMAN, *Proc. Roy. Soc.*, 1948, A. **195**, 150.

TABLE VI, 7

ELECTROKINETIC POTENTIALS ζ IN V. CALCULATED FROM THE STERN THEORY
FOR AQUEOUS ELECTROLYTE SOLUTIONS AT THE Ag–H_2O INTERFACE AT 25 °C.

Electrode potential in volts	0·01N HCl	0·3N HCl	$\begin{cases} 0\cdot3N\ HCl \\ 0\cdot2M\ BaCl_2 \end{cases}$	0·6N HCl	$\begin{cases} 0\cdot01\ NHCl \\ 0\cdot2M\ BaCl_2 \end{cases}$
			Electrokinetic potentials in v.		
0	0·0	0·0	0·0	0·0	0·0
0·25	0·13	0·06	0·025	0·05	0·03
0·5	0·16	0·08	0·04	0·07	0·04
0·75	0·18	0·095	0·05	0·085	0·045
1·0	0·195	0·11	0·06	0·10	0·05
1·5	—	—	—	0·12	0·055

These figures show the dependence of ζ upon the "absolute" electrode potential
measured with respect to the potential of zero charge. See Table VI, 8.

O. STERN, *Z. Elektrochem.*, 1924, 30, 508.
Calculated by B. E. CONWAY, *Thesis*, London, 1949.

TABLE VI, 8

POTENTIALS OF ZERO CHARGE IN VOLTS, WITH REFERENCE TO THE
N–CALOMEL ELECTRODE

Electrode Metal	Method	Ref.	Potential	Repro- ducibility
Hg	Electrocapillary curves	1	—0·50 v.	±0·01 v.
	Electrocapillary curves	2	—0·56 v.	±0·01 v.
	Electrocapillary curves	5	—0·475 v.	±0·003 v.
	Deflection of Hg drops	3	—0·53 v.	
Ga	Electrocapillary curves	4	—0·90 v.	±0·05 v.
Pt	Contact angle	12	0·0 v.	±0·1 v.
Ag	Cataphoresis of suspended particles	6	—0·2 v.	
	Motion of massive metal	7	0·1 - 0·2 v.	
	Adsorption of ions	8	0·23 v.	
	Disturbance of potential by rubbing	9	0·19 v.	
	Electrode capacity in very pure so- lution and adsorption of ions in very pure solution	10	—0·24 v.	±0·02 v.

TABLE VI, 8 (Continued)

Electrode Metal	Method	Ref.	Potential	Reproducibility
Ni	Salt effect on H overpotential (Validity of result depends on correctness of theoretical interpretation)	11	—0·54 v.	±0·02 v.

[1] R. Parsons (unpublished).
[2] G. Gouy, Ann. Phys., 1917, 7, (9), 129.
[3] A. N. Frumkin, J. Phys. Chem. U.R.S.S., 1917, 49, 207.
[4] A. N. Frumkin and A. Gorodetzkaya, Z. physik. Chem., 1928, 136, 215.
[5] D. C. Grahame, Chem. Rev., 1947, 41, 441.
[6] J. Billiter, Monatshefte, 1929, 53-54, 813.
[7] A. Garrison, J. Am. Chem. Soc., 1923, 45, 37.
[8] M. Proskurnin and A. N. Frumkin, Z. physik. Chem., 1931, 155, 29.
[9] K. Bennewitz and J. Shulz, ibid., 1926, 124, 115.
[10] V. I. Veselovsky, Acta Physicochim. U.R.S.S., 1939, 11, 815.
[11] P. Lukovtsev, S. Levina and A. N. Frumkin, Acta Physicochim. U.R.S.S., 1939, 11, 21.
[12] A. N. Frumkin et al., Physik. Z. der Sowietunion, 1932, 1, 255; 1934, 5, 418.

TABLE VI, 9

POTENTIAL OF THE ELECTROCAPILLARY MAXIMUM OF MERCURY IN AQUEOUS SOLUTIONS AT 25 °C. ALL VALUES HAVE NEGATIVE SIGN

Subst.	Conc. N	Method†	A*	B	C	D	E	F
LiCl	1·0	IV	0·557	—	—	0·557	0·550	0·557
	0·1	I	0·5580	0·5510	0·5582	0·5051	—	—
		IV	0·559	0·552	0·560	0·506	—	—
		VI	0·5592	0·5522	0·5594	0·5063	—	—

† For methods used see end of this group of tables.
* A E.c.max. in volts relative to calomel electrode in solution named.
  B E.c.max. in volts relative to tenth-normal calomel electrode in KCl before correcting for liquid junction potential.
  C E.c.max. in volts relative to tenth-normal calomel electrode in KCl after correcting for liquid junction potential.

TABLE VI, 9 (*Continued*)

POTENTIAL OF THE ELECTROCAPILLARY MAXIMUM OF MERCURY IN AQUEOUS SOLUTIONS AT 25 °C. ALL VALUES HAVE NEGATIVE SIGN.

Subst.	Conc. N	Method†	A*	B	C	D	E	F
NaCl	1·0	IV	0·557	—	—	0·557	0·552	0·557
	0·1	I	0·558	0·554	0·559	0·505	—	—
		II	0·562	0·557	0·562	0·509	—	—
		III	0·560	0·555	0·560	0·507	—	—
		IV	0·559	0·554	0·559	0·506	—	—
		V	0·558	0·553	0·558	0·505	—	—
		VI	0·5591	0·5545	0·5592	0·5062	—	—
KCl	1·0	I	0·5557	0·6086	0·6094	0·5557	0·5557	0·5557
		II	0·555	0·608	0·609	0·555	0·555	0·555
		IV	0·557	0·610	0·611	0·557	0·557	0·557
		V	0·556	0·609	0·610	0·556	0·556	0·556
		VI	0·5555	0·6084	0·6092	0·5555	0·5555	0·5555
	0·7	VI	0·5535	0·5979	0·5988	0·5450	0·5450	0·5448
	0·3	VI	0·5515	0·5762	0·5767	0·5234	0·5234	0·5228
	0·1	I	0·5589	0·5589	0·5589	0·5060	0·5060	0·5052
		II	0·559	0·559	0·559	0·506	0·506	0·505
		III	0·560	0·560	0·560	0·507	0·507	0·506
		IV	0·560	0·560	0·560	0·507	0·507	0·506
		V	0·556	0·556	0·556	0·503	0·503	0·502
KCl	0·01	II	0·600	0·546	0·545	0·493	0·493	0·491
		VI	0·5936	0·5396	0·5385	0·4867	0·4867	0·4847
	0·001	V	0·640	0·530	0·528	0·477	0·477	0·474
RbCl	0·1	I	0·558	0·559	0·558	0·505	—	—
		IV	0·558₅	0·560	0·559	0·506	—	—
		VI	0·5576	0·5592	0·5583	0·5047	—	—
CsCl	1·0	IV	0·556	—	—	0·556	0·557	0·556₅
	0·1	I	0·5578	0·5591	0·5585	0·5049	—	—
		IV	0·559	0·560	0·559	0·506	—	—
		VI	0·5564	0·5577	0·5571	0·5035	—	—

D E.c.max. in volts relative to normal calomel electrode in salt named.

E E.c.max. in volts relative to normal calomel electrode in KCl before correcting for liquid junction potential.

F E.c.max. in volts relative to normal calomel electrode in KCl after correcting for liquid junction potential.

TABLE VI, 9 (*Continued*)

POTENTIAL OF THE ELECTROCAPILLARY MAXIMUM OF MERCURY IN AQUEOUS SOLUTIONS AT 25 °C. ALL VALUES HAVE NEGATIVE SIGN.

Subst.	Conc. N	Method†	A*	B	C	D	E	F
HCl	0·1	I	0·5566	0·5837	—	0·5037	—	—
		IV	0·559	0·586	—	0·506	—	—
		VI	0·558	0·586	—	0·505	—	—
NH$_4$Cl	0·1	I	0·5582	0·5582	—	0·5053	—	—
		IV	0·559	0·559	—	0·506$_5$	—	—
		VI	0·5587	0·5587	—	0·5058	—	—
MgCl$_2$	0·1	I	0·5576	0·5471	—	0·5047	—	—
		IV	0·559	0·549	—	0·506$_5$	—	—
		VI	0·5590	0·5485	—	0·5061	—	—
CaCl$_2$	0·1	I	0·5589	0·5491	—	0·5060	—	—
		IV	0·559	0·549	—	0·506	—	—
		VI	0·5586	0·5488	—	0·5057	—	—
SrCl$_2$	0·1	I	0·5582	0·5482	—	0·5053	—	—
		IV	0·559	0·549	—	0·506	—	—
		VI	0·5588	0·5488	—	0·5069	—	—
BaCl$_2$	0·1	I	0·5581	0·5483	—	0·5052	—	—
		IV	0·560	0·550	—	0·507	—	—
		VI	0·5587	0·5489	—	0·5058	—	—
MnCl$_2$	0·1	I	0·5573	0·5467	—	0·5044	—	—
		IV	0·559	0·548	—	0·506	—	—
		VI	0·5589	0·5483	—	0·5060	—	—
CoCl$_2$	0·1	I	0·5576	0·5473	—	0·5047	—	—
		IV	0·5588	0·5485	—	0·5059	—	—
		VI	0·5585	0·5482	—	0·5056	—	—
NiCl$_2$	0·1	I	0·5573	0·5468	—	0·5044	—	—
		IV	0·558	0·547	—	0·505	—	—
		VI	0·5588	0·5481	—	0·5059	—	—

TABLE VI, 9 (*Continued*)

POTENTIAL OF THE ELECTROCAPILLARY MAXIMUM OF MERCURY IN AQUEOUS SOLUTIONS
AT 25 °C. ALL VALUES HAVE NEGATIVE SIGN.

Subst.	Conc. N	Method†	A*	B	C	D	E	F
$AlCl_3$	0·1	I	0·5583	0·5460	—	0·5054	—	—
		IV	0·559	0·547	—	0·506	—	—
		VI	0·5585	0·5462	—	0·5056	—	—
$LaCl_3$	0·1	I	0·5570	0·5447	—	0·5041	—	—
		IV	0·558	0·546	—	0·505	—	—
		VI	0·5588	0·5465	—	0·5059	—	—
NaF	1·0	V	—	—	0·525	—	0·471	0·472
	0·1	V	—	0·526	0·525$_5$	—	0·473	0·472
KF	0·1	VI	—	0·5284	0·524	—	0·4755	0·471
		VII	—	0·529	0·524$_5$	—	0·476	0·471
$KHCO_3$	0·1	VI	—	0·5318	0·526	—	0·4789	0·472
		VII	—	0·536$_5$	0·530	—	0·484	0·477
K_2CO_3	0·1	VI	—	0·5321	0·526	—	0·4792	0·473
K_2SO_4	0·1	VI	—	0·5295	0·523	—	0·4766	0·470
		VII	—	0·531	0·525	—	0·468	0·471
KOH	0·1	VI	—	0·514	0·530	—	—	0·476
		VII	—	0·516	0·532	—	0·463	0·478
$KC_2H_3O_2$	0·1	VI	—	0·5482	0·541	—	0·4953	0·488
		VII	—	0·551	0·544	—	0·498	0·491
$KClO_4$	0·1	VI	—	0·5618	0·560	—	0·5089	0·507
		VII	—	0·562	0·561	—	0·510	0·508
KNO_3	0·1	VI	—	0·5703	0·569$_5$	—	0·5174	0·516
		VII	—	0·569	0·568	—	0·516	0·514

TABLE, VI, 9 (*Continued*)

POTENTIAL OF THE ELECTROCAPILLARY MAXIMUM OF MERCURY IN AQUOUS SOLUTIONS
AT 25 °C. ALL VALUES HAVE NEGATIVE SIGN.

Subst.	Conc. N	Method†	A *	B	C	D	E	F
KBr	0·1	VI	0·499	0·627	0·627	—	0·574	0·573
		VII	0·501	0·629	0·629	—	0·576	0·575
KCNS	0·1	VI	0·625	0·681	0·679	—	0·628	0·625
		VII	0·629	0·685	0·683	—	0·632	0·629
KI	0·1	VI	0·477	0·785	0·785	—	0·732	0·731
		VII	0·481	0·789	0·789	—	0·736	0·735

Results obtained by method VI to be regarded as final values.

† Methods of determination of electrocapillary maximum potentials.

I. Measurement of isotension potentials, D. C. GRAHAME, R. P. LARSEN and M. A. POTH, *J. Am. Chem. Soc.*, 1949, **71**, 2978.

II. Location of arrest potentials as a method of measuring iso-tension potentials from which the electrocapillary maximum potential is calculated.

III. Measurement of drop times for determination of iso-tension potentials; see D. C. GRAHAME, R. P. LARSEN and M. A. POTH, *loc.cit.*

IV. Determination of iso-tension potentials close to the electrocapillary maximum potential.

V. Determination of the potential of a streaming mercury electrode under rigourously controlled conditions.

VI. Use of one reference electrode in the streaming method together with suitable correction for liquid junction potential.

VII. Comparison of differential capacity of the mercury electrode in two different solutions.

For further details of these methods see, D. C. GRAHAME, E. M. COFFIN and J. I. CUMMINS, *Office of Naval Research, Tech.Report No. 2*, August 11, 1950, Research Contract N8 - onv - 66903.

TABLE VI, 10

POTENTIAL OF THE ELECTROCAPILLARY MAXIMUM ACCORDING TO ERDEY-GRUZ AND SZARVAS [5] (INTERPOLATED VALUES) AND COMPARISON OF RESULTS WITH THOSE OF GRAHAME [6] AND OF OTHERS **. ALL VALUES HAVE NEGATIVE SIGN.

Subst.	Conc. N	E-G-S [5]	GRAHAME [6] *	GOUY [1]	CRAXFORD [2]	WINKEL and SIEBERT [7]
NaCl	4·0	0·600	—	—	—	—
	2·0	0·575	—	—	—	—
	1·0	0·552	0·5557	0·56	0·56	—
	0·1	0·498	0·5052	0·52 [3]	0·525	—
	0·01	0·481	0·4847	0·52 [3]	0·52	—
CaCl$_2$	1·0	0·552	—	0·55	—	—
	0·1	0·495	0·496	—	—	—
	0·01	0·481	—	—	—	—
Na$_2$SO$_4$	1·0	0·466	—	0·48	—	0·454
	0·1	0·465	0·470	—	—	0·489
	0·01	0·466	—	—	—	0·473
NaClO$_4$	1·0	0·529	—	—	—	—
	0·1	0·497	0·507	—	—	—
	0·01	0·476	—	—	—	—
NaNO$_3$	2·0	0·568	—	—	—	—
	1·0	0·552	—	0·56	—	0·563
	0·1	0·515	0·516	—	—	0·502
	0·01	0·496	—	0·52	—	0·487

* E.c.max. in volts relative to tenth-normal mercurous salt electrode in electrolyte named.

** All values in this table relative to normal calomel electrode in KCl corrected for liquid junction potentials where possible.

[1] G. GOUY, *Ann. chim. phys.*, 1903 (7), **29**, 145.

[2] S. R. CRAXFORD †, *Trans. Faraday Soc.*, 1940, 36, 85.

[3] These values obtained by a long extrapolation. See reference 4, page 2983 for a discussion and recalculation of one of these values.

[4] D. C. GRAHAME et al., *J. Am. Chem. Soc.*, 1949, **71**, 2978.

[5] T. ERDEY-GRUZ and P. SZARVAS, *Z. physik. Chem.*, 1936, A **177**, 277.

[6] D. C. GRAHAME, E. M. COFFIN and J. I. CUMMINS, *Office of Naval Research, Tech. Report No. 2*, August 11, 1950, Research Contract N8 - onv - 66903.

[7] A. WINKEL and H. SIEBERT, *Z. Elektrochem.*, 1938, **44**, 127.

† CRAXFORD also gives values for KNO$_3$, KI and CaBr$_2$ solutions.

TABLE VI, 10 (*Continued*)

Subst.	Conc. N	E-G-S [5]	GRAHAME [6] *	GOUY [1]	CRAXFORD [2]	WINKEL and SIEBERT [7]
NaBr	4·0	0·679	—	—	—	—
	2·0	0·655	—	—	—	—
	1·0	0·632	—	0·66	0·611	—
	0·1	0·570	0·573	0·58(CaBr$_2$)	0·567	—
	0·01	0·517	—	0·54(CaBr$_2$)	0·526	—
	0·001	0·504	—	—	—	—
KCNS	1·0	0·715	—	0·72	—	—
	0·1	0·628	0·625	0·62	—	—
	0·01	0·582	—	0·59	—	—
NaI	4·0	0·883	—	—	—	—
	2·0	0·849	—	—	—	—
	1·0	0·819	—	0·83	0·708	—
	0·1	0·724	0·731	0·72	0·666	—
	0·01	0·654	—	0·66	0·613	—
	0·001	0·599	—	—	0·530	—
KCN	2·0	0·827	—	—	—	—
	1·0	0·790	—	—	—	—
	0·1	0·684	—	—	—	—
	0·01	0·582	—	—	—	—

TABLE VI, 11

SURFACE CHARGE DENSITY, σ, OF THE ELECTRICAL DOUBLE LAYER AT THE MERCURY
ELECTRODE IN TENTH-NORMAL AQUEOUS SOLUTIONS OF METALLIC CHLORIDES AT 25 °C.

E^- v.	σ in μ coul./cm.^{2}							
	LiCl	NaCl	KCl	RbCl	CsCl	HCl	NH$_4$Cl	MgCl$_2$
0·08	19·57	19·56	19·66	19·68	19·70	19·40	19·58	19·80
0·10	18·28	18·26	18·33	18·34	18·36	18·32	18·28	18·46
0·12	17·17	17·15	17·21	17·21	17·21	17·03	17·16	17·32
0·14	16·18	16·14	16·20	16·19	16·20	16·05	16·16	16·29
0·16	15·26	15·23	15·28	15·26	15·26	15·14	15·24	15·35
0·18	14·40	14·37	14·41	14·38	14·38	14·28	14·38	14·47
0·20	13·61	13·54	13·58	13·54	13·55	13·46	13·55	13·62
0·25	11·60	11·58	11·61	11·55	11·57	11·51	11·59	11·64
0·30	9·70	9·68	9·70	9·64	9·65	9·62	9·69	9·71
0·35	7·77	7·76	7·78	7·70	7·72	7·71	7·76	7·77
0·40	5·79	5·79	5·81	5·73	5·74	5·74	5·68	5·80
0·45	3·81	3·80	3·83	3·75	3·76	3·76	3·80	3·81
0·50	1·924	1·923	1·942	1·870	1·872	1·879	1·917	1·920
0·55	0·261	0·258	0·271	0·210	0·205	0·203	0·250	0·236
0·60	−1·149	−1·156	−1·148	−1·201	−1·220	−1·221	−1·167	−1·218
0·65	−2·364	−2·378	−2·373	−2·425	−2·467	−2·452	−2·394	−2·504
0·70	−3·46	−3·48	−3·48	−3·53	−3·61	−3·55	−3·50	−3·68
0·80	−5·44	−5·48	−5·50	−5·57	−5·71	−5·52	−5·54	−5·80
0·90	−7·24	−7·31	−7·34	−7·44	−7·64	−7·29	−7·40	−7·67
1·00	−8·92	−9·01	−9·06	−9·19	−9·28	−8·94	−9·14	−9·40
1·10	−10·51	−10·63	−10·70	−10·87	−11·44	—	−10·82	−11·02
1·20	−12·06	−12·21	−12·31	−12·52	−12·95	—	−12·47	−12·60
1·30	−13·60	−13·79	−13·92	−14·18	−14·70	—	−14·13	−14·18
1·40	−15·16	−15·38	−15·56	−15·89	−16·48	—	−15·83	−15·79
1·50	−16·76	−17·03	−17·26	−17·66	−18·32	—	−17·62	−17·46
1·60	−18·42	−18·74	−19·04	−19·51	−20·25	—	—	−19·21
1·70	−20·17	−20·53	−20·93	−21·48	−22·29	—	—	−21·08
1·80	−22·02	−22·40	−22·93	−23·57	−24·45	—	—	−23·07
1·90	−24·00	−24·40	−25·10	−25·84	−26·79	—	—	—
1·95	−25·06	−25·47	−26·28	−27·08	−28·06	—	—	—
e.c. max. volts	0·5586	0·5585	0·5589	0·5569	0·5567	0·5566	0·5582	0·5576

TABLE VI, 11 (*Continued*)

SURFACE CHARGE DENSITY, σ, OF THE ELECTRICAL DOUBLE-LAYER AT THE MERCURY
ELECTRODE IN TENTH-NORMAL AQUEOUS SOLUTIONS OF METALLIC CHLORIDES AT 25 °C.

E^- v.	σ in μ coul./cm.^{2}							
	$CaCl_2$	$SrCl_2$	$BaCl_2$	$MnCl_2$	$NiCl_2$	$CoCl_2$	$AlCl_3$	$LaCl_3$
0·08	19·87	19·97	20·04	19·76	19·84	19·78	20·02	20·17
0·10	18·51	18·60	18·64	18·42	18·50	18·52	18·65	18·76
0·12	17·36	17·43	17·46	17·29	17·35	17·31	17·47	17·58
0·14	16·32	16·39	16·42	16·27	16·33	16·28	16·44	16·52
0·16	15·38	15·44	15·46	15·33	15·39	15·34	15·49	15·55
0·18	14·49	14·55	14·57	14·45	14·50	14·46	14·59	14·64
0·20	13·64	13·70	13·72	13·61	13·66	13·62	13·74	13·78
0·25	11·64	11·70	11·71	11·63	11·67	11·63	11·74	11·76
0·30	9·72	9·77	9·78	9·71	9·74	9·71	9·80	9·81
0·35	7·78	7·83	7·84	7·77	7·80	7·77	7·84	7·85
0·40	5·81	5·84	5·85	5·78	5·81	5·79	5·84	5·84
0·45	3·83	3·85	3·85	3·79	3·81	3·80	3·84	3·83
0·50	1·949	1·949	1·950	1·904	1·911	1·915	1·942	1·922
0·55	0·274	0·256	0·253	0·226	0·227	0·236	0·258	0·221
0·60	—1·180	—1·216	—1·217	—1·223	—1·234	—1·219	—1·217	—1·267
0·65	—2·474	—2·525	—2·529	—2·509	—2·530	—2·509	—2·545	—2·613
0·70	—3·66	—3·72	—3·73	—3·69	—3·71	—3·69	—3·77	—3·85
0·80	—5·80	—5·87	—5·88	—5·81	—5·84	—5·81	—5·96	—6·06
0·90	—7·70	—7·78	—7·79	—7·69	—7·74	—7·70	—7·88	—8·01
1·00	—9·44	—9·53	—9·54	—9·42	—	—9·43	—9·62	—9·79
1·10	—11·09	—11·19	—11·20	—11·06	—	—11·06	—	—11·48
1·20	—12·71	—12·81	—12·82	—12·67	—	—	—	—13·13
1·30	—14·33	—14·45	—14·46	—14·28	—	—	—	—14·80
1·40	—15·98	—16·12	—16·14	—15·93	—	—	—	—16·51
1·50	—17·71	—17·86	—17·88	—	—	—	—	—
1·60	—19·52	—19·68	—19·70	—	—	—	—	—
1·70	—21·45	—21·61	—21·63	—	—	—	—	—
1·80	—23·48	—23·62	—23·66	—	—	—	—	—
e.c. max. volts	0·5589	0·5582	0·5581	0·5573	0·5573	0·5576	0·5583	0·5570

E^- = —electrode potential of mercury electrode with respect to calomel electrode
in the same solution.

TABLE VI, 12

DIFFERENTIAL CAPACITY OF MERCURY IN $N/10$ SOLUTIONS OF METALLIC CHLORIDES AT 25 °C; POTENTIALS RELATIVE TO CALOMEL ELECTRODE IN THE SAME SOLUTION. CAPACITIES IN $\mu F./cm^2$.

E volts	LiCl	NaCl	KCl	RbCl	CsCl	HCl	NH$_4$Cl	MgCl$_2$
0·063	94·1	94·9	97·2	102·4	103·8	95·4	96·6	94·1
0·08	72·0	72·7	73·8	76·5	77·4	72·6	73·4	74·7
·12	52·1	52·4	52·8	54·0	54·2	52·2	52·6	54·2
·16	44·52	44·61	44·79	45·51	45·51	44·39	44·66	45·64
·24	38·67	38·58	38·64	39·04	38·95	38·37	38·54	39·14
·32	38·43	38·35	38·37	38·53	38·51	38·15	38·45	38·62
·41	39·84	39·85	39·85	39·84	39·96	39·76	39·87	39·93
·46	38·62	38·58	38·67	38·63	38·75	38·73	38·66	38·77
·54	31·75	31·82	31·88	31·88	32·08	32·21	31·90	32·37
·62	24·58	24·72	24·78	24·85	25·32	25·03	24·85	26·03
·70	21·00	21·19	21·31	21·44	22·12	21·10	21·43	22·68
·86	17·90	18·14	18·30	18·57	19·27	17·62	18·50	18·59
1·00	16·32	16·57	16·77	17·11	17·86	16·12	17·07	16·71
1·16	15·46	15·78	16·06	16·50	17·29	—	16·45	15·78
1·32	15·47	15·87	16·28	16·86	17·66	—	16·88	15·96
1·48	16·17	16·64	17·22	17·93	18·67	—	18·16	16·89
1·64	17·42	17·80	18·70	19·51	20·21	—	—	18·51
1·80	19·00	19·24	20·76	21·66	22·32	—	—	20·52
1·94	21·37	21·76	24·03	25·02	25·76	—	—	—

For references, see p. 232.

TABLE VI, 12 (*continued*)

E volts	$CaCl_2$	$SrCl_2$	$BaCl_2$	$MnCl_2$	$CoCl_2$	$NiCl_2$	$AlCl_3$	$LaCl_3$	$PrCl_3$
0·063	99·2	96·4	103·6	99·1	98·7	99·7	98·5	106	107·4
0·08	75·9	77·5	78·7	75·6	75·4	76·0	77·0	80·0	80·7
·12	54·3	54·9	55·3	54·0	54·0	54·2	55·0	56·3	56·6
·16	45·82	46·09	46·36	45·60	45·64	45·78	46·18	46·98	47·25
·24	39·16	39·27	39·34	38·67	39·10	39·18	39·41	39·71	39·73
·32	38·65	38·71	38·73	38·67	38·63	38·78	38·98	39·15	38·65
·41	39·82	40·09	40·16	40·03	40·03	40·17	40·34	40·49	39·56
·46	38·51	38·92	38·98	38·79	38·74	39·02	38·94	39·22	38·31
·54	32·10	32·50	32·59	32·29	32·31	32·39	32·37	32·82	32·18
·62	26·12	26·49	26·53	26·06	26·14	26·27	26·83	27·30	26·79
·70	22·85	23·06	23·11	22·70	22·72	22·81	23·63	23·88	23·42
·86	18·81	18·89	18·89	18·67	18·71	18·71	19·02	19·26	18·98
1·00	16·92	16·98	16·97	16·79	16·74	—	16·90	17·29	17·09
1·16	16·12	16·25	16·25	16·02	—	—	—	16·51	16·39
1·32	16·40	16·59	16·62	16·33	—	—	—	16·94	16·86
1·48	17·49	17·63	17·64	—	—	—	—	—	—
1·64	19·13	19·11	19·11	—	—	—	—	—	—
1·80	20·91	20·63	20·96	—	—	—	—	—	—

D. C. GRAHAME, *J. Electrochem. Soc.*, 1951, **98**, 343.
See also *J. Am. Chem. Soc.*, 1949, **71**, 2975.

TABLE VI, 13

EFFECT OF FREQUENCY ON THE DIFFERENTIAL CAPACITY (C) OF THE DOUBLE LAYER
BETWEEN MERCURY AND AQUEOUS SOLUTIONS AT THE DROPPING MERCURY ELECTRODE

Solution	Capillary	E volts	% deviation of capacity when frequency changed from 1000~ to		$C \, \mu F/\text{cm.}^2$
			240~	5000~	
1N NaCl	Fine	0·11	0·3	0·1	43.0
		—0·24	0·5	—0·1	20·4
		—0·64	0·1	0·2	16·2
	Blunt	0·11	0·2	—1·8	43·0
		—0·04	0·2	—1·2	35·0
		—0·24	0·2	—0·8	20·4
		—0·64	0·3	—0·8	16·2
		—1·04	0·0	—0·4	18·5
1N KNO$_3$	Blunt	0·50	0·6	—0·6	25·7
		0·00	0·5	—0·7	31·5
		—0·20	0·7	—0·8	25·2
		—0·50	1·1	—0·8	16·8
0·1N NaCl	Fine	0·36	0·2	—0·2	39·5
		0·06	0·5	—0·3	35·1
		—0·24	0·4	—0·4	18·6
		—0·64	0·4	—0·2	15·6
	Blunt	0·31	2·1	—6·4	37·7
		0·11	2·4	—5·5	38·2
		0·01	2·2	—6·1	30·2
		—0·24	1·7	—4·8	18·6
		—0·64	0·3	—5·3	15·6
		—1·24	0·4	—2·5	19·0
1N KI	Blunt	—0·14	—1·0	—3·0	69·3
		—0·44	0·5	—1·2	39·4
		—0·84	—0·2	0·0	18·3
1N KNO$_3$	Fine	0·70	0·3	0·4	33·6
	Stationary	0·60	0·6	—0·4	28·4
		0·00	0·2	—0·3	31·5
		—0·50	0·3	—0·3	16·8

Accuracy: $\pm 0·3\%$, blunt capillary.

           $\pm 0·5\%$, fine capillary.

Potentials (E) were measured with respect to the electrocapillary maximum of Hg in the same solution.

D. C. GRAHAME, *J. Am. Chem. Soc.*, 1946, **68**, 301.

TABLE VI, 14

CAPACITY OF THE DOUBLE LAYER BETWEEN Hg AND $1N$ aq. KNO_3
SATURATED WITH OCTYL ALCOHOL AT 25 °C.

E volts	Capacity $\mu F/cm.^2$ at indicated frequency $\sim$				
	240 $\sim$	480 $\sim$	1000 $\sim$	5000 $\sim$	10,000 $\sim$
0·8	43·0	42·8	42·3	42·2	41·7
0·5	27·2	27·2	27·0	26·8	26·5
0·475	28·9	28·6	27·8	27·6	27·0
0·45	56·5	45·5	41·5	31·8	29·3
0·40	11·0	10·6	10·5	10·1	10·0
0·30	5·21	5·21	5·20	5·15	5·14
0·00	4·00	4·03	4·00	4·03	4·05
—0·20	4·30	4·28	4·30	4·30	4·33
—0·50	8·36	8·08	7·88	7·71	7·66
—0·55	14·1	13·5	12·6	11·8	11·6
—0·60	49·6	41·4	35·5	28·1	26·1
—0·65	36·1	34·2	32·4	27·6	25·3
—0·70	22·7	22·4	22·2	21·8	21·4
—0·90	18·8	18·7	18·7	18·7	18·7

Potentials (E) were measured with respect to the electrocapillary maximum of Hg
in absence of octyl alcohol.

D. C. GRAHAME, *J. Am. Chem. Soc.*, 1946, **68**, 301.

TABLE VI, 15

SERIES RESISTANCE OF THE ELECTRICAL DOUBLE LAYER BETWEEN MERCURY AND
$1N$ aq. KNO_3 SATURATED WITH OCTYL ALCOHOL AT 25 °C.

E volts	Resistance in ohm.cm.^{2} at indicated frequency $\sim$			
	240 $\sim$	480 $\sim$	1000 $\sim$	5000 $\sim$
0·80	0·05	0·08	0·04	0·01
0·50	0·40	0·10	0·01	0·00
0·475	0·42	0·24	0·09	0·00
0·45	3·90	1·38	0·74	0·11
0·40	3·25	1·11	0·35	0·01
0·30	5·71	1·53	0·54	0·03
0·00	2·42	0·65	0·14	0·01

TABLE VI, 15 (*Continued*)

E volts	Resistance in ohm.cm.^{2} at indicated frequency $\sim$.			
	240 $\sim$	480 $\sim$	1000 $\sim$	5000 $\sim$
—0·20	1·79	0·79	0·13	0·03
—0·50	2·17	1·38	0·66	0·08
—0·55	3·83	2·26	1·03	0·12
—0·60	4·60	2·47	1·22	0·21
—0·65	1·68	1·03	0·69	0·19
—0·70	0·14	0·15	0·15	0·04
—0·90	0·72	0·22	0·02	0·01

Potentials (E) were measured with respect to the electrocapillary maximum potential of Hg in absence of octyl alcohol.

D. C. GRAHAME, *J. Am. Chem. Soc.*, 1946, **68**, 301.

TABLE VI, 16

FREE ENERGY OF TRANSFER OF MERCUROUS SALT OF ANION OF ELECTROLYTE FROM SOLID STATE TO INTERFACE OF POLARIZED MERCURY ELECTRODE AT POTENTIAL OF THE ELECTROCAPILLARY MAXIMUM AT 25 °C.

Subst.	Conc. N	$-\Delta G$ k.cal. equiv.	Subst.	Conc. N	$-\Delta G$ k.cal. equiv.
KCl	1·0	12·813	NaI	4·0	12·41
	0·7	12·767		2·0	12·09
	0·3	12·721		1·0	11·79
	0·1	12·892		0·1	10·82
	0·01	13·692		0·01	10·45
	0·001	14·76		0·001	10·50
NaBr	4·0	11·86	KCN	4·0	4·64
	2·0	11·76		2·0	3·94
	1·0	11·63		1·0	3·48
	0·1	11·42		0·1	2·26
	0·01	11·44		0·01	1·15
	0·001	12·46			
			Na$_2$SO$_4$	1·0	18·78
KCNS	1·0	15·27		0·1	19·98
	0·1	14·41		0·01	21·24
	0·01	14·67			

TABLE VI, 16 (*Continued*)

Subst.	Conc. N	$-\Delta G$ k.cal. equiv.	Subst.	Conc. N	$-\Delta G$ k.cal. equiv.
Na_2S	2·0	7·10	$CaCl_2$	1·0	12·73
	1·0	6·46		0·1	12·885
	0·1	4·36			
	0·01	3·53	RbCl	0·1	12·86
			NH_4Cl	0·1	12·887
NaCl	4·0	12·99	$MgCl_2$	0·1	12·894
	2·0	12·86	$SrCl_2$	0·1	12·889
	1·0	12·84	$BaCl_2$	0·1	12·887
	0·1	12·896	$MnCl_2$	0·1	12·892
	0·01	13·56	$CoCl_2$	0·1	12·882
			$NiCl_2$	0·1	12·889
LiCl	1·0	12·85	$AlCl_3$	0·1	12·882
	0·1	12·899	$LaCl_3$	0·1	12·889
			KBr	0·1	11·51
CsCl	1·0	12·82	KI	0·1	11·00
	0·1	12·834	K_2SO_4	0·1	20·09
			K_2CO_3	0·1	13·15

D. C. GRAHAME, E. M. COFFIN and J. I. CUMMINS, *Office of Naval Research, Tech. Report No.* 2, August 11 1950, Research Contract N 8 - onv - 66903.

TABLE VI, 17

ENTROPY AND ENTHALPY OF TRANSFER OF CALOMEL
AT POTENTIAL OF THE ELECTROCAPILLARY MAXIMUM IN KCl AT 25 °C.

Conc. N	dE^s/dT mv./deg.	dE^t/dT mv./deg.	dE^A/dT mv./deg.	ΔS e.u. equiv.	$T\Delta S$ cal. equiv.	ΔG k.cal. equiv.	ΔH k.cal. equiv.
1·0	—0·66	0·59 *	—0·07	—1·6	—481	—12·813	—13·294
0·1	—0·68	0·77 **	+0·18	4·2	1265	—12·892	—11·627

dE^s/dT is temperature coefficient of e.c.max. measured relative to a calomel electrode held at constant temperature. A negative value indicates that the potential of the calomel electrode becomes smaller as the temperature of the polarized electrode increases.

dE^t/dT is the temperature coefficient of two identical calomel cells in the electrolyte named when the temperature of one is changed. A positive value indicates that the warmer cell is positive to the cooler.

dE^A/dT is the temperature coefficient of the e.c.max. measured relative to a calomel electrode in the same electrolyte at the same temperature.

* Data of T. W. RICHARDS, Z. *physik. Chem.*, 1897, **24**, 39. Corrected to 25 °C.
** Data of T. W. RICHARDS *(loc. cit.)* confirmed by measurements made by GRAHAME.

D. C. GRAHAME, E. M. COFFIN and J. I. CUMMINS *loc. cit.*, see Table VI, 9

TABLE VI, 18

ELECTROCAPILLARY DATA FOR ALLOYS IN FUSED SALT ELECTROLYTES

Sn — Zn

Electrolyte KCl-LiCl⎱ Interfacial tension in dyne/cm.
Eutectic at 430 °C. ⎰

Potential of capillary electrode in v. *	mol. % Zn								
	0	5	10	25	50	75	90	95	100
0·0	492	451	438	494	521	522	524	528	700
0·1	507	455	441	499	523	525	527	531	703
0·2	511	457	442	500	524	526	530	533	706
0·3	511	456	442	507	527	528	531	535	714
0·4	501	456	442	501	529	532	532	536	725
0·5	491	454	434	494	526	532	532	538	730
0·6	477	443	422	482	518	523	532	533	730
0·7	468	435	410	471	506	506	514	522	727
0·8	450	429	392	448	487	490	500	503	722
0·9	426	412	375	439	465	486	489	484	707
1·0	413	401	357	425	445	457	465	462	691
1·1	379	391	337	408	436	430	455	454	675
1·2	362	377	321	382	420	414	439	446	661
1·3	342	366	314	—	410	398	433	434	646
1·4	326	361	304	—	406	385	416	415	626
1·5	311	350	—	—	396	375	—	407	617
1·6	299	343	—	—	387	366	—	395	612
1·8	—	—	—	—	—	—	—	377	607
2·0	—	—	—	—	—	—	—	388	576

Electrolyte KI + LiI, 70 mol.% LiI at 430 °C.

	0	5	10	25	50	75	90	95	100
0·0	391	414	429	438	436	438	453	—	542
0·1	410	419	434	444	439	440	455	—	547
0·2	417	421	435	446	441	461	459	—	553
0·3	425	427	436	455	447	443	464	—	563
0·4	423	429	440	455	458	453	475	—	590
0·5	418	425	439	455	454	464	477	—	604
0·6	412	419	435	444	457	474	474	—	609
0·7	402	412	428	435	445	452	465	—	605
0·8	393	405	424	426	—	431	457	—	594
0·9	388	398	417	414	—	423	444	—	581
1·0	384	393	412	403	—	—	—	—	—
1·1	378	388	—	—	—	—	—	—	—
1·2	374	382	—	—	—	—	—	—	—

TABLE VI, 18 (*Continued*)

Thallium-Amalgam.

KI + LiI 70 mol.% LiI at 420 °C. in closed vessel.

Interfacial tension in dyne/cm.

Potential of capillary electrode in v. *	mol.% Tl.						
	0	2	5	20	40	80	100
0·6	321	—	—	—	—	—	—
0·5	347	—	—	—	—	—	—
0·4	377	—	—	—	—	—	—
0·14	386	—	—	—	—	—	—
0·00	387	378	380	377	385	385	388
—0·10	—	—	—	—	—	—	404
—0·20	387	386	391	388	390	404	416
—0·30	—	—	—	398	—	416	429
—0·40	380	383	420	405	412	414	441
—0·50	—	—	—	—	—	—	446
—0·60	373	372	397	408	429	434	455
—0·70	—	—	—	—	—	—	450
—0·80	355	356	—	407	418	433	446
—0·90	—	—	—	—	—	—	440
—1·00	—	339	—	400	412	416	430
—1·10	—	—	—	—	—	—	423
—1·20	—	320	—	388	407	404	—

ELECTROCAPILLARY MAXIMUM POTENTIALS

* Relative to Pb electrode in KCl + LiCl eutectic		max. potential in v.
	Hg	0·1
	Sn	0·23
	Pb	0·47
	Zn	0·55
	Tl	0·65
	Cd	0·63

S. KARPATSCHOFF and A. STROMBERG, *Acta Physicochim. U.R.S.S.*, 1940, **12**, 523.

CHAPTER VII

TRANSPORT AND GENERAL PROPERTIES OF COLLOIDS AND MACROMOLECULAR ELECTROLYTES OF BIOLOGICAL IMPORTANCE

The principal part of this chapter is devoted to the electrophoretic mobilities of a number of proteins. In most cases mobilities have been measured using the TISELIUS electrophoresis apparatus except in a small number of cases, *e.g.*, for the observations of blood cells, where the micro-electrophoretic technique has been used.

Effects of ionic strength on observed mobilities are given for certain materials. Computed values of apparent valency or net charge are given for some proteins. These values depend on assumptions made (but supported in some cases by frictional ratio data) concerning the axial ratio of the molecule.

The use of electrophoretic mobilities in the characterisation of proteins is stressed in a number of tables in which characteristic mobilities and mobility ranges of serum and plasma fractions are given. Deviations of apparent electrophoretic composition from known relative concentrations in artifical protein mixtures are given as a basis for formulating true composition corrections when unknown mixtures are dealt with. The mean electrophoretic composition, from Schlieren diagrams, of human plasma pools is given in Table VII, 10. The relation of observed mobilities of human sera components to dialysis time is given in Table VII, 11 and enables appropriate standardisation of the times of preliminary dialysis for electrophoresis runs to be made.

A series of buffer solutions of ionic strength 0·1 and 0·2 of pH from 2 to 12 for electrophoretic determinations is given in the Table 15 in Chapter V. For a continuous series of buffers of a range of pH's and ionic strengths utilising phosphate, acetate and acetic acid, the reader is referred to A. A. GREEN, *J. Am. Chem. Soc.*, 1933, **55,** 3712, where buffer compositions for various pH's and ionic strengths are shown graphically.

Factors involved in theoretical electrophoretic mobility computations using HENRY's theory are given in Table VII, 13, and functions for the derivation of ζ potential at a charged cylinder are tabulated. Conversion tables for relating frictional to axial ratios for assymmetric macromolecules, from Perrin's equations are included.

It should be noted that values of axial ratios obtained from frictional ratios derived from sedimentation and diffusion data depend on assumptions made concerning the total and inner hydration of the protein or other macromolecule in question. This factor, however, is often a completely unknown quantity.

Specific refactive increments used in accurate interpretation of Schlieren diagrams are given for some important well characterised proteins. The dependence of the increment upon net charge is shown in Table VII, 20. For most purposes this factor may be neglected.

TABLE VII, 1

VALENCY AND MOBILITY OF OVALBUMIN FROM ELECTROPHORETIC DATA
AT $I_{(m)} = 0.1$, $0\ °C$.

Buffer	pH	U $\left(\dfrac{\mu.\sec.^{-1}}{\text{volt cm.}^{-1}}\right)$	Valence calc. for sphere	Valence calc. for cylinder
G	3·05	0·625	11·06	13·13
A/NaCl	3·62	0·389	6·89	8·17
A/NaCl	3·91	0·279	4·94	5·86
A	4·64	—0·020	—0·35	—0·42
A	5·33	—0·282	—4·99	—5·91
A	5·65	—0·353	—6·24	—7·40
C-NaCl	6·12	—0·446	—7·89	—9·34
P-NaCl	6·17	—0·546	—9·68	—11·4
B	7·83	—0·592	—10·5	—12·4
G	10·28	—0·621	—11·0	—13·0
G	10·88	—0·700	—12·4	—14·7
G	11·81	—0·931	—16·5	—19·6
P	6·12	—0·494	—8·74	—10·4
P	6·80	—0·592	—10·5	—12·4
P	* 7·10	—0·670	—11·9	—14·1

U = electrophoretic mobility. A = Acetate B = Barbiturate
G = Glycine C = Cacodylate P = Phosphate

From L. G. LONGSWORTH, *Ann. N. Y. Acad. Sci.*, 1941, **41**, 267, and
* A. TISELIUS and H. SVENSSON, *Trans. Faraday Soc.*, 1940, **36**, 16.

TABLE VII, 2

MOBILITY OF OVALBUMIN AT $0.5\ °C$., pH 7·10 IN PHOSPHATE BUFFER SOLUTION OF
VARYING IONIC STRENGTH, $I_{(m)}$

$I_{(m)}$	Mobility $\times 10^5$ cm.sec.$^{-1}$/volt cm.$^{-1}$
0	(20·35) extrapolated
0·00143	15·6
0·00442	13·2
0·00941	11·6
0·0244	9·45
0·0944	7·60
0·100	6·70
0·140	6·29
0·200	0·75

$\varepsilon = 87.7$ for the solution.
A. TISELIUS and H. SVENSSON, *Trans. Faraday Soc.*, 1940, **36**, 17.

TABLE VII, 3

VALENCY AND MOBILITY OF OVALBUMIN

1. Sodium acetate/Acetic acid $I_{(m)} = 0.02$, temp. $= 20$ °C.

pH	Mobility (μ.sec.$^{-1}$/volt cm.$^{-1}$)	Valency calc. for sphere	Valency calc. for cylinder
4·27	0·31	2·1	2·5
4·43	0·17	1·2	1·4
4·44	0·14	1·0	1·1
4·68	—0·14	—1·0	—1·1
4·74	—0·19	—1·3	—1·5
4·90	—0·34	—2·3	—2·7
5·04	—0·49	—3·4	—3·9
5·05	—0·47	—3·2	—3·7
5·27	—0·66	—4·5	—5·3

2. Barium acetate/Acetic acid $I_{(m)} = 0.06$, temp. $= 20$ °C.

4·27	0·36	3·2	3·7
4·51	0·11	0·97	1·1
5·11	—0·30	—2·6	—3·1

A. TISELIUS, *Nova Acta reg. Soc. Sci. Upsaliensis*, 1930, No. 4, 7.

TABLE VII, 4

ELECTROPHORETIC MOBILITIES OF OVALBUMINS AND HAEMOGLOBINS

Albumin [1]	Mobility (μ.sec.$^{-1}$/volt cm.$^{-1}$)	Haemoglobin [2]	Mobility (μ.sec.$^{-1}$/volt cm.$^{-1}$)
Chicken	—0·354	Rabbit	—0·215
Guinea Hen	—0·376	Sheep	—0·23
Turkey	—0·353	Dog	—0·24
Duck	—0·427	Horse	—0·30
Goose	—0·460	Guinea Pig	—0·30
		Chicken	—0·16

Accuracy of mobilities ±0.002, [1] and ±0.005, [2].

[1] K. LANDSTEINER, L. G. LONGSWORTH and J. VAN DER SCHEER, *Science*, 1938, **88**, 83. In 0·02M acetate buffers at pH 5·20, at 0 °C.

[2] *Ditto*, in 0·1 $I_{(m)}$ phosphate buffers pH 7·95 at 0 °C. Mobilities determined by moving boundary method.

TABLE VII, 5

MOBILITY AND VALENCY OF SERUM ALBUMINS
FROM ELECTROPHORETIC MEASUREMENTS

1. Sodium acetate/Acetic acid buffer $I_{(m)} = 0.02$, temp. $= 20$ °C.

pH	Mobility $\mu.\text{sec.}^{-1}/\text{volt cm.}^{-1}$	* Valency calc. for sphere	* Valency calc. for cylinder $(l/2a = 5)$
4·19	0·847	8·17	8·73
4·36	0·588	5·67	6·06
4·67	0·168	1·60	1·73
4·97	—0·225	—2·17	—2·32
5·28	—0·439	—4·24	—4·53
5·49	—0·595	—5·74	—6·13

R. A. KEKWICK, *Biochem. J.*, 1938, **32**, 552. (Horse serum albumin B.)

2. Sodium acetate/Acetic acid buffer $I_{(m)} = 0.10$, temp. $= 25$ °C.

pH	Mobility $\mu.\text{sec.}^{-1}/\text{volt cm.}^{-1}$	* Valency calc. for sphere	* Valency calc. for cylinder $(l/2a = 5)$
4·03	0·640	8·16	8·92
4·36	0·356	4·54	4·96
4·76	0·00	0	0
5·67	—0·487	—6·21	—6·79
5·86	—0·750	—9·56	—10·4
6·52	—1·00	—12·8	—13·9
7·00	—1·23	—15·7	—17·1
7·68	—1·33	—17·0	—18·5

With rabbit serum-albumin-coated quartz particles.

$l/2a$ = axial ratio, where l = length of cylinder of radius a.

* These are values of valency computed for spherical or cylinderical models from the observed mobility data.

Accuracy of mobilities, ± 0.005.

L. S. MOYER and E. Z. MOYER, *J. Biol. Chem.*, 1940, **132**, 373.

TABLE VII, 6

MOBILITIES OF RED BLOOD CELLS DETERMINED BY DIFFERENT METHODS

Method *	Mobilities (μ.sec.$^{-1}$/volt cm^{-1}.)				
	Man	Rat	Rabbit	Mouse	Guinea Pig
1. Moving boundary	—	1·45	0·60	1·42	1·16
2. Horizontal Micro-electrophoresis	1·31	1·45	0·55	1·35	1·11
3. Horizontal Micro-electrophoresis	1·30	—	—	—	—
4. Vertical Micro-electrophoresis	1·25	—	—	—	—

* All mobilities measured at pH 7·4 in 0·067M phosphate buffer.

[1] F. O. Howitt, *Biochem. J.*, 1934, **28**, 1165.
[2] H. A. Abramson, *J. Gen. Physiol.*, 1929, **12**, 711.
[3] L. S. Moyer, *J. Bact.*, 1936, **31**, 531.
[4] H. A. Abramson, L. S. Moyer and A. Voet, *J. Am. Chem. Soc.*, 1936, **58**, 2362.

TABLE VII, 7

EFFECT OF IONIC STRENGTH ON ELECTROPHORETIC MOBILITY
AND NET CHARGE DENSITY OF HUMAN RED BLOOD CELLS

At pH 7·3 in isotonic solutions of glucose and salt.

Ionic strength	$1/\varkappa \times 10^7$ cm.	Mobility $\left(\dfrac{\mu.\text{sec.}^{-1}}{\text{volt cm.}^{-1}} \right)$	Net Charge Density σ $\sigma = \dfrac{\varkappa\eta\,U}{1 + \varkappa r_i}$ ($r_i = 2.5$ Å)
0·0043 (pH 6·8)	4·65	3·63	2240
0·0069	3·67	3·44	2620
0·0086	3·29	3·21	2600
0·0172	2·33	2·78	3100
0·043	1·47	1·92	3060
0·086	1·04	1·35	2820
0·172	0·735	1·04	2840

$1/\varkappa$ = mean double layer thickness.
η = viscosity.
r_i = mean ion radius.
U = electrophoretic mobility.

R. L. Furchgott and E. Ponder, *J. Gen. Physiol.*, 1941, **24**, 447.

TABLE VII, 8

(1) ELECTROPHORETIC MOBILITIES OF SOME ANIMAL SERA COMPONENTS
AT pH 7·7

Serum	Mobility (μ.sec.$^{-1}$/volt cm.$^{-1}$)			
	Albumin	a *	β *	γ *
Horse antipneumococcus I serum	0·55	0·37	0·30	0·09
Normal horse serum	0·57	0·38	0·31	0·10
Pig antipneumococcus I serum	0·57	0·35	0·27	0·11
Monkey antipneumococcus III serum	0·52	0·43	0·30	0·07
Rabbit anti-ovalbumin serum	0·60	0·36	0·29	0·11

In 0·02M phosphate, 0·15M NaCl buffer; 0·5 °C.
All components present as anions.
* Globulins.

(2) ELECTROPHORETIC MOBILITIES OF PURIFIED ANTIBODIES (ANTIPNEUMOCOCCUS)
IN μ.sec.$^{-1}$/volt cm.$^{-1}$

pH	Horse	Cow	Pig	Rabbit		
				Salt dissociated	Ba dissociated	Isolated by electrophoresis
7·72	0·17	0·13	0·13	0·09	0·08	0·12
6·70	0·13	0·12	0·10	0·08	0·06	0·07
5·86	0·11	0·098	0·06	0·00	0·00	0·00
4·81	0·06	0·00	+0·05	+0·10	+0·11	+0·09
4·02	+0·11	+0·14	+0·21	—	—	—
3·18	+0·22	—	—	—	—	—
Isoelectric pH	4·4	4·8	5·1	5·8	5·8	5·8

Net charges are negative except where indicated positive.
A. TISELIUS and E. A. KABAT, *J. Expt. Med.*, 1939, **69**, 119.

TABLE VII, 9

OBSERVED RANGES OF MOBILITIES ($-U \cdot 10^5$ cm.sec.$^{-1}$/volt cm^{-1}) USED FOR IDENTIFICATION OF ELECTROPHORETIC COMPONENTS IN HUMAN PLASMA AND PLASMA FRACTIONS   (SODIUM DIETHYLBARBITURATE BUFFER pH 8·6, $I_{(m)} = 0·1$)

Material	Electrophoretic components						
	Albumins	α_1-Globulins	α_2-Globulins	β_1-Globulins	β_2-Globulins	Fibrinogen	γ-Globulins
Plasma[a]	5·7 — 6·2	4·6 — 5·1	3·6 — 4·1	2·8 — 3·2	2·5 — 2·8	1·7 — 2·3	0·8 — 1·3
Chief Fractions							
Fraction I[b,c]	5·8 — 6·2	4·9 — 5·4	3·6 — 4·3	2·6 — 3·2		1·7 — 2·2	0·5 — 1·0
Fraction II, III[a,d,e,j]	5·9 — 6·4	4·8 — 5·4	3·9 — 4·5	3·1 — 3·8	2·4 — 3·0	1·7 — 2·2	0·7 — 1·2
Fraction IV-1[d,e,f,g]	5·9 — 6·4	4·8 — 5·3	3·8 — 4·3	2·7 — 3·1	2·4 — 2·8	1·7 — 2·3	0·8 — 1·3
Fraction IV-1[d,e,f,g]	5·8 — 6·3	4·7 — 5·3	4·0 — 5·5	2·7 — 3·9			0·9 — 1·2
Fraction IV-4	5·7 — 6·3	4·8 — 5·3	3·8 — 4·3	2·6 — 3·0		1·6 — 1·9	
Fraction V	5·8 — 6·2	4·8 — 5·2	3·7 — 4·2	2·8 — 3·4			
Fraction VI	5·8 — 6·2	4·8 — 5·2	3·7 — 4·2	2·8 — 3·4			
Sub Fractions							
Fraction I-1 (purified fibrinogen)[b,c]				2·5 — 3·2		1·7 — 2·2	0·8 — 1·3
Fraction II-1, 2 (purified γ-globulin)					1·8 — 2·3		0·6 — 1·0
Fraction II-3 (purified γ-globulin)					2·2 — 3·5		0·6 — 1·2
Fraction III-0 (β-lipoprotein)[g,j]	6·0 — 7·0	4·9 — 5·4		3·9 — 4·3	2·2 — 2·5		0·8 — 1·2
Fraction III-0, 2 ("x" lipoprotein)[i]	5·9 — 6·3	4·4 — 5·5		4·1 — 5·6			
Fraction III-2 (prothrombin)[j]				3·2 — 3·7	1·9 — 2·6		
Fraction III-1 (isoagglutinins)	5·7 — 6·3	4·8 — 5·5		3·1 — 3·7	2·1 — 2·8		0·7 — 1·2
Fraction IV-1, 1W (α_1-lipoprotein)[f,h]	5·9 — 6·4	6·1 — 7·5		2·7 — 3·7			0·8 — 1·2
Fraction IV-6, 2 (purified α_2-globulin)			3·8 — 4·2				
Crystalline albumin	5·8 — 6·2						

See notes p. 248.

TABLE VII, 10

DEVIATIONS OF APPARENT ELECTROPHORETIC DISTRIBUTIONS FROM KNOWN RELATIVE
CONCENTRATIONS IN ARTIFICIAL MIXTURES OF PURIFIED PROTEINS

Conditions of electrophoresis			Known relative albumin concn. %	Apparent electrophoretic relative albumin concn. %	Dev. of apparent electrophoretic from known albumin concn. %	Protein Components
pH	$I_{(m)}$	Protein, g./100 ml.				
$8 \cdot 6^a$	0·05	2·0	$9 \cdot 8^d$	9·4	—0·4	
$8 \cdot 6^a$	0·05	2·0	$89 \cdot 3^d$	90·2	0·9	Albumin/
$8 \cdot 6^a$	0·05	2·0	$50 \cdot 8^d$	53·0	2·2	fibrinogen
$8 \cdot 6^a$	0·2	1·0	$50 \cdot 8^d$	51·4	0·6	
$8 \cdot 6^a$	0·05	3·0	$50 \cdot 0^e$	52·0	2·0	Albumin/
$8 \cdot 6^a$	0·1	2·0	$50 \cdot 0^e$	52·0	2·0	γ-globulin
$8 \cdot 6^a$	0·1	1·0	$50 \cdot 0^e$	52·0	1·0	(bovine)
$7 \cdot 7^b$	0·2	2·5	$51 \cdot 0^f$	56·0	5·0	
$8 \cdot 6^c$	0·1	1·2	$34 \cdot 0^d$	42·0	6·0	
$8 \cdot 6^c$	0·1	1·3	$66 \cdot 0^d$	74·0	8·0	Albumin/
$8 \cdot 6^a$	0·1	2·0	$31 \cdot 0^e$	38·0	7·0	β-globulin
$8 \cdot 6^a$	0·1	2·0	$65 \cdot 0^e$	71·0	5·0	
$8 \cdot 6^a$	0·2	2·0	$65 \cdot 0^e$	68·0	3·0	
$8 \cdot 6^a$	0·2	1·0	$65 \cdot 0^e$	67·0	2·0	
$8 \cdot 6^a$	0·05	2·5	$51 \cdot 0^d$	58·0	7·0	
$8 \cdot 6^a$	0·05	1·5	$51 \cdot 0^d$	56·0	5·0	Albumin/
$8 \cdot 6^a$	0·05	1·0	$51 \cdot 0^d$	55·0	4·0	α_2-globulin
$8 \cdot 6^a$	0·3	1·0	$51 \cdot 0^d$	51·0	0	

[a] Sodium diethylbarbiturate. [b] Potassium phosphate. [c] Sodium diethylbarbiturate
and citrate. [d] Determined by refractive increment measurements. [e] Determined by
both refractive increment measurements and protein and non-protein nitrogen analyses. [f] Determined by nitrogen analysis.

See notes p. 248.

S. H. ARMSTRONG, Jr., M. J. E. BUDKA and K. C. MORRISON, *J. Am. Chem. Soc.*,
1947, **69**, 416.

TABLE VII, 10 (*Continued*)

DISTRIBUTION OF COMPONENTS IN ELECTROPHORETIC SCHLIEREN DIAGRAMS OF NORMAL
HUMAN PLASMA POOLS ANALYSED IN SODIUM DIETHYL-BARBITURATE
BUFFER $I_{(m)} = 0{\cdot}1$, pH $8{\cdot}6$

	Albumins	Total α-globulins	β-Globulins	γ-Globulins	Fibrinogen	$α_1$-Globulins
wt.%	55·2	14·0	13·4	11·0	6·5	5·3
Standard Deviation	1·3	0·8	1·6	0·7	0·6	0·5

Values given are average wt.% composition of each of the components from 20 different plasma pools and represent a reliable mean composition of plasma.

S. H. ARMSTRONG, Jr., M. J. E. BUDKA and K. C. MORRISON, *J. Am. Chem. Soc.*, 1947, **69**, 416.

NOTES ON TABLES VII, 9 AND VII, 10

(a) Resolution of $β_1$- and $β_2$-globulins is not sufficiently clear-cut to give reproducible apparent distributions.

(b) For satisfactory resolution of fibrinogen and the adjacent slow-moving β-globulin peaks, the duration of electrophoresis at a potential gradient of 6 to 8 volts per cm. approximates four to five hours. Whereas under these conditions albumin and α-globulin boundaries will be out of the field, agreement between fibrinogen determinations by electrophoresis and by clottable nitrogen is close. (See also J. T. EDSALL, R. M. FERRY and S. H. ARMSTRONG, Jr., *J. Clin. Investigation*, 1944, **23**, 557.)

(c) Fibrinogen has an extremely high temperature coefficient of solubility between 0 and 5 °C. To avoid precipitation in the cell in runs of material high in fibrinogen, it is advisable to carry out analyses at approximately 8 °C. under continuous observation in order that boundary disturbances due to thermal convection currents may be forestalled when necessary by lowering the field strength.

(d) Occasionally in Fraction II, III and certain of its subfractions, and uniformly in Fraction IV and Fraction IV-1, a small component (absent from the Schlieren diagram of whole plasma) separates from the chief albumin peak; its mobility varies from $-7{\cdot}0$ to $-7{\cdot}5 \times 10^{-5}$. It has been included with the albumins in distribution data.

(e) Speed and maintenance of low temperatures are particularly essential in preparing alcohol-containing samples of Fractions II, III, IV, and the subfractions high in lipoids for analysis. When dialyses are set up immediately following separation of fractions, a very small portion of the material present in the precipitate paste of Fraction IV is insoluble in routine buffer and can be removed by high-speed centrifugation at 0 °C. With increasing periods of storage, the amount of insoluble material increases as does the spread of the individual component peaks, thus rendering quantitative interpretation of analyses increasingly difficult.

(^{f}) Part of the component migrating in this fraction with mobility characteristic of albumin, either as in plasma or as crystallized, differs strikingly from chemically separated albumin both with respect to lipoid content and solubility characteristics.

(^{g}) In solution of lipoproteins whose turbidity is sufficient to interfere with analysis, clarification can generally be effected by filtration through an 8-SEITZ pad. If such filtration is carried out under comparable conditions in following successive fractionations, the distribution data, although subject to correction for selective adsorption of proteins on the filter material, have proved useful for comparative purposes.

(^{h}) It is possible to store this fraction either in aqueous solution sterilized by SEITZ filtration or as dried from the frozen state. Under the latter circumstances, mobilities have in general been unaffected by periods of storage up to one year. In the former, mobilities have been found to increase by as much as -1×10^{-5} cm.^{2}/volt/sec. in a period of 1 month. This behaviour is in contrast with materials low in lipoid, e.g., Fraction II, Fraction III-1, Fraction V, and crystalline albumin, whose mobilities would appear to be independent of storage conditions under ordinary circumstances.

(^{i}) Separated ultra-centrifugally from Fraction III-0. Whereas mobility in the parent material is consistent with β_1-globulin, highest mobility for the purified fraction was observed when this fraction was added in artificial mixture to lipoprotein IV-1,1. When added to plasma in artificial mixture, it appeared to migrate chiefly with the α_2-globulins (mobility $-4 \cdot 1 \times 10^{-5}$). Further studies on factors affecting mobility are in progress.

(^{j}) Resolution of α_1- and α_2-globulins is not sufficiently clean-cut for reproducible distributions.

The methods used in these fractionations of plasma and a more detailed description of the fractions are given in the relevent biochemical literature (q.v.) by E. J. COHN and his collaborators.

S. H. ARMSTRONG, Jr., M. J. E. BUDKA and K. C. MORRISON, *J. Am. Chem. Soc.*, 1947, **69**, 416.

T

Mo

Dialysis time, hrs.	Descending or Ascending boundary (D or A)	Mobili 10^{-5} cm.^{2} p		
		Albumin	a_1-Globulin	a_2-Glo
				Pho
0	D.	4·7	††	3·2
	A.	4·6	4·1	3·1
24	D.	4·7	††	3·2
	A.	4·8	4·3	3·5
48	D.	4·5	††	3·0
	A.	4·6	††	3·4
				Barbi
0	D.	5·7	4·8	3·7
	A.	5·6	4·6	3·7
24	D.	6·2	5·3	4·1
	A.	6·5	5·5	4·5
48	D.	5·5	4·6	3·7

Mobilities are determined in the TISELIUS apparatus using a micro cell of 2 ml. capacity. Schlieren photographic measurements were obtained by the LONGS-WORTH SCANNING technique.

D. H. MOORE et al., J. Biol. Chem., 1949, **180**, 1147.

HUMAN SERUM

ponents

| obulin | γ-Globulin | Relative Refractivities † | | Conductance 10^{-3} mho.cm.$^{-1}$ | |
		Buffer vs. water	Protein vs. buffer	Buffer	Protein
*					
2·1	0·3	1·01	2·43	9·8	8·74
2·3	0·6				
2·2	0·5	1·01	2·14	9·8	9·28
2·5	0·4				
2·0	0·3	1·01	2·17	9·8	9·31
2·3	0·4				
*					
2·5	0·8	2·42	1·9	3·11	4·35
2·5	0·9				
2·9	1·1	2·42	2·26	3·11	3·04
3·1	1·3				
2·5	0·9	2·42	2·31	3·11	3·08

† Zeiss interferometer readings with 1 cm. cell.
* Phosphate buffer pH 7·4, 0·02M Na$_2$HPO$_4$, 0·15M NaCl.
Barbiturate buffer pH 8·6, 0·1M Sodium diethyl-barbiturate 0·02M diethyl-barbituric acid.
†† α_1-Globulin not resolved.

TABLE VII, 12

MOBILITIES OF GLYCINE, ALANINE AND GLYCYL-GLYCINE
IN cm.^{2}/sec./volt . 10^4 AT 0 °C.

pH	Glycine in HCOOH	Alanine in		Glycyl-glycine in HCOOH
		HCOOH	CH$_3$COOH	
2·3	10·35	8·6		12·6
2·4	9·3	7·7		12·2
2·6	7·3	6·1	5·5	11·25
2·7	6·35	5·3	4·7	10·7
2·9	4·6	3·85	3·35	9·3
3·0	3·9	3·2	2·8	8·6
3·2	2·65	2·2	1·9	6·95
3·6				3·9
3·8				2·8
3·9				2·3

pH	Glycine in NH$_3$ aq.	Alanine in NH$_3$ aq.
9·3	—4·2	—2·6
9·4	—4·9	—3·1
9·6	—6·6	—4·4
9·8	—8·3	—5·9
9·9	—9·2	—6·7
10·1	—10·8	—8·35
10·2	—11·5	—9·1
10·4	—12·7	—10·5
10·5	—13·2	—11·1
10·7	—13·9	—12·1
10·8	—14·2	—12·5

H. SVENSSON, A. BENJAMINSSON and I. BRATTSTEN, *Acta Chem. Scand.*, 1949, 3, 307.

TABLE VII, 13

THEORETICAL ELECTROPHORETIC MOBILITY (U) OF SPHERES OF RADIUS r

$$U = \frac{\zeta \varepsilon}{6 \pi \eta} \cdot f(\varkappa r)$$

where ζ is the electrokinetic potential, ε and η the dielectric constant and viscosity of the medium respectively.

FACTORS FOR SPHERES FROM HENRY'S THEORY

$\varkappa r$	$6/f(\varkappa r)$	$\varkappa r$	$6/f(\varkappa r)$
0	6·000	5	5·113
1	5·844	10	4·843
2	5·631	25	4·38
3	5·450	100	4·11
4	5·298	∞	4·00

See: D. C. HENRY, *Proc. Roy. Soc.*, London, 1931, A **133**, 106.
M. H. GORIN, *J. Phys. Chem.*, 1941, **45**, 371 and *J. Chem. Phys.*, 1939, **7**, 405.

TABLE VII, 14

FIRST ORDER GRONWALL-LA MER CORRECTION TERMS FOR PROTEINS

Protein radius $r = 27\cdot5$ Å; Mean radius of ions in ionic atmosphere taken as $r_i = 2\cdot5$ Å. $U =$ mobility.

$\varkappa(r + r_i)$	Correction factor y for spheres of charge q and valency z.					
	$z = 5$	$z = 10$	$z = 15$	$z = 20$	$z = 25$	$z = 30$
0·312	1·007	1·034	1·081	1·157	1·247	1·437
0·494	1·008	1·041	1·097	1·178	1·325	1·547
0·696	1·011	1·043	1·104	1·200	1·353	1·603
0·987	1·005	1·032	1·075	1·140	1·236	1·343
1·392	1·003	1·021	1·049	1·091	1·149	1·213
3·11	1·000	1·003	1·007	1·013	1·020	1·030
4·40	1·000	1·000	1·000	1·000	1·000	1·000

for use in the relation $\quad U = \dfrac{q(1 + \varkappa r_i) \cdot f(\varkappa r)}{6 \pi \eta r y [1 + \varkappa(r + r_i)]}$.

Values calculated for $r = 27\cdot5$ Å, *i.e.*, $r + r_i = 30$ Å. For other values of $r + r_i$ table can be used by changing the actual valency z to a new valence function z' by the relationship

$$z' = z \left(\frac{30}{r_i + r} \right)^2$$

See: M. H. GORIN, *J. Phys. Chem.*, 1941, **45**, 371.

TABLE VII, 15

ASSYMETRIC MACRO-MOLECULES: VALUES OF AXIAL RATIOS CORRESPONDING TO
VARIOUS FRICTIONAL RATIOS FOR PROLATE AND OBLATE ELLIPSOIDS

If ϱ is the ratio b/a where $b = $ equatorial radius and $a = $ one half the length of the axis of rotation,

$$f/f_0 = \frac{\sqrt{1-\varrho^2}}{\varrho^{2/3}\log\dfrac{1+\sqrt{1-\varrho^2}}{\varrho}}, \quad (\varrho < 1), \quad \text{for prolate ellipsoids}$$

$$f/f_0 = \frac{\sqrt{1-\varrho^2}}{\varrho^{2/3}\arctan\sqrt{\varrho^2-1}}, \quad (\varrho > 1), \quad \text{oblate ellipsoids.}$$

Prolate ellipsoids				Oblate ellipsoids			
$1/\varrho$	f/f_0	$1/\varrho$	f/f_0	ϱ	f/f_0	ϱ	f/f_0
1·0	1·000	12	1·645	1·0	1·000	12	1·534
1·2	1·003	14	1·739	1·2	1·003	14	1·604
1·4	1·010	16	1·829	1·4	1·010	16	1·667
1·6	1·020	20	1·996	1·6	1·019	20	1·782
1·8	1·031	25	2·183	1·8	1·030	25	1·908
2·0	1·044	30	2·356	2·0	1·042	30	2·020
3·0	1·112	35	2·518	3·0	1·105	35	2·119
4·0	1·182	40	2·668	4·0	1·165	40	2·212
5·0	1·255	50	2·946	5·0	1·224	50	2·375
6·0	1·314	60	3·201	6·0	1·277	60	2·518
7·0	1·375	70	3·438	7·0	1·326	70	2·648
8·0	1·433	80	3·658	8·0	1·374	80	2·765
9·0	1·490	90	3·867	9·0	1·416	90	2·873
10·0	1·543	100	4·067	10·0	1·458	100	2·974

R. O. HERZOG, R. ILLIG and H. KUDAR, Z. physik. Chem., 1933, A 167, 329 and F. PERRIN, J. Phys. Rad., 1936, 7, vii, 1. See also introductory notes at beginning of this chapter.

TABLE VII, 16

VALUES OF THE BESSEL FUNCTIONS, $K_0(\varkappa a)$ AND $K_1(\varkappa a)$ IN THE EQUATION FOR THE ζ POTENTIAL AT A CYLINDER OF CHARGE, q. AXIAL RATIO $l/2a$ IN A MEDIUM OF DIELECTRIC CONSTANT ε

$$\zeta = \frac{2q}{\varepsilon\,(l + 2a)} \cdot \frac{K_0(\varkappa a)}{\varkappa a\,.\,K_1(\varkappa a)}$$

$\varkappa a$	$\dfrac{K_0\,(\varkappa a)}{K_1\,(\varkappa a)}$	$\dfrac{K_0\,(\varkappa a)}{\varkappa a\,K_1(\varkappa a)}$
0·06	0·1770	2·950
0·08	0·2140	2·675
0·10	0·2463	2·463
0·14	0·3012	2·151
0·20	0·3760	1·835
0·40	0·5100	1·275
0·60	0·5965	0·9942
1·00	0·7176	0·7176
1·40	0·7595	0·5426
2·00	0·8141	0·4071
3·00	0·8616	0·2872
4·00	0·8939	0·2235

For theoretical computation of mobilities see Tables VII, 13, 17.

TABLE VII, 17

ELECTROPHORETIC MOBILITIES OF MOLECULAR CYLINDERS
AT DIFFERENT IONIC STRENGTHS, $I_{(m)}$

Assymmetry or Axial ratio	Ratio of mobility to that of a sphere of same molecular volume for different values of $I_{(m)}$.				
	$I_{(m)} = 0\cdot0$	$I_{(m)} = 0\cdot005$	$I_{(m)} = 0\cdot02$	$I_{(m)} = 0\cdot1$	$I_{(m)} = 0\cdot2$
2·5	0·920	0·856	0·774	0·738	0·715
5·0	0·800	0·715	0·653	0·624	0·604
10·0	0·648	0·545	0·503	0·490	0·485
22·5	0·477	0·379	0·361	0·362	0·357
45	0·350	0·263	0·254	0·256	0·259

TABLE VII, 18

VALUES OF THE F FACTOR IN THE ELECTROPHORETIC MOBILITY EQUATION

$$U = \zeta\varepsilon/F\pi\eta \text{ FOR CYLINDERS}$$

where U = mobility, ε the dielectric constant of the medium of viscosity η.

$\varkappa a$	F	F'
0·00	8·00	6·67
0·40	7·73	6·49
1·00	7·36	6·26
1·40	6·87	5·91
2·00	6·51	5·67
2·40	6·34	5·56
3·00	6·10	5·40
∞	4·00	4·00

F = Factor for long cylinder perpendicular to electric field.

F' = Factor for long cylinder randomly oriented.

a = Radius of cylinder; $\dfrac{1}{\varkappa}$ = double layer thickness.

See: H. A. ABRAMSON *et al.*, *Chem. Rev.*, 1939, **24**, 364.
Compare Table VII, 13.

TABLE VII, 19

SPECIFIC REFRACTIONS (k) OF SOME PROTEINS IN BUFFER SOLUTIONS AT 0·5 °C.

Protein	R = diethyl barbiturate						R = $NaHPO_4'$			
	BSA	BSA	BSA	BSA	EA	LG	BSA	HSA	EA	LG
pH	8·56	8·59	8·60	8·60	8·60	8·60	7·67	7·71	7·74	7·68
Protein concentration in g./100 ml.	2·010	2·056	1·919	5·024	1·812	2·695	3·498	2·994	2·357	2·832
Buffer concentration c_{NaR} .	0·2118	0·0461	0·0963	0·0905	0·0971	0·0931	0·1220	0·1286	0·1297	0·1202
Buffer concentration c_{HR} .	0·005	0·01	0·02	0·02	0·02	0·02	0·0078	0·0078	0·0079	0·0078
k (Na Proteinate) . . .	0·001981	0·002025	0·001982	0·001976	0·001970	0·002020	0·001915	0·001904	0·001882	0·001892
k (Na Proteinate for $I_{(m)} \to 0$). .	0·001935	0·001935	0·001935	0·001935	0·001902	0·001909	0·001923	0·00191	0·001899	0·001901

Notes:

BSA = Bovine serum albumin,
HSA = Human serum albumin
EA = Egg albumin
LG = β-Lactoglobulin
c_{NaR} = and c_{HR} are given as g.mol/l.

Refractive indices are determined by a differential prism method (L. G. LONGSWORTH, *Ind. Eng. Chem.*, *Anal. Ed.*, 1946, **18**, 219) in conjunction with the optical system of a LONGSWORTH-TISELIUS electrophoresis apparatus. Specific refraction k is given by $k = (n_{solution} - n_{solvent})/P$ where n refers to the refractive index of the medium and P is the protein concentration in g./1000 ml. Values of k are given for wave length of light of 5780 A. Accuracy of k is c. ±0·000003.

G. E. PERLMANN and L. G. LONGSWORTH, *J. Am. Chem. Soc.*, 1948, **70**, 2719.

TABLE VII, 20
EFFECT OF CHARGE ON THE SPECIFIC REFRACTION (k)
OF CRYSTALLINE EGG ALBUMIN AND BOVINE SERUM ALBUMIN AT 0·5 °C.

Protein concentration g./100 ml.	pH	Mol NaOH . 10^5 per 1 g. protein	k' . 10^6	a
		Egg albumin		
6·451	4·95	0·00	1877	—
5·951	5·70	13·03	1888	45
5·739	6·20	19·28	1894	47
5·545	7·26	25·38	1898	44
5·334	8·7	32·67	1908	53
5·128	10·1	42·3	1904	36
5·025	10·5	44·6	1909	34
				Mean 44
		Bovine serum albumin		
4·740	5·02	0·00	1902	—
4·340	7·22	19·59	1919	46
4·077	8·32	34·44	1934	49
3·782	10·10	53·68	1944	41
3·606	10·58	64·75	1951	50
3·525	10·72	72·97	1979	56
				Mean 46

k' is given by $k' = k (1 + aze^-_0)$, where k is the isoelectric specific refraction, and k' varies proportionally to the net charge ze^-_0 where a is the proportionality factor. The net charge is given by the amount of added NaOH since at the given pH values all the added alkali reacts. The protein concentration is that for the isoelectric solution after correction for the dilution due to the added alkali.

G. E. PERLMANN and L. G. LONGSWORTH, *J. Am. Chem. Soc.*, 1948, **70**, 2719.

TABLE VII, 21

INTERFACIAL POTENTIAL AND TRANSPORT ENERGY FOR THE TRYPSIN WATER INTERFACE

pH	ζ mv.	$-\zeta e_0$ cal./g.mol *
2	360	8290
4	306	7050
6	188	4330
8	104	2400
10	80	1840
12	72	1660

* ζe_0 = energy to bring single negative ion of unit charge e_0 from bulk to enzyme surface.
(Sample of trypsin from Northrop).
H. SCHULMAN and E. K. RIDEAL, *Biochem. J.*, 1933, 27, 1581.

TABLE VII, 22

pH OPTIMA FOR THE ACTION OF CERTAIN ENZYMES

Enzyme	Substrate	Optimum pH	Iso-electric pH
Trypsin	Proteins	7·8	7·50
Urease	Urea	6·6 - 6·8	5·50
Pepsin	Ovalbumin	1·5	2·85
Pepsin	Casein	1·8	
Pepsin	Haemoglobin	2·2	
Pepsin	Gelatin	2·2	
Yellow enzyme	Proteins	5·3	
Zymase	Glucose	6·2	
β-l-Fructosidase	Sucrose	5·7	8·25
α-Glucosidase	α-Methylglucoside	5·4	
α-Glucosidase	Maltose	7·0	
Catalase	Hydrogen peroxide	6·8	5·58
Peroxidase (horseradish)	Guaiacol-H_2O_2	4·5 - 6·5	
	o-Cresol-H_2O_2	3·5 - 5·0	
Ribonuclease	Ribonucleic acid	7·6	
Deoxyribonuclease	Deoxyribonucleic acid	6·8 - 8·2 Requires Mg or Mn ions	5·0

TABLE VII, 22 (*Continued*)

Enzyme	Substrate	Optimum pH	Iso-electric pH
Papain	{ Ovalbumin	7·4 - 7·6	5·2
	{ Gelatin	5·0	
Amylase (Aspergillus Oryzae)		4·5 - 6·0	
Amylase (Malt)	} Starch maltose formation	4·5 - 6·0	
Amylase (Pancreatic)		6·0 - 7·3	
Carboxypeptidase	{ Polypeptides	7·0 - 7·5	
	{ Carbobenzoxyglycyl- phenylalanine	7·4	
Yeast invertase	{ Sucrose	4·8 - 5·8	
	{ Inulin	3·2 - 4·0	
Lactase { Dog intestine		5·4 - 6·0	
Calf intestine	{ β-Galactosides	5·0	
Yeast	{ β-Lactose	7·0	
Almond		4·2	
Beef kidney alkaline phosphomonoesterase	Naβ-Glycerophosphate+Mg¨	9·2	
Erythrocyte acid- phosphomonoesterase	α- or β-Glycerophosphate	5·6	
Liveracid- phosphomonoesterase	α- or β-Glycerophosphate	5·5	
"Topyeast"phosphatase	Most phosphoric esters	4·0	
Pancreatic Lipase	Fats	Increases from 7 to 8·8 with increasing number of C atoms in the fatty acid of the tri-glyceride	

CHAPTER VIII

ELECTROCHEMISTRY OF MELTS AT HIGH TEMPERATURES

In this chapter data on various electrochemical aspects of the physical chemistry of melts have been collected together. It was felt to be more satisfactory to collect the high temperature data on conductance, activity and thermodynamic functions together in a separate section rather than to disperse the material amongst the other relevant chapters in the book. Accordingly numerical data on densities, specific and equivalent conductance of fused salts and fused mixtures including silicates and some glasses is given together with conductance data for solid oxides and solid oxide mixtures.

TABLE VIII, 1

ACTIVITY AND ACTIVITY COEFFICIENTS OF

$MgCl_2$ IN $MgCl_2$ - KCl AND $MgCl_2$ - NaCl FUSED SALT MIXTURES

A = $MgCl_2$,　B = NaCl or KCl.

	Mol. Fraction of A	B = KCl					B = NaCl				
		0·900	0·833	0·667	0·500	0·333	0·900	0·833	0·667	0·500	0·333
Activity	650 °C.	0·75	0·53	0·27	0·045	0·008	0·87	0·69	0·43	0·14	0·044
	700	0·79	0·59	0·33	0·063	0·013	0·90	0·75	0·52	0·18	0·061
	750	0·82	0·65	0·40	0·087	0·020	0·92	0·81	0·62	0·23	0·081
	800	0·85	0·70	0·47	0·117	0·028	0·95	0·87	0·72	0·29	0·105
Activity coefficient	650 °C.	0·84	0·63	0·41	0·090	0·026	0·99	0·82	0·65	0·27	0·13
	700	0·88	0·70	0·50	0·126	0·040	1·00	0·90	0·79	0·36	0·18
	750	0·91	0·77	0·59	0·174	0·059	1·03	0·97	0·93	0·47	0·24
	800	0·95	0·85	0·70	0·234	0·084	1·05	1·05	1·09	0·59	0·31

From oxidation equilibrium of fused salts mixtures.

Standard state: pure $MgCl_2$ at the given temperature.

R. TSUCHIYA, *J. Electrochem. Soc. Japan*, 1949, **17**, 76.

TABLE VIII, 2

ACTIVITY COEFFICIENTS OF FUSED SALTS

	Mol. Fraction AgCl	1·00	0·8	0·6	0·45	0·3	0·2	0·1
AgCl in $PbCl_2$								
$f_\pm$ (500 °C.)		1·000	1·001	0·980	0·982	0·980	0·981	1·021
$f_\pm$ (600 °C.)		1·000	1·000	0·980	0·980	0·982	0·993	1·034

Standard state: pure AgCl at the given temperature.

E. J. SALSTRÖM, *J. Am. Chem. Soc.*, 1934, **56**, 1272.

TABLE VIII, 2 (*Continued*)

PbBr₂ in PbCl₂

Mol. Fraction PbBr$_2$	1·00	0·80	0·60	0·50	0·45
$f_\pm$ (450 °C.)	1·000	0·873	0·766	0·682	0·588
$f_\pm$ (500 °C.)	1·000	0·586	0·737	0·667	0·581
$f_\pm$ (550 °C.)	1·000	0·845	0·713	0·652	0·576

Standard state: pure PbBr$_2$ at the given temperature.

E. J. SALSTRÖM and J. H. HILDEBRAND, *J. Am. Chem. Soc.*, 1930, **52**, 4641.

AgBr in LiBr

Mol. Fraction AgBr	1·0000	0·5937	0·4086	0·2548	0·1100
$f_\pm$ (500 °C.)	1·0000	1·211	1·477	2·040	2·651
$f_\pm$ (550 °C.)	1·0000	1·199	1·432	1·950	2·457
$f_\pm$ (600 °C.)	1·0000	1·194	1·408	1·887	2·303

Standard state: pure AgBr at the given temperature.

E. J. SALSTRÖM and J. H. HILDEBRAND, *J. Am. Chem. Soc.*, 1930, **52**, 4050.

PbCl₂ in ZnCl₂

Mol. Fraction PbCl$_2$	1·000	0·885	0·688	0·595	0·490	0·301
$f_\pm$ 500 °C.	1·000	0·930	0·865	0·770	0·675	0·575
$f_\pm$ 600 °C.	1·000	0·945	0·840	0·750	0·685	0·515

Accuracy of these determinations: e.m.f. measured to $\pm 0·2$ mv. Calculated $f_\pm$ accurate to $\pm 0·001$.

Standard state: pure PbCl$_2$ at the given temperature.

A. WACHTER and J. H. HILDEBRAND, *J. Am. Chem. Soc.*, 1930, **52**, 4655.

TABLE VIII, 3

ACTIVITIES AND ACTIVITY COEFFICIENTS OF SiO_2 IN MOLTEN SLAGS OF THE SYSTEM

CaO - SiO_2

Temp. °C.	Mol. fraction of SiO_2									
	0·483		0·508		0·533		0·558		0·583	
	a	$f_\pm$	a	$f_\pm$	a	$f_\pm$	a	$f_\pm$	a	$f_\pm$
1600	0·334	0·69	0·509	1·00	0·527	0·99	0·603	1·08	0·710	1·22
1575	0·366	0·76	0·549	1·08	0·563	1·06	0·639	1·15	0·746	1·28
1550	0·401	0·83	0·594	1·17	0·605	1·14	0·680	1·22	0·787	1·35
1525	—	—	—	—	0·651	1·22	0·722	1·29	0·831	1·42
1500	—	—	—	—	—	—	0·772	1·38	0·880	1·51

a = activity ⎫ referred to β-cristobalite as the
$f_\pm$ = activity coefficient ⎰ standard state at the same temperature.

Values of $f_\pm$ accurate to approx $\pm 0·005$ - $\pm 0·01$.

L. CHING CHANG and G. DERGE, *Technical Pub.* No. 2101 (Class C. Metals Technology 1946) Am. Inst. of Mining and Metall. Engineers.

TABLE VIII, 4

STANDARD E.M.F. OF SiC - C (GRAPHITE) ELECTRODE PAIR IN CaO-SiO_2 MELTS

Temp. °C.	Chemical Composition of Standard State					E_0 volts
	Wt.%		Mol.%		Mol. ratio CaO/SiO_2	
	CaO	SiO_2	CaO	SiO_2		
1600	32·0	68·0	33·5	66·5	0·504	0·1054
1575	32·8	67·2	34·3	65·7	0·522	0·0989
1550	33·5	66·5	35·0	65·0	0·538	0·0924
1525	34·0	66·0	35·6	64·4	0·553	0·0857
1500	34·5	65·5	36·1	63·9	0·565	0·0790

Measured e.m.f. values accurate to $\pm 4·6$ mv. Thermoelectromotive-force corrections are large and introduce further errors.

L. CHING CHANG and G. DERGE, *loc.cit.*, see Table VIII, 3.

TABLE VIII, 5

THERMODYNAMIC FUNCTIONS FOR $CaO\text{-}SiO_2$ SLAGS (see Tables VIII 3 and 4).

Mol. fraction of SiO_2 in slag.	Free energy change in cell reaction (cal.)	Partial molal free energy of SiO_2 (cal.)	Partial molal heat content of SiO_2 (cal.)
0·483	—40,100 + 18·8T	24,900 — 15·5T	26,100
0·508	—20,400 + 3·3T	21,600 — 12·9T	22,700
0·533	—8,720 — 3·3T	19,700 — 11·8T	20,100
0·558	10,500 — 15·2T	16,500 — 9·80T	16,670
0·583	22,400 — 23·5T	14,500 — 8·42T	14,700

The LEWIS-RANDALL sign convention is used. T = absolute temperature.
Standard state as in Table VIII, 3.
L. CHING CHANG and G. DERGE, *loc.cit.*, see Table VIII, 3.

E_0 and $\varDelta G^0$ VALUES OF THE CELL REACTION (see Table VIII, 4) AT 1500 °C. FOR
SLAGS OF THE SYSTEM $CaO\text{-}SiO_2$ - Al_2O_3

% Al_2O_3 by wt.	Standard State 1500 °C.	CaO/SiO_2 mol. ratio, slag composition in equilibrium with standard state	E_0 volts	$\varDelta G^0$ cal.
0	Pure β-cristobalite	0·565	0·0790	—21,800
5	β-Cristobalite (may contain displaced Al atoms)	0·400	0·138	—38,200
10	Same as 5% Al_2O_3 mixture	0·197	0·164	—45,400
15	Mullite	0·074	0·131	—36,300
20	Mullite	0·119	0·116	—32,100

L. CHING CHANG and G. DERGE, *loc.cit.*, see Table VIII, 3.

TABLE VIII, 6

SPECIFIC CONDUCTANCE OF PURE CHLORIDES
Values of $\varkappa$ in mho.cm.$^{-1}$

Salt	950 °C.	900 °C.	850 °C.	800 °C.	750 °C.
KCl	—	2·48	2·36	2·24	—
NaCl	4·06	3·91	3·77	—	—
$CaCl_2$	2·78	2·56	2·34	2·12	—
$MgCl_2$	—	1·44	1·33	1·22	1·11

E. K. LEE and E. P. PEARSON, *Trans. Electrochem. Soc.*, 1945, **88**, 171.

TABLE VIII, 7

EQUIVALENT CONDUCTANCE OF SOME FUSED SALTS

Salt	Temp. range °C.	Equivalent Conductance $\Lambda_v^t = \Lambda_v^{800} [1 + c\,(t - 800)]$ where t is in °C.
LiCl	600 - 1000	$\Lambda_v^t = 196 \quad [1 + 0{\cdot}000782\,(t - 800)]$
NaCl	800 - 1000	$133{\cdot}2\,[1 + 0{\cdot}00115 \quad (t - 800)]$
KCl	768 - 1035	$108{\cdot}3\,[1 + 0{\cdot}00142 \quad (t - 800)]$
RbCl	726 - 915	$92 \quad [1 + 0{\cdot}00167 \quad (t - 800)]$
CsCl	645 - 831	$91 \quad [1 + 0{\cdot}00168 \quad (t - 800)]$
KBr	728 - 860	$100{\cdot}5\,[1 + 0{\cdot}00152 \quad (t - 800)]$
KI	682 - 1000	$101{\cdot}2\,[1 + 0{\cdot}00151 \quad (t - 800)]$
NaBr	740 - 940	$138 \quad [1 + 0{\cdot}00111 \quad (t - 800)]$

Accuracy: $\Lambda_v^{800} \pm 0{\cdot}5\%$; $c \pm 0{\cdot}5\%$.

PICRATES

$$\Lambda_v^t = \Lambda_v^{140} [1 + c\,(t - 140)].$$

Salt	Λ^{140}	c
$N(C_2H_5)_2(C_3H_7)_2$. Pic.	4·654	0·0238
$N(C_2H_5)_3C_3H_7$. Pic.	4·50	0·0242
$N(CH_3)_2\,(C_3H_7)_2$. Pic.	4·386	0·0248
$N(CH_3)\,(C_3H_7)_3$. Pic.	4·26	0·0260
$N(C_2H_5)\,(C_3H_7)_3$. Pic.	4·25	0·0262
$N(C_3H_7)_4$. Pic.	4·10	0·0272
$N(C_4H_9)_4$. Pic.	3·45	0·0310
$N(C_5H_{11})$. Pic.	2·92 (150 °C.)	0·034 [Use factor $(t - 150)$]

Accuracy: Λ_v^{140} is $\pm 0{\cdot}01$; $c \pm 1\%$.

P. WALDEN, Z. *physik. Chem.*, 1931, A 157, 389.

TABLE VIII, 8

SPECIFIC CONDUCTANCE OF SOME MOLTEN CHLORIDES

Chloride	t °C.	$\varkappa$ mho.cm.$^{-1}$
$BeCl_2$	450	$0\cdot00318 \pm 0\cdot0001$
	460	$0\cdot00572 \pm 0\cdot0001$
	472	$0\cdot00867 \pm 0\cdot0001$
UCl_4	570	$0\cdot34$
	598	$0\cdot42 \pm 0\cdot005$
	620	$0\cdot48$
$ThCl_4$	814	$0\cdot61$
	843	$0\cdot67$
	866	$0\cdot71$
	889	$0\cdot76$
	922	$0\cdot78$
$LaCl_3$	950	$1\cdot30$
	1000	$1\cdot42$
	1050	$1\cdot56$
	1100	$1\cdot70$
	1135	$1\cdot77$
$NdCl_3$	775	$0\cdot63$
	807	$0\cdot71$
	827	$0\cdot765$
	847	$0\cdot81$
	873	$0\cdot88$
	900	$0\cdot945$
$TeCl_2$	206	$0\cdot0420$
	221	$0\cdot0589$
	250	$0\cdot0893$
	271	$0\cdot114 \pm 0\cdot001$
	290	$0\cdot134$
	305	$0\cdot151$

TABLE VIII, 8 (*Continued*)

Chloride	$t\,°C.$	$\varkappa$ mho.cm.$^{-1}$
TeCl$_4$	236	0·1145
	254	0·136
	277	0·161
	290	0·175
	316	0·203
BiCl$_3$	266	0·442 $\pm$ 0·001
	295	0·481
	315	0·506
	335	0·533
	350	0·555
PrCl$_3$	824	0·82
	875	0·97
	902	1·06
	935	1·16
	965	1·26
MoCl$_5$	216	$1{\cdot}8 \cdot 10^{-6}$
	234	$4{\cdot}1 \cdot 10^{-6}$
	258	$7{\cdot}5 \cdot 10^{-6}$
WCl$_5$	250	$0{\cdot}67 \cdot 10^{-6}$
	260	$0{\cdot}97 \cdot 10^{-6}$
	270	$1{\cdot}22 \cdot 10^{-6}$
	290	$1{\cdot}70 \cdot 10^{-6}$
	300	$1{\cdot}84 \cdot 10^{-6}$
WCl$_6$	280	$1{\cdot}98 \cdot 10^{-6}$
	290	$2{\cdot}28 \cdot 10^{-6}$
	300	$2{\cdot}60 \cdot 10^{-6}$
	320	$4{\cdot}05 \cdot 10^{-6}$
	330	$6{\cdot}94 \cdot 10^{-6}$

A. Voigt and W. Biltz, *Z. anorg. Chem.*, 1924, **133**, 277.

TABLE VIII, 9

CONDUCTANCE OF FUSED SALTS

$$\varkappa = a + b \cdot 10^{-3} \, (t - t_1)$$

Substance	a (mho.cm.$^{-1}$)	b (mho.cm.$^{-1}$°C.$^{-1}$)	t_1 °C.
LiF	20·3	100	905
LiCl	7·59	1·0	780
NaF	3·15	8·3	1000
NaCl	3·66	2·2	850
KF	4·14	4·5	860
KCl	2·19	2·1	800
KBr	1·66	2·0	760
KI	1·35	2·3	710
RbCl	1·49	2·1	733
CsCl	1·14	2·0	660
CuCl	3·27	2·45	430
CuI	1·82	1·78	605
AgCl	4·44	1·84	600
AgBr	3·39	1·70	600
AgI	2·17	0·61	600
BeCl$_2$	0·0032	26	451
MgCl$_2$	1·05	1·7	729
KCl . MgCl$_2$	0·93	2·1	570
CaCl$_2$	1·99	3·5	795
SnCl$_2$	1·98	2·9	900
BaCl$_2$	1·71	3·0	900
ZnCl$_2$	0·051	1·5	460
CdCl$_2$	1·93	2·0	576
CdBr$_2$	1·06	2·0	571
CdI$_2$	0·19	2·1	389
Hg$_2$Cl$_2$	1·00	1·8	529
HgCl$_2$	0·00052	0·0005	294
AlCl$_3$	0·56 . 10^{-6}	—	—
AlCl$_3$. NH$_3$	0·0143	0·26	136
ScCl$_3$	0·56	2·8	959
YCl$_3$	0·40	2·0	714
LaCl$_3$	1·14	3·3	868
PrCl$_3$	0·90	3·7	824
NdCl$_3$	0·69	2·8	775
InCl$_3$	0·42	9·0	594
InCl$_2$	0·47	2·0	356
InCl	0·97	6·4	242

TABLE VIII, 9 (*Continued*)

Substance	a (mho.cm.$^{-1}$)	b (mho.cm.$^{-1}$°C.$^{-1}$)	t_1 °C.
TlCl	1·17	3·5	450
ThCl$_4$	0·67	1·8	814
SnCl$_2$	0·89	5·7	263
PbCl$_2$	1·48	4·6	508
BiCl$_3$	0·44	1·4	266
MoCl$_5$	1·8 . 10^{-6}	—	—
Na$_2$MoO$_4$	1·41	1·75	843
WCl$_6$	1·9 . 10^{-6}	—	280
WCl$_5$	0·67	2·3	250
Na$_2$WO$_4$	1·091	1·82	752
UCl$_4$	0·34	2·8	570
TeCl$_4$	0·12	1·1	236

Accuracy: No statement is made. Accuracy is probably of order ±5% for low melting compounds and is less satisfactory for those of higher melting points.

P. DROSSBACH, *Electrochemistry of Molten Salts*, Berlin, 1938.

TABLE VIII, 10

ENERGY OF ACTIVATION FOR CONDUCTANCE OF FUSED SALTS

$$\varkappa = A \, e^{-E/RT}$$
$$\Lambda_V = A' \, e^{-E'/RT}$$
$$\eta = \text{const.} \, . \, e^{B/RT}, \quad \Lambda_V = \frac{\varkappa \, W_e}{d}, \quad \varrho = \text{density.}$$

W_e = Equivalent weight.

Salt	Λ_V	E in k.cal.	E' in k.cal.	B in k.cal.	A mho.cm.$^{-1}$
LiCl	183	1·15	1·72	8·8	11·5
NaCl	150	1·54	2·70	9·4	7·3
KCl	120	2·30	3·26	7·8	6·5
RbCl	94	2·83	3·66	—	6·5
CsCl	86	3·33	3·75	—	6·6
LiBr	177	1·75	—	6·0	13·5
NaBr	148	1·84	2·51	10·6	7·4
KBr	109	2·55	3·42	7·9	5·8
NaI	150	1·25	2·00	7·4	4·8
KI	104	2·75	3·70	9·2	5·5
AgCl	118	0·99	1·20	5·3	7·4

TABLE VIII, 10 (Continued)

Salt	Λ_V	E in k.cal.	E' in k.cal.	B in k.cal.	A mho.cm.$^{-1}$
AgBr	99	0·70–1·00	0·99	4·5–5·4	—
AgI	105	0·80	0·90	5·8	4·0
CuCl	94	0·85	1·06	5·5	6·2
MgCl$_2$	35	3·56	3·97	—	6·4
CaCl$_2$	64	4·10	4·72	9·5	13·5
SrCl$_2$	69	4·00	4·65	—	11·0
BaCl$_2$	77	4.15	4·35	—	10·5
CdCl$_2$	58·5	2·30	2·13	4·5	7·3
CdBr$_2$	41·2	2·75	—	—	5·4
PbCl$_2$	53·0	2·3–4·5	4·20	6·6	—
PbBr$_2$	27	4·35	4·32	9·2	16·0

Accuracy of Λ_V is $\pm 0\cdot 2\%$. Temperature coefficient data from which E and E' are derived is accurate to $\pm 0\cdot 2\%$. Accuracy of E and E' is of the order of $\pm 0\cdot 4\%$. H. BLOOM and E. HEYMANN, Proc. Roy. Soc., 1947, **188A**, 392.

TABLE VIII, 11

CONDUCTANCE AND FREE ENERGY, ENTHALPY AND ENTROPY OF ACTIVATION
FOR CONDUCTANCE IN SILICATE MELTS

Cation	Composition of melt (M_xO_y/SiO_2)	$\varkappa_{1750}$ (mho.cm.$^{-1}$)	Λ_{1750}	$\Delta H^{\neq}_{1750}$ (k.cal./g. equiv.)	$\Delta G^{\neq}_{1750}$ (k.cal./g. equiv.)	$\Delta S^{\neq}_{1750}$ (cal./g. equiv./deg.)
K·	1 : 2	1·5	71·8	8·2	24·6	—8·2
	1 : 1	2·4**	82·7	8·0	24·0	—8·0
Na·	1 : 2	2·1	83·3	12·0	24·0	—6·0
	1 : 1	4·8**	126·0	13·5	22·3	—4·4
Li·	1 : 2	2·5	77·8	11·6	24·2	—6·5
	1 : 1	5·5	109·0	10·6	22·9	—6·1
	2 : 1	23·2**	332·0	9·6	18·4	—4·4
Ba··	1 : 2	0·18	6·4	33·2	37·1	—2·0
	1 : 1	0·60	16·2	17·5	33·4	—8·0
	2 : 1	1·32**	29·9	9·0	30·8	—10·9
Sr··	1 : 2	0·21	7·7	36·0	36·5	—0·2
	1 : 1	0·63	15·7	26·7	33·5	—3·4
	2 : 1	1·4**	26·8	17·0	31·4	—7·2
Ca··	1 : 2	0·31	11·4	30·0	34·7	—2·4
	1 : 1	0·83	18·4	20·0	32·8	—6·4
	2 : 1	1·15**	18·8	20·0	32·7	—11·4

TABLE VIII, 11 (*Continued*)

Cation	Composition of melt (M_xO_y/SiO_2)	$\varkappa_{1750}$ (mho.cm.$^{-1}$)	Λ_{1750}	$\Delta H^{\neq}_{1750}$ (k.cal./g. equiv.)	$\Delta G^{\neq}_{1750}$ (k.cal./g. equiv.)	$\Delta S^{\neq}_{1750}$ (cal./g. equiv./deg.)
Mn··	1 : 2	0·55**	18·2	24·0	32·9	—4·5
	1 : 1	1·8	35·1	16·0	30·2	—7·1
	2 : 1	6·3	85·5	12·0	26·6	—7·3
Fe··	1 : 1	1·82***	44·0	15·0	29·4	—7·2
Mg··	1 : 2	0·23**	6·5	34·0	37·1	—1·6
	1 : 1	0·72	12·2	24·0	34·5	—5·3
	2 : 1	2·15**	24·7	17·0	31·7	—7·4
Al···	10 wt.%	3×10^{-3}	0·202	22·0	52·5	—15·3
Ti····	10 wt.%	$6·3 \times 10^{-4}$	0·051	35·7	59·3	—11·8

** Extrapolated values. *** Extrapolated from WEJNARTH's data, (*Trans. Electrochem. Soc.*, 1934, **65**, 177).

Note: The conductance is predominantly cationic and Λ is the equivalent conductance with respect to the cation in the silicate mixture. See also Table VIII, 14.

J. O'M. BOCKRIS, J. A. KITCHENER, S. IGNATOWICZ and J. W. TOMLINSON, *Trans. Faraday Soc.*, 1952, **48**, 75.

ELECTRICAL RESISTIVITIES IN OHM.CM.

I. Vitreous

t °C.	Composition (Mo						
	0	1·74	3·82	6·19	8·89	11·57	16·41
100	—	—	—	—	—	—	—
150	—	—	—	—	—	—	40.10⁶
200	—	—	—	—	25.10⁶	12.10⁶	33.10⁵
250	—	—	—	—	40.10⁵	18.10⁵	40.10⁴
300	—	—	40.10⁶	10.10⁶	80.10⁴	36.10⁴	75.10³
350	—	55.10⁶	80.10⁵	20.10⁵	20.10⁴	95.10³	20.10³
400	—	16.10⁶	22.10⁵	60.10⁴	65.10³	28.10³	6300
450	—	50.10⁵	80.10⁴	20.10⁴	23.10³	10.10³	2500
500	—	18.10⁵	30.10⁴	85.10³	10.10³	4000	1000
550	50.10⁶	72.10⁴	12.10⁴	38.10³	4200	190	400
600	20.10⁶	32.10⁴	48.10³	18.10³	2000	100	—
650	10.10⁶	16.10⁴	25.10³	8.10³	1200	—	—
700	5.10⁶	10.10⁴	—	—	—	—	—

TABLE VIII, 12
ELECTRICAL CONDUCTANCE OF CaO-SiO₂-Al₂O₃ SLAGS

Slag composition %			Electrical conductance in mho.cm.$^{-1}$			
SiO₂	Al₂O₃	CaO	1600 °C.	1550 °C.	1500 °C.	1450 °C.
41·7	11·6	46·7	0·817	0·671	0·551	0·442
40·1	14·8	45·1	0·758	0·538	0·361	0·236
40·05	9·9	50·05	0·762	0·587	0·447	0·337
45·0	5·0	50·0	0·730	0·560	0·424	0·327
50·0	5·0	45·0	0·671	0·543	0·459	0·350
36·1	14·8	49·1	0·637	0·434	0·290	0·188
43·3	8·3	48·3	0·563	0·423	0·311	0·225
50·05	9·9	40·05	0·479	0·352	0·256	0·188
45·05	9·9	45·05	0·469	0·358	0·251	0·146
43·0	14·0	43·0	0·439	0·289	0·197	0·138
35·15	19·7	45·15	0·383	0·290	0·194	0·129
45·15	19·7	35·15	0·333	0·218	0·180	0·099
40·15	19·7	40·15	0·297	0·209	0·144	0·098
50·1	14·8	35·1	0·282	0·203	0·144	0·101
45·1	14·8	40·1	0·248	0·175	0·135	0·090

Conductance is predominantly cationic.

A. E. MARKIN and G. DERGE, *Technical Pub.* No. 1569, (Class C, No. 334) Amer. Inst. Mining and Metall. Engineers, 1943.

3

ı Na₂O - SiO₂ (VITREOUS AND CRYSTALLINE).

0 mol. SiO₂)								
4	34·81	44·98	55·12	65·10	75·17	80·24	90·34	99·97
	—	—	25.10⁶	65.10⁵	24.10⁶	18.10⁶	28.10⁶	35.10⁶
10⁶	65.10⁶	50.10⁵	12.10⁵	55.10⁴	13.10⁵	10.10⁵	18.10⁵	22.10⁵
10⁵	50.10⁵	40.10⁴	12.10⁴	65.10³	12.10⁴	10.10⁴	16.10⁴	20.10⁴
10⁴	62.10⁴	52.10³	20.10³	10.10³	15.10³	15.10³	20.10³	25.10³
10³	12.10³	10.10³	3500	2500	28	3000	400	54
10³	3300	2800	1000	700	66	730	100	13
	1000	800	310	270	20	250	30	40
	36	260	110	900	64	80	82	12
	13	100	400	—	—	—	—	—
	—	—	—	—	—	—	—	—
	—	—	—	—	—	—	—	—
	—	—	—	—	—	—	—	—
	—	—	—	—	—	—	—	—

II. Crystalline

$t\,°C.$				Composition (Mol.			
	0	1·74	3·82	6·19	8·89	11·57	21·28	29
200	—	—	—	—	—	—	—	
250	—	—	—	—	—	—	—	
300	—	—	—	—	—	—	—	
350	—	—	—	—	40.10^6	30.10^6	20.10^6	2
400	—	—	20.10^6	12.10^6	80.10^5	62.10^5	40.10^5	4
450	—	20.10^6	65.10^6	30.10^5	24.10^5	15.10^5	90.10^4	1
500	—	70.10^5	20.10^5	11.10^5	70.10^4	40.10^4	26.10^4	4
550	—	25.10^5	72.10^4	38.10^4	25.10^4	15.10^4	82.10^3	6
600	—	10.10^5	28.10^4	18.10^4	10.10^4	60.10^3	31.10^3	2
650	—	50.10^4	11.10^4	80.10^3	40.10^3	27.10^3	14.10^3	800
700	40.10^6	21.10^4	50.10^3	40.10^3	20.10^3	12.10^3	5000	300
750	16.10^6	90.10^3	11.10^3	6500	5500	4000	1500	100
800	—	—	—	—	—	—	—	
900	—	—	—	—	—	—	—	

M. Foex, *Bull. Soc. Chim.*, 1944 (5), **11**, 456.

TABLE VIII, 14

CONDUCTANCE AND FREE ENERGY, ENTHALPY AND ENTROPY OF ACTIVATION FOR
CONDUCTANCE IN MIXED SILICATE MELTS

Composition	$\varkappa_{1750}$ mho.cm.$^{-1}$	Λ_{1750}	$\Delta H^{\neq}$	$\Delta G^{\neq}$	$\Delta S^{\neq}$
System: $CaO.SiO_2 + MnO.SiO_2$					
$CaO.SiO_2$	0·89	19·9	18·6	32·5	—7·0
0·5 CaO ⎱ SiO₂ / 0·5 MnO ⎰	1·07	22·2	16·0	32·1	—8·1
0·25 CaO ⎱ SiO₂ / 0·75 MnO ⎰	1·28	25·9	14·5	31·5	—8·5
$MnO.SiO_2$	1·8	35·1	12·0	30·2	—9·1
System: $MnO + MnS + SiO_2$					
$MnO.SiO_2$	1·8	35·1	12·0	30·2	—9·1
0·8 MnO ⎱ SiO₂ / 0·2 MnS ⎰	1·67	35·0	12·9	30·1	—8·6

13 *(Continued)*

CM.)

0 mol. SiO$_2$)

80	50·03	60·07	70·24	80·24	90·34	99·97	110·07	120·32
	—	—	—	—	—	—	—	—
	—	—	—	—	—	—	40.10^6	50.10^5
	—	18.10^6	20.10^6	20.10^6	30.10^6	—	72.10^5	10.10^5
10^6	—	36.10^5	42.10^5	40.10^5	70.10^5	20.10^6	18.10^5	32.10^4
10^5	34.10^6	10.10^5	10.10^5	12.10^5	18.10^5	40.10^5	58.10^4	10.10^4
10^5	65.10^5	35.10^4	30.10^4	43.10^4	65.10^4	12.10^5	20.10^4	40.10^3
10^4	15.10^5	15.10^4	12.10^4	16.10^4	20.10^4	42.10^4	75.10^3	20.10^3
10^4	42.10^4	62.10^3	50.10^3	56.10^3	85.10^3	17.10^4	32.10^3	9000
10^3	13.10^4	28.10^3	24.10^3	30.10^3	40.10^3	70.10^3	17.10^3	4800
10^3	46.10^3	15.10^3	12.10^3	14.10^3	20.10^3	30.10^3	9000	3800
	16.10^3	7000	5000	7000	10.10^3	17.10^3	5000	1700
	5500	2200	1800	3000	7000	9000	3000	1000
	1800	900	640	800	3000	5000	1100	300
	—	—	—	—	—	—	440	120

TABLE VIII, 14 *(Continued)*

See notes in Table VIII, 11.

J. O'M. Bockris, J. A. Kitchener, S. Ignatowicz and J. W. Tomlinson, *Trans. Faraday Soc.*, 1952, **48**, 75.

TABLE VIII, 15

SPECIFIC CONDUCTANCE ($\varkappa$) OF NICKEL OXIDE NiO IN OXYGEN AT PRESSURE P

log (P_{O_2}) mm. Hg	log $\varkappa$ (mho./cm.)		
1·2	—0·49 ⎫		—
1·4	—0·46 ⎪		—
1·6	—0·39 ⎪		—0·68 ⎫
1·8	—0·35 ⎬ 1000 °C.		—0·60 ⎪
2·0	—0·30 ⎪		—0·56 ⎬ 900 °C.
2·4	—0·18 ⎪		—0·47 ⎭
2·8	—0·09 ⎭		

H. H. V. Baumbach and C. Wagner, *Z. physik. Chem.*, 1934, **B 24**, 59.

TABLE VIII, 16

ELECTRICAL CONDUCTANCE OF SOLID OXIDE MIXTURES AT 15 °C.

1. CuO - MnO$_2$

Mixture		Specific resistance (ohm.cm.)	Specific conductance (mho.cm.$^{-1}$)
100% CuO		—	~ 0
90% CuO	10% MnO$_2$	—	~ 0
80% ,,	20% ,,	276,520	36 . 10^{-7}
70% ,,	30% ,,	91,380	109 . 10^{-7}
60% ,,	40% ,,	20,416	490 . 10^{-7}
50% ,,	50% ,,	9,195	1,100 . 10^{-7}
40% ,,	60% ,,	6,519	1,530 . 10^{-7}
30% ,,	70% ,,	4,700	21·2 . 10^{-5}
20% ,,	80% ,,	3,874	26 . 10^{-5}
10% ,,	90% ,,	2,291	44 . 10^{-5}
0% ,,	100% ,,	1,469	68 . 10^{-5}

2. PbO$_2$ - MnO$_2$

90% PbO$_2$	10% MnO$_2$	2·65	377 . 10^{-3}
80% ,,	20% ,,	2·70	370 . 10^{-3}
70% ,,	30% ,,	5·90	170 . 10^{-3}
60% ,,	40% ,,	8·7	115 . 10^{-3}
50% ,,	50% ,,	36·3	30 . 10^{-3}
40% ,,	60% ,,	507·5	2 . 10^{-3}
30% ,,	70% ,,	1,683	0·6 . 10^{-3}
20% ,,	80% ,,	1,747	0·57 . 10^{-3}

3. MnO$_2$ - KBr

95% MnO$_2$	5% KBr	669·2	15 . 10^{-4}
90% ,,	10% ,,	228·3	44 . 10^{-4}
80% ,,	20% ,,	309·3	32 . 10^{-4}
70% ,,	30% ,,	1,223	8·2 . 10^{-4}
60% ,,	40% ,,	1,132	8·8 . 10^{-4}
50% ,,	50% ,,	1,168	8·6 . 10^{-4}
40% ,,	60% ,,	2,276·6	4·4 . 10^{-4}

TABLE VIII, 16 (*Continued*)

Mixture		Specific resistance (ohm.cm.)	Specific conductance (mho.cm.$^{-1}$)
4. MnO$_2$ (fresh, H$_2$O free) - KBr			
100% MnO$_2$		1,140·2	87·7 . 10^{-5}
90% MnO$_2$	10% KBr	397·3	25·2 . 10^{-4}
80% ,,	20% ,,	432·4	23·1 . 10^{-4}
70% ,,	30% ,,	690·3	14·5 . 10^{-4}
60% ,,	40% ,,	893	11·2 . 10^{-4}
50% ,,	50% ,,	1,040·6	9·6 . 10^{-4}
40% ,,	60% ,,	3,397	2·9 . 10^{-4}
5. 3MnO$_2$. 2H$_2$O - KBr			
100% 3MnO$_2$ · 2H$_2$O		32,000	0·3 . 10^{-4}
90% ,,	10% KBr	2,318·6	4·3 . 10^{-4}
80% ,,	20% ,,	9,524	7·1 . 10^{-4}

P. FISCHER, *Z. Elektrochem.*, 1926, 32, 538.

TABLE VIII, 17

CONDUCTANCE OF SOME HIGH MELTING POINT OXIDES AND SUPLHIDES
Specific conductance $\varkappa$ in mho.cm.$^{-1}$ × 10^6; T in °K.

1. Alumina, Al$_2$O$_3$			
In Vacuum		In N$_2$, 1 atmosphere	
T	$\varkappa$	T	$\varkappa$
1783	19	1783	7·5
1873	25	1873	12·5
After heating to glowing for a long period		1898	19
2000	22	1953	30
2083	34	Evacuated	
2148	45	2000	19
1873	12·3	H$_2$ admitted, 1 atmosphere	
		1913	38
After short heating to glowing			
1893	52		
1998	83		
2048	150		
2093	268		

TABLE VIII, 17 (*Continued*)

2. Magnesium oxide, MgO

In Vacuum		In N_2, 1 atmosphere		In H_2, 1 atmosphere	
T	$\varkappa$	T	$\varkappa$	T	$\varkappa$
1773	16·5	1778	10·7	1783	125
2183	375	1883	94	2000	940
Long period of heating		1973	375		
1773	7·5	2053	620		
1913	50	2113	830		
2053	150				
2273	750				

3. Calcium oxide, CaO

In Vacuum		In N_2, 1 atmosphere	
T	$\varkappa$	T	$\varkappa$
1783	45	1783	390
1913	410	1868	1090
1963	1000	1913	1640

4. Zirconium oxide, ZnO

In Vacuum		
T	$\varkappa$	
1573	12	*Note*: The zirconia was of uncertain purity owing to the difficulty of purification of this material (PODZUS, see below).
1773	600	

5. Thoria, ThO_2

In Vacuum		In N_2, 1 atmosphere		In H_2, 1 atmosphere	
T	$\varkappa$	T	$\varkappa$	T	$\varkappa$
1823	30	1883	93	1798	500
1913	47	1933	200	1943	2500
2053	107	2138	600		
2128	180	2273	2000		
2233	300				

TABLE VIII, 17 (*Continued*)

6. Boron nitride, BN

In Vacuum		In N_2, 1 atmosphere	
T	$\varkappa$	T	$\varkappa$
1783	7·5	1873	6·5
1873	75	1978	10
1953	375	2073	16
2023	1500	2173	33
1873	75		

Note: $\varkappa$ depends strongly on degree of purity and comparisons with other work must be made with caution.

Von E. PODZUS, Z. *Elektrochem.*, 1933, **39**, 75.

TABLE VIII, 18

DENSITIES (ϱ) OF BINARY FUSED SALT MIXTURES OF NaCl-CaCl$_2$

NaCl: $\varrho = 1\cdot549 - 0\cdot0005$ $(t - 800\ °C.)$, $(800 \sim 900\ °C.)$, $(t$ in $°C.)$,

CaCl$_2$: $\varrho = 2\cdot085 - 0\cdot00044$ $(t - 800\ °C.)$, $(780 \sim 870\ °C.)$.

	NaCl — CaCl$_2$									
Temp. °C.	550	600	650	675	700	725	750	800	850	900
Mol.% of NaCl										
0	—	—	—	—	—	—	—	2·085	2·063	—
20	—	—	—	—	2·032	2·021	2·010	1·988	1·966	—
40	—	—	1·951	1·940	1·930	1·919	1·909	1·888	1·867	—
50	—	1·928	1·906	1·895	1·886	1·877	1·868	1·846	1·824	—
55	1·935	1·913	1·891	1·880	1·874	1·870	1·859	1·837	1·815	—
60	—	—	1·876	1·864	1·852	1·840	1·828	1·804	1·780	—
70	—	—	—	1·792	1·783	1·774	1·765	1·747	1·729	—
80	—	—	—	—	—	—	1·703	1·683	1·663	—
100	—	—	—	—	—	—	—	1·549	1·524	1·499

Values determined by buoyancy method.

G. FUSEYA and K. OUCHI, *J. Electrochem. Soc.*, *Japan*, 1949, **17**, 254.

TABLE VIII, 19

DENSITY (ϱ_t) OF FUSED SALTS AT TEMPERATURE $t°$ C.

given by $\varrho_t = a - b \cdot 10^{-4} \cdot (t - t_1)$ where t and t_1 are in $°C.$

Compound	a (g./cc)	b (g./cc./°C.	t_1 °C.
LiF	1·798	4·4	850
LiCl	1·501	4·3	600
NaF	1·942	5·6	1000

TABLE VIII, 19 (*Continued*)

Compound	a (g./cc.)	b (g./cc./°C.)	t_1 °C.
NaCl	1·505	6·0	850
NaI	2·698	10·6	700
NaBr	2·306	7·2	780
NaOH	1·771	4·9	350
KF	1·878	6·69	900
KCl	1·539	5·947	750
KBr	2·106	7·99	750
KI	2·431	10·22	700
KOH	1·717	4·4	400
RbF	2·873	9·7	825
RbCl	2·252	8·7	714
RbBr	2·688	11·0	700
RbI	2·798	11·1	700
CsF	3·611	12·3	700
CsCl	2·786	10·8	650
CsBr	3·125	13·4	650
CsI	3·175	12·2	640
CuCl	3·677	7·9	422
Hg_2Cl_2	5·90	4·0	525
$HgCl_2$	5·118	3·38	240
$BeCl_2$	1·512	11·0	416
$MgCl_2$	1·686	2·9	712
$KCl . MgCl_2$	1·711	7·8	570
$CaCl_2$	2·03	4	850
$SrCl_2$	2·69	4·5	900
$BaCl_2$	3·12	6	1000
$ZnCl_2$	2·532	5·8	318
$ZnBr_2$	3·405	9·1	500
$CdCl_2$	3·32	6·9	600
$AlCl_3$	1·33	25	190
AlI_3	2·78	—	382
$AlBr_3$	2·26	—	265
$AlCl_3 . NH_3$	1·504	8·3	125
Na_3AlF_6	2·04	8·0	1035
$ScCl_3$	1·07	—	940
YCl_3	2·52	5	700
$LaCl_3$	3·155	5	860
$GaCl_3$	2·063	20·5	78
$GaBr_3$	3·138	29·5	125
GaI_3	3·600	22·4	211
$InCl_3$	2·14	21	586
$InCl_2$	3·05	16	235

TABLE VIII, 19 (*Continued*)

Compound	a (g./cc.)	b (g./cc./°C.)	t_1 °C.
InCl	3·74	14	225
TlCl	5·628	18	430
ThCl$_4$	3·3	—	765
SnCl$_2$	3·394	12	245
PbCl$_2$	4·947	16·4	500
PbBr$_2$	5·305	14·5	600
SbCl$_3$	2·671	21·7	75
BiCl$_3$	3·860	23·2	250
Na$_2$MoO$_4$	2·795	6·29	700
Na$_2$WO$_4$	$3·673 - 9·275\,(t - 930) + 3·37 \cdot 10^{-7}\,(t - 930)^2$		

No statement of the accuracy of these data is given.
P. Drossbach, *Electrochemistry of Fused Salts*, Berlin, 1938.

TABLE VIII, 20

FUSION AND VAPOURISATION OF 1 : 1 SALTS

Substance	T_f	ref.	T_b	ref.	L_f	ref.	L_b	ref.
LiCl	614	1	—	—	5·00	1	—	—
LiBr	822	1	—	—	4·00	1	—	—
LiI	723	1	—	—	3·0	1	—	—
NaCl	1,077	1	1,712	2	7·22	1	44·3	2
NaBr	1,028	1	1,666	2	6·0	1	38·6	2
NaI	934	1	—	—	5·0	1	—	—
KCl	1,045	1	1,690	2	6·41	1	40·5	2
KBr	1,003	1	1,649	2	6·0	1	38·2	2
KI	963	1	—	—	$5·0 - 3·66$	1	—	—
NaNO$_3$	581	4	—	—	3·69	4	—	—
KNO$_3$	606	4	—	—	2·58	4	—	—
AgCl	728	1	1,827	3	3·05	3	44·3	3
AgBr	703	1	—	—	2·37	3	—	—
AgI	825	3	—	—	—	—	—	—

L_f and L_b are heats of fusion and vapourisation respectively in k.cal./mol.;
T_f and T_b are corresponding temperatures in °K.

References:
[1] A. Leontjewa, *Acta Physicochim. U.R.S.S.*, 1939, **11**, 861.
[2] R. Lorenz, *Z. physik. Chem.*, 1912, **79**, 63.
[3] R. Lorenz and A. Hochberg, *Z. anorg. Chem.*, 1916, **94**, 317.
[4] R. S. Dantmura, *ibid.*, 1928, **175**, 1.

TABLE VIII, 21

DENSITIES (ϱ_t) OF MOLTEN SALT MIXTURES. VALUES OF THE CONSTANTS a AND b IN THE EQUATION $\varrho_t = a - b\,(t - 600)$

$PbCl_2$–$CdCl_2$ ($\pm 0.2\%$) *

mol. % $PbCl_2$	100	79.4	67.2	41.8	20.1	0
a	4.802 (4.763 LFJ)	4.544	4.388	4.018	3.693	3.366 (3.320 LFJ)
$b \cdot 10^3$	1.50 (1.44 LFJ)	1.43	1.39	1.18	1.02	0.84 (0.69 LFJ)
Range in °C.	516 - 710	545 - 680	480 - 680	515 - 700	540 - 680	582 - 725

$CdCl_2$–$CdBr_2$ ($\pm 0.1\%$)

mol. % $CdCl_2$	100	70.3	54.4	34.7	0
a	3.366	3.598	3.709	3.832	4.040
$b \cdot 10^3$	0.84	0.90	0.91	0.93	1.08
Range in °C.	582 - 725	580 - 680	590 - 710	606 - 705	580 - 720

$CdCl_2$–$NaCl$ ($\pm 0.2\%$)

mol. % $CdCl_2$	100	77.8	64.8	55.5	44.3	34.3	0
a	3.366	3.108	2.919	2.763	2.574	2.398	(1.675)
$b \cdot 10^3$	0.84	0.95	1.04	0.92	0.86	0.83	(0.63 J)
Range in °C.	582 - 725	580 - 700	540 - 680	570 - 680	500 - 690	580 - 690	Above 800

PbCl$_2$–KCl (±0·6%)

mol. % PbCl$_2$	100	82·1	63·8	47·4	0
a	4·802	4·293	3·745	3·282	(1·628 J)
$b \cdot 10^3$	1·50	1·42	1·28	1·13	(0·60 J)
Range in °C.	516 - 700	565 - 700	580 - 680	490 - 680	Above 750

PbCl$_2$–PbBr$_2$ (±0·15%)

mol. % PbCl$_2$	100	80·3	49·7	15·4	0
a	4·802	4·928	5·095	5·264	5·348 (5·305 LFJ)
$b \cdot 10^3$	1·50	1·52	1·55	1·71	1·65 (1·45 LFJ)
Range in °C.	516 - 570	492 - 620	465 - 640	410 - 600	505 - 600

PbCl$_2$–AgCl (±0·10%)

mol. % PbCl$_2$	100	80·6	70·9	61·1	53·4	42·6	20·3	0
a	4·802	4·790	4·782	4·778	4·775	4·764	4·739	4·698 (4·715 LH)
$b \cdot 10^3$	1·50	1·45	1·42	1·34	1·28	1·26	1·08	0·94 (0·92 LH)
Range in °C.	516 - 710	520 - 700	470 - 680	445 - 670	444 - 680	380 - 700	478 - 660	480 - 680

TABLE VIII, 21 (*Continued*)

AgCl–AgBr (±0·15%)

mol. % AgCl	100	77·3	59·7	34·2	0
a	4·698	4·875	5·006	5·190	5·402 (5·405 LH)
b . 10³	0·94	1·08	1·12	1·07	1·04 (1·03 LH)
Range in °C.	480 - 630	440 - 580	420 - 590	420 - 580	440 - 600

AgCl–KCl (±0·3%)

mol. % AgCl	100	80·6	68·0	47·8	0
a	4·698	3·893	3·425	2·758	(1·628 J)
b . 10³	0·94	0·95	0·96	0·88	(0·60 J)
Range in °C.	480 - 630	433 - 670	385 - 640	560 - 745	Above 750

AgBr–KBr (±0·25%)

mol. % AgBr	100	79·2	60·1	39·5	0
a	5·400 (5·405 LH)	4·484	3·758	3·098	(2·226 J)
b . 10³	1·05 (1·03 LH)	1·12	1·03	0·98	(0·80 J)
Range in °C.	440 - 600	380 - 600	380 - 600	593 - 700	Above 750

CdCl₂–KCl ($\pm 0.2\%$)

mol. % CdCl₂	100	83·1	59·2	40·0	24·8	0
a	3·366	3·049	2·608	2·299	2·063	(1·628 J)
$b \cdot 10^3$	0·84	0·96	0·95	0·82	0·72	(0·60 J)
Range in °C.	582 - 725	534 - 700	464 - 680	460 - 680	604 - 750	Above 750

PbCl₂–BaCl₂

mol. % PbCl₂	100	86·2	80·3	69·4	0
a	4·802	4·620	4·540	4·394	(3·850 AG)
$b \cdot 10^3$	1·50	1·35	1·36	1·27	(0·52 AG)
Range in °C.	516 - 710	565 - 700	575 - 690	660 - 710	Above 1000

CdCl₂–BaCl₂

mol. % CdCl₂	100	82·9	64·0	45·8	0
a	3·366	3·438	3·480	3·493	(3·360 AG)
$b \cdot 10^3$	0·84	0·93	0·93	0·96	(0·52 AG)
Range in °C.	582 - 725	597 - 700	580 - 700	600 - 690	Above 1000

From N. K. BOARDMAN, F. H. DORMAN and E. HEYMANN, *J. Phys. and Colloid Chem.*, 1949, **53**, 375.

Values in brackets by other authors

{ LFJ ≡ R. LORENZ, H. FREI and A. JABS, *Z. physik. Chem.*, 1907, **61**, 468.
J ≡ F. M. JAEGER, *Z. anorg. Chem.*, 1917, **101**, 175.
LH ≡ R. LORENZ and A. HOCHBERG, *ibid.*, 1916, **94**, 305.
AG ≡ K. ARNDT and A. GESSLER, *Z. Elektrochem.*, 1908, **14**, 665.

a is in the units g./cc. and b in g./cc./°C.

* Values in these brackets are accuracies of constants a and b.

TABLE VIII, 22

MOLAR VOLUMES OF MOLTEN SALT MIXTURES

$CdCl_2-CdBr_2$ (700 °C.) max. expt. error $\pm 0.1\%$

mol. % $CdCl_2$	100	70·3	54·4	34·7	0			
molar volume in cm.[3]	55·88	59·79	61·88	64·52	69·23			

$PbCl_2-PbBr_2$ (600 °C.) max. expt. error $\pm 0.15\%$

mol. % $PbCl_2$	100	80·3	49·7	15·4	0			
molar volume in cm.[3]	57·92	59·99	63·32	67·04	68·60			

$PbCl_2-AgCl$ (600 °C.) max. expt. error $\pm 0.1\%$

mol. % $PbCl_2$	100	80·6	70·9	61·1	53·4	42·6	20·3	0
molar volume in cm.[3]	58·92	52·60	49·93	47·28	45·10	42·15	36·04	30·50

$AgCl-AgBr$ (600 °C.) max. expt. error $\pm 0.15\%$

mol. % AgCl	100	77·3	59·7	34·2	0			
molar volume in cm.[3]	30·50	31·50	32·20	33·30	34·75			

$PbCl_2-CdCl_2$ (600 °C.) max. expt. error $\pm 0.2\%$

mol. % $PbCl_2$	100	79·4	67·2	41·8	20·1	0		
molar volume in cm.[3]	57·90	56·90	56·30	55·50	54·81	54·46		

N. K. BOARDMAN, F. H. DORMAN and E. HEYMANN, *J. Phys. and Colloid Chem.*, 1949, 53, 378.

TABLE VIII, 23

E.M.F.'S OF MOLTEN SALT DANIELL CELLS IN VOLTS

Pb | PbBr$_2$ (1) + PbCl$_2$ | Br$_2$

Mol. fraction N$_1$		1·000	0·800	0·600	0·500	0·450
450 °C.	e.m.f.	1·0624	1·0736	1·0866	1·0959	1·1038
500 °C.	e.m.f.	1·0321	1·0447	1·0593	1·0687	1·0768
550 °C.	e.m.f.	1·0017	1·0156	1·0318	1·0415	1·0496

Ag | AgBr (1) + LiBr | Br$_2$

Mol. fraction N$_1$		1·0000	0·5937	0·4086	0·2548	0·1100
500 °C.	e.m.f.	0·7865	0·8085	0·8202	0·8301	0·8686
550 °C.	e.m.f.	0·7720	0·7961	0·8100	0·8216	0·8648
600 °C.	e.m.f.	0·7577	0·7836	0·7993	0·8128	0·8610

Zn | ZnCl$_2$ | Cl$_2$

Temp. °C.	501·0	527·8	541·0	565·2	575·5
e.m.f.	1·5721	1·5529	1·5440	1·5277	1·5199

E.m.f. data accurate to ±0·2 mv.

E. J. SALSTRÖM and J. H. HILDEBRAND, *J. Am. Chem. Soc.*, 1930, **52**, 4648.

Pb	PbCl$_2$	Cl$_2$	e.m.f.	$1·2467 - 6·5 \;.\; 10^{-4}\,(t - 550)$
Cd	CdCl$_2$	Cl$_2$	e.m.f.	$1·3421 - 6·29\;.\;10^{-4}\,(t - 599)$
Zn	ZnCl$_2$	Cl$_2$	e.m.f.	$1·6050 - 4·6 \;.\; 10^{-4}\,(t - 427) - 8·93.10^{-7}\,(t - 427)$
Mg	MgCl$_2$	Cl$_2$	e.m.f.	$2·5112 - 6·73\;.\;10^{-4}\,(t - 700)$

Accuracy: ±0·2 mv. t = temperature in °C.

R. LORENZ and H. VELDE, *Z. anorg. Chem.*, 1929, **183**, 81.

Ag	AgCl	Cl$_2$	Temp. 525 °C.	e.m.f. 0·892
Pb	PbCl$_2$	Cl$_2$	Temp. 525 °C.	e.m.f. 1·255

Accuracy: ±1 mv.

S. A. PLATENEV and V. ROZOV, *Acta Physicochim. U.R.S.S.*, 1937, **7**, 341.

CHAPTER IX

REVERSIBLE ELECTRODE PROCESSES

The data presented in this chapter are concerned principally with reversible electrode processes. A number of data on standard electrode potentials collected together by BOCKRIS and HERRINGSHAW (*Discuss. Faraday Soc.*, 1947, **43**, 328), are presented here together with estimates of their reliability.

Recent data on standard potentials of some half-elements in non-aqueous media by HARNED and others are given in Tables IX, 6, 7, 8 and 9. A number of selected redox potentials of inorganic and organic systems together with those of some systems of biological importance are given in the Tables IX, 12 and 17. In the biological work activities of the components are usually unknown and so the apparent or "formal" non-thermodynamic redox potentials are given. This also applies to the data on uranium and some transuranic elements. For the latter only a limited number of systems are considered, since most of this work is still classified as secret by the Atomic Energy Commission. Further notes on the transuranic couples will be found in the appropriate tables.

A number of polarographic half wave potentials for various processes are given. As the literature on this subject is now so voluminous a selection of potentials for important processes has been given. For further data reference should be made to the extensive recent compilation of P. ZUMAN (*Coll. Czech. Chem. Comm.*, 1950, **15**, 1107).

The electrochemical equivalents of the elements calculated by ROUSCH in 1938 and corrected to the 1942 Atomic weights are given in Table IX, 33. These values are computed with respect to a rounded value of 96,500 coulombs for the Faraday (see Table I, 1).

Data on *irreversible* electrode processes are given in Chapter X.

TABLE IX, 1

STANDARD ELECTRODE POTENTIALS AT 25 °C.

Irreproducibility of Measurements. The large effect of the state of the electrode surface, often stressed as a factor governing the potential associated with an irreversible electrode process, is generally contrasted with the small effect of this factor on reversible electrode potentials. A detailed examination of the literature does not support this contention. Effects of surface characteristics on reversible electrode potentials are probably partly due to the different degrees of mechanical strain in the metal induced by different modes of preparation. Impurities, particularly occluded gases, present in varying quantities, may have a considerable effect on the electrode potential by introducing other reactions at the electrode-solution interface. Lack of complete reversibility of the electrode reaction may also cause irreproducible measurements.

Arrangement of Values of Standard Electrode Potentials. The agreement between the results of independent work is relatively poor, except for some of the softer metals where concordance of about 1 mv. is found among several independent determinations. For many elements, much larger discrepancies occur due partly to the difficulties of determination described above, but more frequently to lack of relevant data which makes for the accurate evaluation of e_0. On this account, the present collection distinguishes three classes of values.

In Table I, Column A refers to those elements for which there are apparently reliable independent data, concordant to within about 1 mv., which lead to an evaluation of the standard electrode potential.

Column B refers to those elements for which insufficiently reliable data are available for an accurate evaluation of the standard electrode potential. In this case, the most accurate results in the literature concerning the standard electrode potential are given with explanatory notes. The concordance between independent determinations is of the order of 1 cv.

Column C refers to those electrode potentials the values of which are of an extremely provisional nature.

Table IX, 2 refers to the standard potentials of some well-known half-cells, the values given being of an accuracy comparable with that of the values in column A.

TABLE IX, 1 (*Continued*)

Electrode Reaction	e_0 (Volts)			Notes	References
	±1 mv. A	±1 cv. B	± ?v. C		
$\frac{3}{2}N_2 + e_0^- \rightleftharpoons N_3'$	—	—	-3·2	Calc. exptl. values irreproducible; electrode reaction irreversible (15, 90)	13, 89
$Li\cdot + e_0^- \rightleftharpoons Li$	—	-3·01	—	Exptl. and calc. values somewhat discrepant. Mean value given; see also 33	2, 3
$Rb\cdot + e_0^- \rightleftharpoons Rb$	—	-2·98	—	Fair agreement of independant determinations; but see 33	2, 5 (calc.); 3 (exptl.)
$Cs\cdot + e_0^- \rightleftharpoons Cs$	—	-2·92	—	Calc. and exptl. values agree; but see also 2, 33	34 (calc.) 35 (exptl.)
$K\cdot + e_0^- \rightleftharpoons K$	—	-2·92	—	Good concordance of results; but see 33	2, 5 (calc.) 3, 36 (exptl.)
$Ba\cdot\cdot + 2e_0^- \rightleftharpoons Ba$	—	-2·92	—	Calc. value; exptl. value -2·15 from fused salts measurement (33)	2, 37, 38
$Sr\cdot\cdot + 2e_0^- \rightleftharpoons Sr$	—	-2·89	—	Calc. value; exptl. value -2·86 (38), but see 33	2, 37, 38
$Ca\cdot\cdot + 2e_0^- \rightleftharpoons Ca$	—	-2·84	—	Calc. value; exptl. values -1·90 (33) to -2·76 (39)	2, 37
$Na\cdot + e_0^- \rightleftharpoons Na$	-2·713	—	—		2, 3, 4, 5, 6
$La\cdot\cdot\cdot + 3e_0^- \rightleftharpoons La$	—	—	-2·4	Calc. and exptl. values very discrepant; see also (91)	2
$Mg\cdot\cdot + 2e_0^- \rightleftharpoons Mg$	—	-2·38	—	See 2, 34, 38, 41 for other calc. values; see also 42 and 43 for discrepant exptl. values	40

TABLE IX, I (*Continued*)

Electrode Reaction	e_0 (Volts)			Notes	References
	±1 mv. A	±1 ev. B	±? v. C		
$Th^{····} + 4e_0^- \rightleftharpoons Th$	—	—	−2·1	Calc. value	2
$Ti^{··} + 2e_0^- \rightleftharpoons Ti$	—	—	−1·75	Calc. value	2
$HfO^{··} + 2H^· + 4e_0^- \rightleftharpoons Hf + H_2O$	—	—	−1·7	Calc. value	2
$Be^{··} + 2e_0^- \rightleftharpoons Be$	—	−1·70	—	Calc. value: exptl. values, −1·1 to −1·9 (84, 85)	2, 83
$Al^{···} + 3e_0^- \rightleftharpoons Al$	—	−1·66	—	Mean of two calc. values; exptl. values very doubtful, see 45 and 46	34, 44
$ZrO^{··} + 2H^· + 4e_0^- \rightleftharpoons Zr + H_2O$	—	—	−1·5	Calc. values	2
$V^{··} + 2e_0^- \rightleftharpoons V$	—	—	−1·5	Calc. values (± 0·3)	2
$WO_4'' + 4H_2O + 6e_0^- \rightleftharpoons 8OH' + W$	—	—	−1·1	Calc. from est. value of entropy of WO_4''	2
$Mn^{··} + 2e_0^- \rightleftharpoons Mn$	—	—	−1·05	Calc. values	2, 92, 93
$Te + 2e_0^- \rightleftharpoons Te''$	—	—	−0·92	Calc. value; second dissociation const. of H_2Te not available; exptl. value, −0·84 (94)	13, 75
$UO_2' + 4H^· + 6e_0^- \rightleftharpoons U + 2H_2O$	—	—	−0·82	Calc. entropy of ion uncertain	2
$Se + 2e_0^- \rightleftharpoons Se''$	—	−0·78	—	Calc. values (independant data)	13, 47
$Zn^{··} + 2e_0^- \rightleftharpoons Zn$	−0·763	—	—		7, 8, 9, 10, 11
$H_3BO_3 + 3H^· + 3e_0^- \rightleftharpoons 3H_2O + B$	—	—	−0·73	Calc. value	2
$Cr^{···} + 3e_0^- \rightleftharpoons Cr$	—	—	−0·71	Calc. value	2
$SbO_2' + 2H_2O + 3e_0^- \rightleftharpoons Sb + 4OH'$	—	−0·67	—	Calc. and exptl. values	76, 77

TABLE IX, 1 (*Continued*)

Electrode Reaction	e_0 (Volts)			Notes	References
	±1 mv. A	±1 cv. B	±?v. C		
$Ga^{\cdots} + 3e_0^- \rightleftharpoons Ga$	—	−0.52	—	Exptl. value	48
$S + 2e_0^- \rightleftharpoons S''$	—	−0.51	—	Calc. values based on thermal data for H_2S; agree with $Ag\,|\,Ag_2S\,|\,H_2S$ electrode measurements; see also 51, 52	49, 50
$Fe^{\cdot\cdot} + 2e_0^- \rightleftharpoons Fe$	—	−0.44	—	Exptl. values	13, 53, 54, 55
$Cd^{\cdot\cdot} + 2e_0^- \rightleftharpoons Cd$	−0.402	—	—	—	5, 11, 12
$In^{\cdots} + 3e_0^- \rightleftharpoons In$	—	−0.34	—	Exptl. values	56, 57
$Tl^{\cdot} + e_0^- \rightleftharpoons Tl$	−0.335	—	—	—	13, 14, 15
$Co^{\cdot\cdot} + 2e_0^- \rightleftharpoons Co$	—	−0.27	—	Exptl. values	58, 59, 60
$Ni^{\cdot\cdot} + 2e_0^- \rightleftharpoons Ni$	—	−0.23	—	See also 14, 63, for data in presence of H_2	61, 62
$Mo^{\cdots} + 3e_0^- \rightleftharpoons Mo$	−0.140	—	−0.2	Calc., mainly from estimated data	2
$Sn^{\cdot\cdot} + 2e_0^- \rightleftharpoons Sn$	—	—	—	—	13 (corrected by the value of e_0 for Pb given here),
$Pb^{\cdot\cdot} + 2e_0^- \rightleftharpoons Pb$	−0.126	—	—	—	16, 17, 18, 19, 20, 21
$D^{\cdot} + e_0^- \rightleftharpoons \frac{1}{2}D_2$	—	−0.003	—	Exptl. value	65
$HAsO_2 + 3H^{\cdot} + 3e_0^- \rightleftharpoons As + 2H_2O$	—	0.25	—	Calc. from exptl. e.m.f. values of reaction $As_2O_3 + 3H_2 \rightleftharpoons 2As + 3H_2O$	2
$BiO^{\cdot} + 2H^{\cdot} + 3e_0^- \rightleftharpoons Bi + H_2O$	—	0.32	—	Exptl. values	66, 67
$Cu^{\cdot\cdot} + 2e_0^- \rightleftharpoons Cu$	—	0.34	—	Exptl. values	68, 69, 70, 71, 72, 73

TABLE IX, 1 (*Continued*)

Electrode Reaction	e_0 (Volts)			Notes	References
	±1 mv. A	±1 cv. B	±? v. C		
$\frac{1}{2}O_2 + H_2O + 2e_0^- \rightleftharpoons 2OH'$	0·401	—	—	Calc. values	78, 79, 80, 81, 82
$Cu^{\cdot} + e_0^- \rightleftharpoons Cu$	—	0·52	—	Calc. from equil., $Cu + Cu^{\cdot\cdot} \rightleftharpoons 2Cu^{\cdot}$	116
$I_2 + 2e_0^- \rightleftharpoons 2I'$	0·536	—	—	—	13, 22, 23
$Te^{\cdots\cdot} + 4e_0^- \rightleftharpoons Te$	—	0·56	—	Calc. and exptl. values	74, 75
$Po^{\cdots} + 3e_0^- \rightleftharpoons Po$	—	—	0·56	Various exptl. data discrepant	95, 96
$Rh^{\cdot\cdot} + 2e_0^- \rightleftharpoons Rh$	—	—	0·6	Calc. value; no knowledge of free energies of solution of oxides	2
$Hg_2^{\cdot\cdot} + 2e_0^- \rightleftharpoons 2Hg$	0·798	—	—	—	13, 24
$Ag^{\cdot} + e_0^- \rightleftharpoons Ag$	0·799	—	—	—	13, 25, 26
$Pd^{\cdot\cdot} + 2e_0^- \rightleftharpoons Pd$	—	—	0·83	Exptl. value; see also 97	99
$Ir^{\cdots} + 3e_0^- \rightleftharpoons Ir$	—	—	1·0	Calc. value	2
$Br_2(l) + 2e_0^- \rightleftharpoons 2Br'$	1·066	—	—	—	27, 28
$Pt^{\cdot\cdot} + 2e_0^- \rightleftharpoons Pt$	—	—	1·2	Calc. from data on $Pt(OH)_2 + 2H^{\cdot} + 2e_0^- \rightleftharpoons Pt + 2H_2O$	2
$Cl_2 + 2e_0^- \rightleftharpoons 2Cl'$	1·358	—	—	Calc. from e.m.f. data (100, 101)	13, 29, 30, 31, 32
$Au^{\cdots} + 3e_0^- \rightleftharpoons Au$	—	—	1·42	Calc. assuming the solubility of AuI to be analogous to that of CuI and AgI	2
$Au^{\cdot} + e_0^- \rightleftharpoons Au$	—	—	1·7		2
$F_2 + 2e_0^- \rightleftharpoons 2F'$	—	2·85	—	Calc.; calc. and exptl. values discrepant (81, 88)	86

TABLE IX, 2

STANDARD POTENTIALS OF SOME WELL-KNOWN HALF-CELLS

Electrode	E_0 (volt)	References
$Pb(Hg) - PbSO_4 . SO_4''$	—0·351	114, 115
$Ag - AgI . I'$	—0·152	102
$Ag - AgBr . Br'$	0·071	98, 103, 104, 105, 106
$Hg - HgO . OH'$	0·098	107, 108
$Hg - Hg_2Br_2 . Br'$	0·140	109
$Ag - AgCl . Cl'$	0·222	98, 110, 111
$Hg - Hg_2Cl_2 . Cl'$	0·268	112, 113
$Hg - Hg_2SO_4 . SO_4''$	0·615	98
$Pb - PbO_2 . PbSO_4 . SO_4''$	1·685	115

Note also:

$$Hg - Hg_2Cl_2, \ 0·1N \ KCl \quad 0·3335$$
$$Hg - Hg_2Cl_2, \quad 1N \ KCl \quad 0·2810 \ \big\} \ \text{values of } E_0' \text{ at 25 °C.}$$
$$Hg - Hg_2Cl_2, \ Satd. \ KCl \quad 0·2420$$

TABLE IX, 1 and 2

References:
[1] V. A. PLESKOV, *Uspekhi Khim.*, 1947, **16**, 254.
[2] W. M. LATIMER, *Oxidation Potentials*, New York, 1938.
[3] G. N. LEWIS, *et al.*, *J. Am. Chem. Soc.*, 1913, **35**, 340; *ibid.*, 1910, **32**, 1659; 1912, **34**, 119; 1915, **37**, 1990.
[4] A. C. TAYLOR, *J. Res. Nat. Bur. Stand.*, 1940, **25**, 731.
[5] E. N. GAPON, *J. Phys. Chem. Russ.*, 1946, **20**, 1209.
[6] J. C. MISCHALEK and T. E. PHIPPS, *J. Chem. Ed.*, 1928, **5**, 197.
[7] R. G. BATES, *J. Am. Chem. Soc.*, 1938, **60**, 2983.
[8] R. H. STOKES and J. M. STOKES, *Trans. Faraday Soc.*, 1945, **41**, 685.
[9] R. A. ROBINSON and R. H. STOKES, *ibid.*, 1940, **36**, 740.
[10] H. N. PARTON and J. W. MITCHELL, *ibid.*, 1939, **35**, 758.
[11] J. SHRAWDER, I. A. COWPERTHWAITE and V. K. LaMER, *J. Am. Chem. Soc.*, 1934, **56**, 2348.
[12] H. S. HARNED and M. E. FITZGERALD, *J. Am. Chem. Soc.*, 1936, **58**, 2624.
[13] G. N. LEWIS and M. RANDALL, *Thermodynamics and the Free Energy of Chemical Substances*, New York, 1923.
[14] R. H. GERKE, *Chem. Rev.*, 1924, **1**, 377.
[15] M. L. BROUTY, *Compt. rend.*, 1942, **214**, 258.
[16] M. M. HARING and J. C. WHITE, *Trans. Electrochem. Soc.*, 1938, **73**, 211.
[17] R. H. GERKE, *J. Am. Chem. Soc.*, 1922, **44**, 1684.

TABLE IX, 1 and 2 (*Continued*)

[18] W. R. CARMODY, *ibid.*, 1929, **51**, 5908.

[19] M. RANDALL and J. Y. CANN, *ibid.*, 1930, **52**, 589.

[20] J. J. LINGANE, *ibid.*, 1938, **60**, 724.

[21] M. M. HARING, M. R. HATFIELD and P. P. ZAPPONI, *Trans. Electrochem. Soc.*, 1939, **75**, 167.

[22] H. H. WILLARD and NING KANG TANG, *J. Am. Chem. Soc.*, 1937, **59**, 1188.

[23] GRINNELL JONES and B. B. KAPLAN, *ibid.*, 1928, **50**, 2066.

[24] W. C. BRAY and A. V. HERSHEY, *ibid.*, 1934, **56**, 1893.

[25] B. B. OWEN and S. R. BRINKLEY, *ibid.*, 1938, **60**, 2233.

[26] J. B. CHLOUPEK and V. Z. DANEŠ, *Coll. Czech. Chem. Comm.*, 1932, **4**, 124.

[27] G. N. LEWIS and H. STORCH, *J. Am. Chem. Soc.*, 1917, **39**, 2544.

[28] GRINNELL JONES and S. BÄCKSTROM, *ibid.*, 1934, **56**, 1524.

[29] G. N. LEWIS and F. F. RUPERT, *ibid.*, 1911, **33**, 299.

[30] R. H. GERKE, *ibid.*, 1922, **44**, 1684.

[31] N. KAMEYAMA, H. YAMAMOTO and O. SKUMPEI, *J. Soc. Chem. Ind. Japan*, 1926, **29**, 679.

[32] M. RANDALL and L. E. YOUNG, *J. Am. Chem. Soc.*, 1928, **50**, 989.

[33] B. NEUMANN and H. RICHTER, *Z. Elektrochem.*, 1925, **31**, 287.

[34] S. MAKISHIMA, *ibid.*, 1935, **41**, 697.

[35] H. E. BENT, G. S. FORBES and A. F. FORZIATTI, *J. Am. Chem. Soc.*, 1939, **61**, 709.

[36] J. L. CRENSHAW, *ibid.*, 1934, **56**, 2525.

[37] W. M. LATIMER, P. W. SCHUTZ and J. F. G. HICKS, *J. Phys. Chem.*, 1934, **2**, 82.

[38] G. DEVOTO, *Z. Elektrochem.*, 1928, **34**, 19.

[39] M. TAMELE, *J. Phys. Chem.*, 1924, **28**, 502.

[40] G. E. COATES, *J. Chem. Soc.*, 1945, 478.

[41] W. M. LATIMER, *J. Phys. Chem.*, 1927, **31**, 1267.

[42] A. SMITS, *Z. Elektrochem.*, 1924, **30**, 223.

[43] L. BOUCHET, *Compt. rend.*, 1929, **188**, 1237.

[44] W. M. LATIMER and B. S. GREENSFELDER, *J. Am. Chem. Soc.*, 1928, **50**, 2202.

[45] A. SMITS and H. GERDING, *Z. Elektrochem.*, 1925, **31**, 304.

[46] H. GERDING, *Z. physik. Chem.*, 1930, **151 A**, 190.

[47] I. A. KARSONOWSKY, *Z. anorg. Chem.*, 1923, **128**, 33.

[48] E. SCHWARZ VON BERGKAMPF, *Z. Elektrochem.*, 1932, **38**, 847.

[49] G. KIMURA, *Bull. Inst. Phys. Chem. Res. Tokyo*, 1935, **14**, 94.

[50] A. A. NOYES and E. S. FREED, *J. Am. Chem. Soc.*, 1920, **42**, 476.

[51] MOTOO WATANABÉ, *Bull. Inst. Phys. Chem. Res. Tokyo*, 1929, **8**, 978.

[52] MOTOO WATANABÉ, *Rep. Tohoku Imp. Univ.* (1), 1933, **22**, 902.

[53] M. RANDALL and M. FRANDSEN, *J. Am. Chem. Soc.*, 1932, **54**, 47.

[54] W. H. HAMPTON, *J. Phys. Chem.*, 1926, **30**, 980.

[55] T. W. RICHARDS and W. T. RICHARDS, *J. Am. Chem. Soc.*, 1924, **40**, 89.

[56] E. M. HATTOX and T. DE VRIES, *ibid.*, 1936, **58**, 2126.

[57] S. HAKOMORI, *J. Am. Chem. Soc.*, 1930, **52**, 2372.

[58] T. HEYMANN and K. JELLINEK, *Z. physik. Chem.*, 1932, **160 A**, 34.

TABLE IX, 1 and 2 (*Continued*)

[59] M. M. HARING and B. B. WESTFALL, *Trans. Electrochem. Soc.*, 1934, **65**, 235.

[60] R. SCHILDBACH, *Z. Elektrochem.*, 1910, **16**, 967.

[61] M. M. HARING and E. G. VANDEN BOSCHE, *J. Phys. Chem.*, 1929, **33**, 161.

[62] L. COLOMBIER, *Compt. rend.*, 1934, **199**, 273, 408.

[63] KWANJI MURATA, *Bull. Chem. Soc. Jap.*, 1928, **3**, 57.

[64] B. FORESTI, *Gazz. Chim. Ital.*, 1940, **70**, 349.

[65] E. ABEL, E. BRATU and O. REDLICH, *Z. physik. Chem.*, 1935, **173 A**, 353.

[66] D. F. SMITH, *J. Am. Chem. Soc.*, 1923, **45**, 360.

[67] E. H. SWIFT, *ibid.*, 1923, **45**, 371.

[68] G. N. LEWIS and W. N. LACY, *ibid.*, 1914, **36**, 804.

[69] F. MÜLLER and H. REUTHER, *Z. Elektrochem.*, 1941, **47**, 640.

[70] F. MÜLLER and H. REUTHER, *ibid.*, 1942, **48**, 682.

[71] M. QUINTIN, *J. Chim. Physique*, 1938, **35**, 300.

[72] R. F. NIELSON and D. J. BROWN, *J. Am. Chem. Soc.*, 1927, **49**, 2423.

[73] R. BURIAN, *Z. Elektrochem.*, 1931, **37**, 238.

[74] F. H. GETMAN, *Trans. Electrochem. Soc.*, 1933, **64**, 201.

[75] I. A. KARSONOWSKY, *Z. anorg. Chem.*, 1923, **128**, 17.

[76] W. M. LATIMER (2), based on results of R. SCHUHMANN, *J. Am. Chem. Soc.*, 1924, **46**, 52.

[77] G. GRUBE and F. SCHWEIGARDT, *Z. Elektrochem.*, 1923, **29**, 257.

[78] W. NERNST and H. VON WARTENBURG, *Z. physik. Chem.*, 1906, **56**, 534.

[79] G. N. LEWIS, *J. Am. Chem. Soc.*, 1906, **28**, 158.

[80] J. N. BRØNSTED, *Z. physik. Chem.*, 1909, **65**, 84.

[81] W. NERNST, *Sitzungsber. Berlin Akad.*, 1909, 255.

[82] G. N. LEWIS and M. RANDALL, *J. Am. Chem. Soc.*, 1914, **36**, 2468.

[83] W. M. LATIMER, *J. Phys. Chem.*, 1927, **31**, 1267.

[84] M. PRYTZ, *Z. anorg. Chem.*, 1930, **193**, 113.

[85] F. H. GETMAN, *Trans. Electrochem. Soc.*, 1934, **66**, 143.

[86] W. M. LATIMER, *J. Am. Chem. Soc.*, 1926, **48**, 2868.

[87] B. NEUMANN and H. RICHTER, *Z. Elektrochem.*, 1925, **31**, 481.

[88] C. S. GARNER and D. M. YOST, *J. Am. Chem. Soc.*, 1937, **59**, 2738.

[89] H. P. STOUT, *Trans. Faraday Soc.*, 1945, **41**, 64.

[90] E. H. RIESENFELD and F. MÜLLER, *Z. Elektrochem.*, 1935, **41**, 87.

[91] F. MÜLLER, *Monatsh.*, 1929, **53**, 215.

[92] KOKICHI SANO, *Kinzoku-no-Kenkyu*, 1935, **12**, 548.

[93] A. N. CAMPBELL, *J. Chem. Soc.*, 1923, 2323.

[94] I. A. KARSONOWSKY, quoted by LATIMER, [2].

[95] H. J. SCHEIDT, *Sitzungsber. Akad. Wiss. Wien.*, 1929, **138**, 755.

[96] M. HAISSINSKY, *J. Chim. Physique*, 1935, **32**, 116.

[97] D. H. TEMPLETON, G. W. WATT and C. S. GARNER, *J. Am. Chem. Soc.*, 1943, **65**, 1608.

[98] H. S. HARNED and B. B. OWEN, *The Physical Chemistry of Electrolytic Solutions*, Reinhold Publ. Corp., New York, 1943.

[99] B. NEUMANN, *Z. physik. Chem.*, 1894, **14**, 1932.

TABLE IX, 1 and 2 (*Continued*)

[100] R. H. GERKE and M. D. ROURKE, *J. Am. Chem. Soc.*, 1927, **49**, 855.
[101] T. F. BUEHRER and W. E. ROSEVEARE, *ibid.*, 1927. **49**, 1989.
[102] B. B. OWEN, *ibid.*, 1935, **57**, 1526.
[103] A. S. KESTON, *ibid.*, 1935, **57**, 1671.
[104] H. S. HARNED, A. S. KESTON and J. G. DONELSON, *ibid.*, 1936, **58**, 989.
[105] H. S. HARNED and J. G. DONELSON, *ibid.*, 1937, **59**, 1280.
[106] B. B. OWEN and L. FOERING, *ibid.*, 1936, **58**, 1575.
[107] F. FRIED, *Z. physik. Chem.*, 1926, **123 A**, 406.
[108] Y. KOBAYASHI and H. Y. WANG, *J. Sci. Hiroshima Univ.*, 1934, **5 A**, 392.
[109] W. D. LARSON, *J. Am. Chem. Soc.*, 1940, **62**, 765.
[110] S. S. PRENTISS and G. SCATCHARD, *Chem. Rev.*, 1933, **13**, 139.
[111] H. S. HARNED and R. W. EHLERS, *J. Am. Chem. Soc.*, 1932, **54**, 1350.
[112] M. RANDALL and L. E. YOUNG, *ibid.*, 1928, **50**, 989.
[113] F. MÜLLER and H. REUTHER, *Z. Elektrochem.*, 1943, **49**, 497.
[114] J. SHRAWDER and I. A. COWPERTHWAITE, *J. Am. Chem. Soc.*, 1934, **56**, 2340.
[115] H. S. HARNED and W. J. HAMER, *ibid.*, 1935, **57**, 33.
[116] F. FENWICK, *J. Am. Chem. Soc.*, 1926, **48**, 860.

TABLE IX, 3

STANDARD POTENTIAL OF THE Ag/AgCl ELECTRODE AS FUNCTION OF TEMPERATURE

Temp. °C.	E_0 v.	Temp. °C.	E_0 v.
0	0·23634	35	0·21563
5	·23392	40	·21200
10	·23126	45	·20821
15	·22847	50	·20437
20	·22551	55	·20035
25	·22239	60	·19620
30	·21912		

Accuracy: $\pm 0\cdot05$ mv.

See also Table IX, 2.

H. S. HARNED and R. W. EHLERS, *J. Am. Chem. Soc.*, 1932, **54**, 1350.

TABLE IX, 4

LIQUID JUNCTION POTENTIALS

| Solution | Composition in mol/l. | | | Total molality |
	HCl	KCl	KNO$_3$	
A	—	4·185	—	4·185
B	—	3·103	1·035	4·138
C	0·043	3·061	1·035	4·139
D	0·043	4·147	—	4·190

1.   Liquid junction potentials calculated from HENDERSON equation.

Junction between the above solutions:	Potential at 25 °C. in mv.
A/B	—0·22
A/D	—0·48
B/C	—0·49
B/D	—0·28
C/D	—0·21
C/A	—0·70

G. G. MANOV, N. J. DE LOLLIS and S. F. ACREE, *J. Res. Nat. Bur. Stand.*, 1944, **33**, 273.

2.   K$_3$Fe(CN)$_6$/K$_4$Fe(CN)$_6$ junctions at 25 °C.

K$_3$Fe(CN)$_6$ conc. (mol/l.)	K$_4$Fe(CN)$_6$ conc. (mol/l.)	Mean conc. (mol/l.)	Liquid junction potential in mv.
0·5	0·05	0·275	31·5
0·4	0·04	0·22	31·0
0·2	0·02	0·11	28·5
0·1	0·01	0·055	25·9
0·1	0·005	0·0525	33·5
0·1	0·001	0·0505	52·2
0·02	0·001	0·0105	26·6
0·01	0·001	0·0055	18·1

E. B. R. PRIDEAUX, *J. Chem. Soc.*, 1944, 606.
For older work, see also:
P. F. BUCHI, *Z. Elektrochem.*, 1924, **30**, 443.
P. B. TAYLOR, *J. Phys. Chem.*, 1927, **31**, 1478.
A. B. LAMB and A. T. LARSON, *J. Am. Chem. Soc.*, 1920, *42*, 229.
E. J. ROBERTS and F. FENWICK, *J. Am. Chem. Soc.*, 1927, **49**, 2787.

TABLE IX, 5

DIFFUSION POTENTIALS IN AQUEOUS AND NON-AQUEOUS MEDIA,
FROM 0·01N TO 0·1N ELECTROLYTE SOLUTION AT 20 °C.

Electrolyte	Diffusion Potential in mv. in the following solvents		
	Water	Aniline	Amyl alcohol
KOH	—26·5	30 ± 3	10 ± 1
KF	9·3	—35 ± 3	— 4 ± 1
KCl	0	—27 ± 3	—12 ± 0·5
KBr	0	—30 ± 1	—13 ± 0·5
KI	0	—37 ± 0·5	—17
NaOH	—35	20 ± 3	6 ± 1
NaF	— 2	—33 ± 3	— 4 ± 1
NaCl	—11·7	—30 ± 3	—11 ± 1
NaBr	—12·3	—33 ± 1	—15 ± 0·5
NaI	—12·1	—37 ± 0·5	—14
NaClO$_4$	— 8·4	—	—16 ± 0·5
NaOAc	11	—	—
Na benzoate	13	—	—
LiOH	—39	25 ± 3	9 ± 1
LiCl	—19	—30 ± 1	—10 ± 1
LiBr	—20	—32 ± 0·05	—13 ± 0·5
LiClO$_4$	—16	—	—18 ± 1
(CH$_3$)$_4$NOH	—36	45	12
(CH$_3$)$_4$NCl	—14	3	—11
(CH$_3$)$_4$NI	—14	— 3·5	—14
C$_6$H$_5$NH$_2$HCl	—19	3	—
HCl	38	—	32 ± 1
HBr	37	—	35 ± 1
HClO$_4$	40	—	36 ± 1

K. H. MEYER, H. HAUPTMANN and J. F. SIEVERZ, *Helv. Chim. Acta*, 1936, **19**, 948.

TABLE IX, 6

MOLAL ELECTRODE POTENTIALS (E_0') OF THE SILVER-SILVER CHLORIDE ELECTRODE
IN METHANOL-WATER MIXTURES

Temp. °C.	Potential in v. (10% Methanol)	Potential in v. (20% Methanol)
0	0·22762	0·22022
5	0·22547	0·21837
10	0·22328	0·21631
15	0·22085	0·21405
20	0·21821	0·21155
25	0·21535	0·20881
30	0·21220	0·20567
35	0·20892	0·20246
40	0·20550	0·19910

The temperature dependence of electrode potential is expressed by the equations:
E_0' (10% MeOH) $= 0 \cdot 21818 - 555 \cdot 63 \times 10^{-6} \ (t - 20) - 4 \cdot 128 \times 10^{-6} \ (t - 20)^2$
and
E_0' (20% MeOH) $= 0 \cdot 21151 - 529 \cdot 10 \times 10^{-6} \ (t - 20) - 4 \cdot 706 \times 10^{-6} \ (t - 20)^2$
Accurate to $\pm 0 \cdot 05$ mv. Composition is given as wt.%.

H. S. HARNED and H. C. THOMAS, *J. Am. Chem. Soc.*, 1935, **57**, 1666. See also Table
IX, 7.

TABLE IX, 7

MOLAL ELECTRODE POTENTIALS (E_0') OF THE SILVER-SILVER CHLORIDE ELECTRODE
IN ETHANOL-WATER MIXTURES

Temp. °C.	Potential in v. (10% Ethanol)	Potential in v. (20% Ethanol)
0	0·22726	0·21606
10	0·22328	0·21367
20	0·21901	0·21013
25	0·21467	0·20757
30	0·21383	0·20587
40	0·20783	0·19962

Accuracy: $\pm 0 \cdot 05$ mv.

TABLE, IX 7 (Continued)

The temperature dependence of electrode potential is expressed by the equation:
$$E_0' = a + b\,(t - 20) + c\,(t - 20)^2 \text{ where the constants are}$$

	a	b	c
10% Ethanol	0·21898	$4\cdot89247 \times 10^{-4}$	$-1\cdot40006 \times 10^{-6}$
20 % Ethanol	0·21011	$4\cdot08604 \times 10^{-4}$	$-5\cdot57748 \times 10^{-6}$

Values of constants for these equations are found by the method of least squares from the experimental e.m.f. data. Composition of solvent is given as wt.%.

A. PATTERSON and W. A. FELSING, *J. Am. Chem. Soc.*, 1942, **64**, 1478.

Silver-silver bromide electrode in anhydrous methanol at 25 °C.
$$E_0' = -0\cdot1328 \text{ v. (molal basis)}$$
and
$$E_0' = -0\cdot1451 \text{ v. (molar basis)}$$

E. W. KANNING and A. W. CAMPBELL, *J. Am. Chem. Soc.*, 1942, **64**, 517.

TABLE IX, 8

THE STANDARD ELECTRODE POTENTIALS OF THE CELL

$$H_2 \text{ (g. 1 atm.)} \mid HCl \mid AgCl_{(s)} \mid Ag_{(s)}$$

IN METHANOL-WATER MIXTURES

Wt.% CH_3OH	Mol % CH_3OH	$E_{0_{25}}$	$a \cdot 10^4$	$b \cdot 10^6$
43·3	30	0·1941	$-7\cdot262$	$-6\cdot594$
64·0	50	0·1764	$-9\cdot512$	$-1\cdot739$
84·2	75	0·1319	$-13\cdot241$	$-4\cdot303$
94·2	90	0·0840	$-14\cdot064$	$-5\cdot435$
100	100	$-0\cdot0103$	$-12\cdot080$	$-4\cdot00$

The temperature dependence of electrode potential may be expressed by the equation:
$$E_{0t} = E_{0_{25}} + a\,(t - 25) + b\,(t - 25)^2$$

J. M. AUSTIN, A. H. HUNT, F. A. JOHNSON and H. N. PARTON, in course of publication. See also Table IX, 6.

TABLE IX, 9

MOLAL ELECTRODE POTENTIAL (E_0') OF THE SILVER-SILVER CHLORIDE ELECTRODE IN DIOXAN-WATER MIXTURES

Temp. °C.	Potential in v. (20% Dioxan)	Potential in v. (45% Dioxan)	Potential in v. (70% Dioxan)
0	0·21983	0·18940	0·10783
5	0·21689	0·18445	0·09982
10	0·21369	0·17947	0·09152
15	0·21033	0·17434	0·08337
20	0·20682	0·16910	0·07475
25	0·20315	0·16344	0·06620
30	0·19920	0·15780	0·05720
35	0·19510	0·15205	0·04855
40	0·19092	0·14612	0·03930
45	0·18650	0·14000	0·03005
50	0·18196	0·13355	0·02040

The temperature dependence of electrode potential may be expressed by the equation:

$$E_0' = E_0'{}_{25} + a\,(t-25) + b\,(t-25)^2$$

where the constants are

	$E_0'{}_{25}$	$a \cdot 10^6$	$b \cdot 10^6$
20% Dioxan	0·20311	− 757·0	—3·58
45% Dioxan	0·16351	—1114·5	—3·24
70% Dioxan	0·06618	—1745·6	—3·25

Values accurate to $\pm 0 \cdot 05$ mv.

H. S. HARNED and J. O. MORRISON, *J. Am. Chem. Soc.*, 1936, **58**, 1908.

TABLE IX, 10

POTENTIALS OF THE $Hg \mid Hg_2SO_4$ ELECTRODE IN METHANOL

$E = $ e.m.f. of the half-element, E_0 the standard electrode potential

Empirical Equations

E_0

$$E_{20}{}^* = 0\cdot54428 + 0\cdot0909m^{1/2} - 0\cdot0500m - 0\cdot0040m^{3/2}$$
$$E_{25} = 0\cdot53920 + 0\cdot1079m^{1/2} - 0\cdot09956m + 0\cdot0467m^{3/2}$$
$$E_{30} = 0\cdot53510 + 0\cdot12008m^{1/2} - 0\cdot11676m + 0\cdot0510m^{3/2}$$
$$E_{35} = 0\cdot53177 + 0\cdot13635m^{1/2} - 0\cdot12847m + 0\cdot0418m^{3/2}$$

$m = $ molal conc. of H_2SO_4.

E_0 values accurate to $\pm 0 \cdot 5$ mv.

* Subscripts refer to temperatures in °C.

E. W. KANNING and W. G. BOWMAN, *J. Am. Chem. Soc.*, 1946, **68**, 2042.

TABLE IX, 11

ELFCTRODE POTENTIALS IN NON-AQUEOUS SOLVENTS

Element	Solvent			
	MeOH [1] 25 °C.	EtOH [2] 25 °C.	H . COOH [4] 25 °C.	NH$_3$ liq. [4] —50 °C.
Li	—3·095 [3]	—3·042	—0·03	—0·31
Na	—2·728	—2·657	0·03	0·08
K	—	—	0.09	—0·05
Rb	—	—	0·0	0·0
Cs	—	—	0·01	—0·02
Ca	—	—	0·25	0·29
Cu/Cu′	0·490	—	—	2·34 [6]
Cu/Cu″	—	—	3·31	2·36
Ag	0·764	0·749	3·62	2·76
Zn	—	—	2·40	1·40
Cd	—0·258	—	2·70	1·73
Hg / $^1/_2$ Hg$_2$··	—	—	3·63	—
Te	—0·379	—0·343	—	—
Pb	—	—	2·73	2·25
H$_2$	0·0	0·0	3·45	1·93
N$_2$/NH$_2$′	—	—	—	0·57
Cl	1·128	1·060	—	3·96 [5]
Br	0·849	0·789	—	3·76 [5]
I	0·369	0·317	—	3·38 [5]
Reference potential	H$_2$ = zero in the same solvent at 25 °C.	H$_2$ = zero in the same solvent at 25 °C.	Rb = zero in the same solvent at 25 °C.	Rb = zero in the same solvent at —50 °C.

References:

[1] P. S. BUCKLEY and H. HARTLEY, *Phil. Mag.*, 1929, **8**, 320.

[2] A. MACFARLANE and H. HARTLEY, *ibid.*, 1932, **13**, 425.

[3] A. MACFARLANE and H. HARTLEY, *ibid.*, 1935, **20**, 611.

[4] V. A. PLESKOV, *Acta Physicochim.*, *U.R.S.S.*, 1946, **21**, 41.

[5] V. A. PLESKOV, *ibid.*, 1945, **20**, 578.

[6] V. A. PLESKOV, *ibid.*, 1940, **13**, 659.

See also V. A. PLESKOV and A. M. MONOSSON, *ibid.*, 1935, **2**, 615, 621 and 679.

TABLE IX, 12

STANDARD OXIDATION-REDUCTION POTENTIALS AT 25 °C.

1. INORGANIC SYSTEMS

Reaction	e_0 volts	Ref.
$Cr^{...} + e_0^- = Cr^{..}$	-0.41	1
$Ti^{...} + e_0^- = Ti^{..}$	-0.37 ± 0.01	2
$Co(CN)_6''' + e_0^- = Co(CN)_6''''$	-0.83	3
$V^{...} + e_0^- = V^{..}$	-0.20	4
$TiO^{..} + 2H^{.} + e_0^- = Ti^{...} + H_2O$	0.10	5
$Sn^{....} + 2e_0^- = Sn^{..}$	0.154 ± 0.001	6
$Cu^{..} + e_0^- = Cu^{.}$	0.167 ± 0.001	7, 8
$VO^{..} + 2H^{.} + e_0^- = V^{...} + H_2O$	0.314	4
$PtCl_6'' + 2e_0^- = PtCl_4'' + 2Cl'$	0.72	9
$Fe(CN)_6''' + e_0^- = Fe(CN)_6''''$	0.356	10
$H_3AsO_4 + 2H^{.} + 2e_0^- = H_3AsO_3 + H_2O$	0.559	11, 8
$I_3' + 2e_0^- = 3I'$	0.535	12, 8
$Fe^{...} + e_0^- = Fe^{..}$	0.771 ± 0.0005	13, 29
$2Hg^{..} + 2e_0^- = Hg_2^{..}$	0.905 ± 0.001	14
$HIO + H^{.} + e_0^- = I' + H_2O$	0.99	15
$V(OH)_4^{.} + 2H^{.} + e_0^- = VO^{..} + 3H_2O$	1.000 ± 0.0005	16, 17
$Tl^{...} + 2e_0^- = Tl^{.}$	1.25	18
$PdCl_6'' + 2e_0^- = PdCl_4'' + 2Cl'$	1.288	19
$Cr_2O_7'' + 14H^{.} + 6e_0^- = 2Cr^{...} + 7H_2O$	1.36	20, 8
$HBrO + H^{.} + 2e_0^- = Br' + H_2O$	1.33	8
$MnO_2 + 4H^{.} + 2e_0^- = Mn^{..} + 2H_2O$	1.236 ± 0.002	21
$ClO_4' + 8H^{.} + 8e_0^- = Cl' + 4H_2O$	1.35	8
$PbO_2 + 4H^{.} + 2e_0^- = Pb^{..} + 2H_2O$	1.456 ± 0.0005	23, 24
$ClO_3' + 6H^{.} + 6e_0^- = Cl' + 3H_2O$	1.45	22, 8
$HClO + H^{.} + 2e_0^- = Cl' + 3H_2O$	1.50	8
$Mn^{...} + e_0^- = Mn^{..}$	1.51	25
$Ce^{....} + e_0^- = Ce^{...}$	1.610 ± 0.001	26
$H_2O_2 + 2H^{.} + 2e_0^- = 2H_2O$	1.77	8
$Co^{...} + e_0^- = Co^{..}$	1.842 ± 0.01	27, 28

TABLE IX, 12 (*Continued*)

References:

1 G. Grube and G. Breitinger, *Z. Elektrochem.*, 1927, **33**, 112.

2 G. S. Forbes and L. P. Hall, *J. Am. Chem. Soc.*, 1924, **46**, 385.

3 H. Lieder and P. Schachterle, *Z. Elektrochem.*, 1926, **32**, 561.

4 F. Foerster and F. Böttcher, *Z. physik. Chem.*, 1930, **151 A**, 321.

5 B. Diethelm and F. Foerster, *Z. physik. Chem.*, 1908, **62**, 129.

6 C. S. Huey and H. V. Tartar, *J. Am. Chem. Soc.*, 1934, **56**, 2585.

7 F. Fenwick, *J. Am. Chem. Soc.*, 1926, **48**, 860.

8 W. M. Latimer, *Oxidation Potentials*, New York, Prentice-Hall, 1938.

9 D. F. Smith, *J. Res. Nat. Bur. Stand*, 1930, **5**, 735.

10 I. M. Kolthoff and W. J. Tomsicek, *J. Phys. Chem.*, 1935, **39**, 945.

11 H. A. Liebhafsky, *J. Phys. Chem.*, 1931, **35**, 1648.

12 Grinnell Jones and B. B. Kaplan, *J. Am. Chem. Soc.*, 1928, **50**, 1845.

13 W. C. Schumb, M. S. Sherrill and S. B. Sweetser, *J. Am. Chem. Soc.*, 1937, **59**, 2360.

14 S. Popoff *et al.*, *J. Am. Chem. Soc.*, 1931, **53**, 1195.

15 W. C. Bray and E. L. Connolly, *J. Am. Chem. Soc.*, 1911, **33**, 1485.

16 J. E. Carpenter, *J. Am. Chem. Soc.*, 1934, **56**, 1847.

17 C. D. Coryell and D. M. Yost, *J. Am. Chem. Soc.*, 1933, **55**, 1909.

18 M. S. Sherrill and A. J. Haas, *J. Am. Chem. Soc.*, 1936, **58**, 953.

19 H. B. Wellman, *J. Am. Chem. Soc.*, 1930, **52**, 985.

20 J. D. Neuss and W. Riemann, *J. Am. Chem. Soc.*, 1934, **56**, 2238.

21 D. J. Brown and H. A. Liebhafsky, *J. Am. Chem. Soc.*, 1930, **52**, 2595.

22 A. R. Olson, *J. Am. Chem. Soc.*, 1920, **42**, 896.

23 H. Fromherz, *Z. physik. Chem.*, 1931, **153**, 387.

24 H. S. Harned and W. J. Hamer, *J. Am. Chem. Soc.*, 1935, **57**, 33.

25 G. Grube and K. Huberich, *Z. Elektrochem.*, 1923, **29**, 17.

26 A. A. Noyes and C. S. Garner, *J. Am. Chem. Soc.*, 1936, **58**, 1265.

27 A. A. Noyes and T. J. Deahl, *J. Am. Chem. Soc.*, 1937, **59**, 1337.

28 A. B. Lamb and A. T. Larson, *J. Am. Chem. Soc.*, 1920, **42**, 2024.

29 D. Bezier, *Ann. Chim.*, 1945, (xi), **20**, 161; *J. Chim. Phys.*, 1944, **41**, 100.

TABLE IX, 12 (*Continued*)

2. ORGANIC SYSTEMS

	Solvent	e_0 volts	
1:4-Naphthoquinone (N.Q.)	A	0·48	
2-Methyl 1:4-N.Q.	B	0·40	
2-Phenyl 1:4-N.Q.	B	0·45	Accuracy: ± 1 cv.
1:2-N.Q.	B	0·57	
4-Methyl 1:2-N.Q.	B	0·53	

A   EtOH 50%,   0·1N HCl,   0·2N LiCl.   N.Q. $\equiv$ Naphthoquinone.
B   EtOH 70%,   0·2N HCl,   0·2N LiCl.

L. F. FIESER and M. FIESER, *J. Am. Chem. Soc.*, 1935, **57**, 491.

Nitrosobenzene-phenylhydroxylamine system in 60% *acetone-water* 0·1N HCl.

	e_0 volts	
Nitrosobenzene (N.B.)	0·58	
2-Methyl-N.B.	0·59	
2:5-Dimethyl-N.B.	0·59	
2-Ethyl-N.B.	0·58	Accuracy: ± 1 cv.
2-Chloro-N.B.	0·59	
2-Bromo-N.B.	0·59	
3-Iodo-N.B.	0·58	

R. E. LUTZ *et al.*, *J. Org. Chem.*, 1937, **2**, 68.   N.B. $\equiv$ Nitrosobenzene.

Anthraquinones	Solvent	e_0 volts	
2-Hydroxy–1:4-anthraquinone	A	0·27	
1 : 4-Anthraquinone	A	0·40	Accuracy: ± 1 cv.

A = 50% aq. EtOH,   0·1N HCl,   0·2N LiCl.

L. F. FIESER, *J. Am. Chem. Soc.*, 1928, **50**, 405.

Quinones in alcoholic solution	e_0 volts	
Benzoquinone	0·71	
Toluquinone	0·66	Accuracy: ± 1 cv.
p-Xyloquinone	0·60	

H. R. BERLINER, *J. Am. Chem. Soc.*, 1946, **68**, 49.

TABLE IX, 13

VARIATION OF POTENTIAL WITH PERCENTAGE OXIDATION, AT CONSTANT pH (30 °C.)
OF DYES

Values of k in the equation:

$$E = E_0 + k \quad \text{where } k = RT/nF \log \frac{[\text{oxidised form}]}{[\text{reduced form}]}$$

Per cent. oxidation	k, volts, for $n = 2$	Tint of indicator dye
99	+0·060	Almost full colour
98	+0·051	
95	+0·038	
90	+0·029	
85	+0·023	
80	+0·018	
75	+0·014	
70	+0·011	
65	+0·008	
60	+0·005	
55	+0·003	
50	0	Half colour
45	—0·003	
40	—0·005	
35	—0·008	
30	—0·011	
25	—0·014	
20	—0·018	
15	—0·023	
10	—0·029	
5	—0·038	
2	—0·051	
1	—0·060	Almost colourless

From L. F. HEWITT, *Oxidation-Reduction Potentials in Bacteriology and Biochemistry*
(Livingstone, Edinburgh, 1950).

T

PERCENTAGE OXIDATION (AND COLOUR) OF VA

E_h (volts)	Phenol-m-sulphonate indo-2 : 6-dibromophenol	m-Chlorophenol indo-2 : 6-dichlorophenol	Phenol-o-sulphonate indo-2 : 6-dibromophenol	o-Chlorophenol indophenol	o-Bromophenol indophenol	Phenol indophenol	Phenol indo-2 : 6-dibromophenol	2 : 6-dichlorophenol indophenol	m-Cresol indophenol	o-Cresol indophenol	2 : 6-dichlorophenol-o-cresol	Thymol indophenol	1-Naphthol 2-SO₃H-indophenol	1-Naphthol-2-SO₃H-In-do-3 : 5-dichlorophenol	Toluylene Blue	Thionine
+0·30	88%	97%	99%	—	—	—	—	—	—	—	—	—	—	—	—	—
+0·25	15%	43%	65%	79%	82%	85%	92%	93%	96%	99%	—	—	—	—	Full colour	—
+0·20	—	2%	4%	8%	9%	12%	20%	21%	35%	66%	81%	88%	—	—	—	—
+0·15	—	—	—	—	—	—	—	—	1%	4%	9%	14%	88%	91%	94%	—
+0·10	—	—	—	—	—	—	—	—	—	—	—	—	15%	19%	24%	95%
+0·05	—	—	—	—	—	—	—	—	—	—	—	—	—	—	—	29%
0	—	—	—	—	—	—	—	—	—	—	—	—	—	—	—	1%
—0·05	—	—	—	—	—	—	—	—	—	—	—	—	—	—	—	—
—0·10	—	—	—	—	—	—	—	Colourless	—	—	—	—	—	—	—	—
—0·15	—	—	—	—	—	—	—	—	—	—	—	—	—	—	—	—
—0·20	—	—	—	—	—	—	—	—	—	—	—	—	—	—	—	—
—0·25	—	—	—	—	—	—	—	—	—	—	—	—	—	—	—	—
—0·30	—	—	—	—	—	—	—	—	—	—	—	—	—	—	—	—
—0·35	—	—	—	—	—	—	—	—	—	—	—	—	—	—	—	—
—0·40	—	—	—	—	—	—	—	—	—	—	—	—	—	—	—	—

$$*E_h = E_0 + \frac{RT}{nF} \ln \frac{\text{(oxidised form)}}{\text{(reduced form)}} \text{, and } E_h = E_0$$

when the system is 50% oxidised. Values of E_0 are given in Table IX, 15.